PELICAN BOOKS

A 201

POTTERY AND CERAMICS

BY ERNST ROSENTHAL

POTTERY
AND CERAMICS

FROM COMMON BRICK TO FINE CHINA

ERNST ROSENTHAL

700
RO

PENGUIN BOOKS

MELBOURNE · LONDON · BALTIMORE

FIRST PUBLISHED 1949
REPRINTED 1952
REVISED EDITION 1954

ACKNOWLEDGEMENTS

A large number of friends, both in and outside the Pottery
Industry, have given valuable help, criticism and suggestions,
and firms manufacturing machinery and tunnel kilns have
given illustrations and descriptions, and reference to them is
made in the appropriate chapters and below the illustrations.
To these, and to the firms who showed me round their factories, and particularly to Mr Leslie Jervis, who kindly read
the manuscript of this book, I would like to express my sincere
thanks.

Ernst Rosenthal, Dr (eng.sc.), M.I.E.E., F.R.I.C.
246 Park West, W.2.

MADE AND PRINTED IN GREAT BRITAIN
FOR PENGUIN BOOKS LTD, HARMONDSWORTH, MIDDLESEX
BY WYMAN AND SONS LTD
COLLOGRAVURE PLATES PRINTED
BY HARRISON AND SONS LTD

LIST OF CONTENTS

GENERAL REMARKS

The reader who wishes to obtain a short and vivid picture is advised firstly to read those sections below which are marked with asterisks and secondly to study the illustrations. In order to give a quick impression of the various branches of the clay ware industry the author describes five typical visits which he made recently. (Please refer to the relevant sections of Chapters 12, 13, 14, 16 and 19.) The reader can then study the remainder of the book at his leisure with very little loss of continuity.

The book falls into two sections:

Section I – Chapters 1 to 11 inclusive – deals with the subject of ceramics (pottery and other clay ware) in broad outline. Raw materials, kilns and other equipment, methods of manufacture, used for all or most types of clay ware, etc., are covered in a general manner.

Section II – Chapters 12 to 20 – deals with the various individual branches of the pottery and clay ware industry and the properties of the finished products. Special manufacturing methods – not covered by Section I – are described.

Contents

Contents

Preface to the Third Edition

THIS third edition incorporates essential details of the progress made by the ceramic industry since the manuscript of the first edition was written. The author's original plan, namely, to cover the whole field of ceramics, from common brick to fine china, in a pleasant, readable form, is maintained. The artist – and indeed all who love beautiful china – will find renewed interest in the chapter, 'Pottery Decoration'. This has been re-written and enlarged. Practically all methods used in the decoration of pottery are included. Fifteen new illustrations, covering modern pottery and modern pottery machinery, are added and the latest figures relating to pottery export are incorporated.

A feature of previous editions of *Pottery and Ceramics* was a tour of typical ceramic factories – the Wedgwood factories in Barlaston, the insulator factories of Bullers in Milton, and the stoneware factories of Doulton in Erith. This section has been brought up to date to include improvements and modernizations carried through since the book was first written.

Recent research work on super-refractories and on other new materials, such as metal powder – ceramic powder combinations used in aircraft power plant construction, is described, and the book includes a new chapter covering the manufacture of refractories for the steel industry, based on a process of extraction from sea water, a recent development in this country.

Whilst on the subject of refractories, it should be pointed out that the present revised edition includes descriptions of one of the most modern factories in the world for producing refractory materials. These factories were not in existence when the first edition was written.

Clay Ware in the Home

(See illustration below)

CLAY ware manufacture is the oldest art in the history of man and from the beginning it has been so connected with the daily round, the common task, that it has been taken for granted.

Archaeologists divide the early history of mankind into 'Stone Age', 'Bronze Age', 'Iron Age', and so on. Having

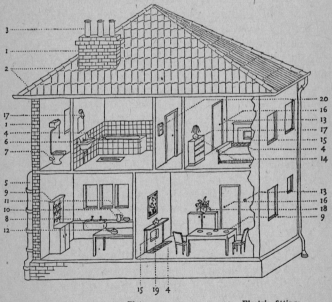

1. Bricks	9. Plates, cups	17. Electric fittings
2. Roofing-Tiles	10. Jug	(Porcelain-Insulation)
3. Chimney pots	11. Mixing-bowl	18. Flower Vase
4. Glazed tiles	12. Fireproof kitchenware	19. Porcelain Figurine
5. Drainpipes	13. Electric switch	20. Fuses
6. Wash-basin	14. Lamp base	(Porcelain-Insulation
7. Closet-bowl	15. Fireplace	
8. Sink	16. Door knobs	

learnt this in our childhood we are inclined to assume that what might have been correct with regard to early history is still true with regard to our age. As soon as a new material is developed, inventors, believing themselves at the same time prophets, predict that archaeologists 10,000 years hence will call our Age the 'Plastic Age', the 'Electronic Age', the 'Atomic Age', as the case may be. The 'Clay Age' (or 'Ceramic Age') seems to have been overlooked, although clay ware has perhaps been used to a larger extent than the materials chosen to epitomize our age.

Potters are unpretentious. They know that clay ware has been manufactured for 10,000 years and that it will still be used, to put it modestly, for many years to come. The competition of new materials obliges them to introduce scientific methods in research and manufacture in order to keep abreast with the achievements of younger industries. They are successful. The illustration proves this. It shows to what extent we are now using clay wares (ceramics) in our homes and daily life. It shows a section of a house made of bricks and covered with tiles. We see the bath, the lavatory W.C. pan and the hand-basin. We notice, furthermore, the glazed tiles round the fireplace in the bedroom, the pots and plates on the dining-room table, fireproof cooking ware in the kitchen and the drain pipes down the side of the house.

Porcelain insulators are found at various places in the lounge, in radio and television sets, telephones, electric fires, wall plugs and sockets. The electricity used in the house indicated is held in check by porcelain insulators on overhead pylons at high voltages before it is stepped down to 200 volts for domestic use, but the overhead transmission lines and pylons are not included in the illustration since it shows only clay ware in the home.

CHAPTER I

Brief History of Pottery

THE manufacture of clay ware is one of the oldest examples of human industry. It probably originated in this way:

In prehistoric times, primeval man left his footprints in clayey soil. These footprints were subsequently dried and hardened by the sun. In addition, his primitive weapons would come in contact with the clayey earth, clay would adhere, dry on, and be difficult to remove. Although he did not realize what was happening, primeval man witnessed, for the first time, the process of plastic clay being deprived of its plastic properties by the drying action of the sun, and its conversion into a hard substance.

Some 15,000 years elapsed before the scientific explanation was available, but probably only a thousand years passed before the first practical use was made of the discovery, when the first bricks were made of rough earth and were dried by exposure to the sun; and when wicker baskets were made temporarily waterproof by coating them with a clay layer.

The fact that the use of clay was known in very ancient times is handed down to us in the Bible, which tells us that God made the first man of clay.

We do not know when the first clay ware was hardened by burning, but we may assume that clay vessels came in contact with fire accidentally, and in this way the first fired ceramic articles were produced.

Burnt ceramic ware found in excavations made in the Nile valley is estimated to have been made 13,000 years ago. The progressive yearly elevation of the soil (caused by the deposition of mud from the river) makes it possible to estimate the age of excavated pieces by noting the depth at which they are found below the present level of the valley.

Excavational discoveries in England, Belgium and Germany teach us that in the glacial epoch clay vessels were made by hand and then burned, and confirm that ceramics go back to about 15,000 B.C. In North and South America as well, prehistoric ceramic articles have been found, thus proving that similar developments took place in the various continents. In these circumstances it seems rather pointless to attribute the original art of making ceramics to any particular race or country.

ANCIENT POTTERY

In attempting to trace the earliest examples of the potter's art we must perforce study ancient oriental history. The information found in old books is a mixture of fact, fable and tradition and it is therefore difficult to arrive at the truth. The only method by which we can verify deductions is by studying actual discoveries on the sites of old dwellings, tombs, temples, etc.

Egypt. – Apart from bricks of even more ancient origin, the oldest pottery articles so far discovered are those which have been found in the Nile Valley. Terra cotta Egyptian vases, designed to carry provisions for the dead, have been found in tombs of the Memphite period (5000 to 3000 B.C.). Besides these vases other wonderful objects of red and black polished terra cotta, modelled by hand, dating back to the period 5000 to 3500 B.C., have been discovered.

At least as early as 3500 B.C. the Egyptians used tiles of a clay-sand composition covered with a blue copper glaze.

Coming to the Theban period (3000 to 1700 B.C.) pictures on the walls of tombs have revealed scenes from the lives of Egyptian potters. From these we can see how they modelled the vases by hand and then fired them in ovens. In pyramids also of this same period the earliest examples of glazed earthenware were found.

From 1700 to 500 B.C. in Egypt the art of earthenware

manufacture reached a high peak of perfection. Many wonderful decorative pieces from temples of this period have been found. (Those from the temple of Tel el Yadouai, built by Rameses III, are of outstanding craftsmanship.)

Babylonia and Assyria. – In these countries, the ancient seats of Mesopotamian civilization, the art of pottery-making reached a high state of perfection many centuries before Christ.

The origin of the processes used by the Babylonians and Assyrians, and also by the Chaldaeans who inhabited the southern part of Babylonia, is not known for certain. They may either have borrowed them from the Egyptians or they may have developed the art themselves. A study of the Babylonian styles and achievements, however, inclines one to the latter opinion.

The ruins of Nineveh and Babylon consist of accumulations of fired bricks of various coloured bodies, very often covered with blue, greyish-blue and yellowish-white glazes. Tombs made in one single piece of ware, or formed from two pieces cemented together, demonstrate the great skill and general high development of the pottery art attained in those ancient times. There are three examples of these coffins in the British Museum. They are made from a yellow clay and the whole of the visible surface is enamelled, rich green on the outside and blue on the oval interior.

The Assyrians and Babylonians from the ninth to the sixth century B.C. also made wall tiles and bricks, decorated in relief and covered with tin glazes.

Herodotus relates that 'the city of Ecbatana, the capital of Media, was surrounded by seven walls painted in seven different colours, the first and largest of a white colour surrounded an area equal in extent to the city of Athens; the second was black; the third purple; the fourth blue; the fifth orange; and the two innermost in different colours, the battlements of the one being plated with silver, the other with gold.' If there is any truth in this story the walls were probably of brick, the surfaces being enamelled in colours.

Persia. – The Persians (who succeeded the Assyrians) carried
the manufacture of ornamental ware to a high degree of perfection. The body they employed was extremely siliceous and
had the appearance of soft stone. Because of the high sand
content of the raw material, its plasticity was very low, and so
one must admire all the more the skill of these ancient potters
in shaping and moulding such a difficult 'body'.

The glazes used were alkaline and very brilliant. The Persians knew how to obtain the various colours (yellow, blue
and green) by adding suitable metal oxides exactly the same as
those still employed to-day by potters all over the world.

To take the place of glazed tiles, they developed a new
type of wall covering – moulded panels covered with figures
and ornaments. Vases and jars were also made, from a more
plastic clay, from the third millennium onwards, hand modelled or formed on a potter's wheel. Funeral urns of this period
were very ornamental and finely wrought.

The potter's wheel. This was an early invention. Its actual
origin is unknown, but it was used in very ancient times by
the Egyptians, Babylonians and Persians, and, to a very great
extent, by the Greeks. Its discovery has been attributed to
various races which have excelled in the art of pottery-making.
The truth probably is that it was invented independently in
various countries.

Certainly the potter's wheel is a great improvement on hand
modelling. It made possible the production of a great variety
of combinations of cylindrical and spherical shapes.

India. – It is possible that the Indian races learned the manufacture of fired bodies and glazes from the Assyrians and
Chaldæans, but here again it is more likely that in prehistoric times they developed their own pottery art. Hand-
modelled red terra-cotta vases from North-West India, made
about the third millennium B.C., exhibit a high state of culture and refinement.

GREEK POTTERY

It is very interesting to note that the Greeks (and also the Romans) did not take over the art of glazing pottery from the Persians (with whom they traded extensively).

Whereas the tiles and bricks of the Babylonians and Persians and the pottery of the Egyptians are often covered with a heavy glaze layer, the vases, bowls and urns of the Greeks are mostly covered by a slight gloss, which we call lustre. How this gloss was obtained is not exactly known, but we can now safely assume that it was formed by applying a clay slip containing silica with a small addition of alkali as a flux.

The dark colour of the lustre is produced by the addition of iron oxide which, during the firing, in reducing atmosphere combines with the metal oxide contained in the clay.

Old Greek pottery is characterized by its ornate decoration and beauty of shape, both in great variety. The clay used in the preparation of the body must have been prepared by washing and sieving, since broken pieces disclose a very fine texture. Firing was carried out at a low temperature. The body is soft and can be scratched with a knife. The decoration was, in most cases, done by hand. Ornaments were scratched on the surface or impressed into the damp body by means of metal dies. The colours were black, yellow, and red brown.

For the purpose of classifying articles according to their style of decoration, Greek pottery can be divided into five periods.

1. Archaic period, previous to the eighth century B.C.
2. Archaic period, from the eighth to the seventh century B.C.
3. Archaic period, from the seventh to the sixth century B.C.
4. The period from the sixth to the fourth century B.C.
5. The Decadence, fourth to the second century B.C.[1]

1. Chaffers, *The Keramic Gallery*.

1. Specimens discovered of the earliest Greek period were rude, painted in brown or black on an ash-coloured ground. They were found at Athens, Corinth, Melos and Rhodes and in Etruria.

2. Pottery of the second Archaic period is usually of cream-coloured clay, painted with crimson and white, but sometimes black and crimson and red on black.

3. The third Archaic period also produced a style very severe, but more artistic than the previous periods. With the exception of the female figures which are painted white, in order to distinguish them from the males, the designs are in black on a red background.

4. The fourth period is the best for Greek art. During this time a process of decoration (now known as 'slipping') was extensively used. This consists in ornamenting the ware by applying in slip form another body of a different colour. This means that the colours used are not enamels but coloured clays painted on the vases after they were shaped. The outline was first sketched on the red clay ware and the black background, then carefully filled in, leaving the figures in red. White details were subsequently painted with thick and thin strokes and other touches as required, clay slip again being used for this purpose.

5. The fifth period – called the decadence – dates from the accession of Alexander the Great in 336 B.C. to approximately 186 B.C., when the fabrication of painted vases practically ceased, as a result of an edict of the Roman Senate against the celebration of the Bacchanalian festivals.

The pottery created during this period was more impressive and elaborate than that of previous epochs. There was a greater profusion of ornament and a certain grandeur in the draughtsmanship.

ROMAN POTTERY

Although in other instances the Romans were very prone to adopt the usages of the nations they conquered, they did not choose the use of glazed ceramics as practised by the

Babylonians, Egyptians and Persians, but only borrowed the Greek style.

The Romans became pre-eminent in the manufacture of bricks and tiles and also in the erection of brick buildings. Their victorious armies carried the art of brick-making with them into the colonies of the Roman Empire, Spain, Germany, and France.

The first fired bricks used by the Romans were for roofing purposes. They employed stones in building walls until the time of the Emperor Augustus. We then learn from his great architect Vitruvius that the Romans of those days started to use fired bricks in the erection of walls, since it was recognized how successfully they had withstood the influence of adverse atmospheric conditions, when employed in roofing.

Roman pottery is of two different types:

(*a*) A red type, called Samian ware.

(*b*) A black (rarer) type, called Etruscan ware.

Evidence of Roman occupation is nearly always manifested by the discovery – during excavation – of numerous fragments of beautiful red coralline Samian ware.

There is one very remarkable fact about this ware. No matter where it is discovered – France, Germany, England – the colour, texture and density are always the same. This has caused considerable discussion as to the place in which Samian ware was originally made. Considering the number of places, at great distances from each other, where specimens have been found, and the difference of the local clays available, it is difficult to understand how, from different materials, Roman potters could make a paste so very similar, in so many different locations.

In Italy, France and Germany, moulds and kilns for producing Samian ware (which is also called *terra sigillata*) have been found.

The decoration in relief on these Samian bowls was produced in the following manner. Stamps, either of bronze or fired clay, were modelled with the designs in relief and were used to impress a pattern on the interior of a mould of soft clay. This mould was then fired to the required hardness and was ready for use. Next the clay paste, from which the Samian bowl was to be made, was pressed into the mould by hand, thus taking its outside shape in every detail, from the inside of the mould.

While still in the mould, and remaining in a soft state, the interior of the vessel was shaped and smoothed by being turned on a lathe. Both the mould and the bowl were then placed in the kiln and baked. A very interesting point may be noted here. The mould had already been fired and would not shrink, whereas the bowl would. This makes it possible to use the mould in two capacities, firstly as a mould purely and simply (we use plaster of Paris moulds nowadays) and then as a 'sagger' or container during the firing process. (Present-day saggers will be discussed later on in the book.)

It can be seen from this short description that the art of mass production had already reached a high state of perfection in those far-off Roman days.

Many chemical analyses of the bodies used by the Romans have been made. It has been found that their composition is very similar to earthenware bodies used nowadays with the following exception.

The Romans used considerable amounts of iron and manganese oxides in order to give the body either a brilliant red or a brownish red colour. Moreover, the Romans added much more magnesium oxide than we do nowadays. It was probably introduced into the body by an admixture of dolomite. This large magnesia content has the great advantage of a high degree of refractoriness during firing. The unbiased potter of to-day must admit that, in this particular respect, the body composition of useful and reliable household articles has advanced very little since Roman times.

The many pottery articles of those days show a very brilliant surface gloss and for a long time it was not known how this type of glaze was produced.

In recent years, however, careful investigations have been

carried out on Etruscan ware (*terra nigra*) and on Samian ware (*terra sigillata*), and optical and electronic microscopes were used to clarify the nature of the body and the glossy surface. These investigations prove that the black Etruscan ware was made by admixing powdered charcoal to the body and by firing the articles in a strongly reducing atmosphere. The glossy surface was produced by covering the article after drying but before firing with a thin slip of a clay emulsion in which particles of only minute size were suspended.

The black decorations of the Greek vases were, however, produced in a different way, namely by using clay containing iron, magnesium, and manganese combinations and firing the articles decorated with such colouring agents in a reducing atmosphere. *Terra sigillata* was fired in oxidising conditions. The glossy surface was not achieved by applying a thin matt glaze as the appearance may suggest. Electro-microscopic investigations reveal that the articles (similarly to the *terra nigra*) after drying were covered with a thin slip emulsion consisting of clay particles of minute size.

The firing was carried out at temperatures of between 800° C. and 1000° C., according to the nature of the clay particles contained in that suspension. After firing, the edges of these minute clay particles softened and fused together. The crystalline structure of the particles can clearly be seen in the thin slices prepared from coatings covering *terra sigillata* articles and photographed under an electro-microscope.

These photos are reproduced in an interesting article by F. Oberlies and N. Köpper published in *Berichte der Deutschen Keramischen Gesellschaft*, May 1953.

In addition to pottery, the Romans made ceramic drain pipes, bath tubs and similar articles. In those far-off days they even produced vitrified stoneware pipes, shaped at the ends for fitting and cementing into each other, just as is done nowadays. Some of the water conduits laid by the Romans in certain towns of Southern France and Italy are still in such a good state of preservation as to be still serviceable to-day.

It will thus be gathered that sanitary pottery manufacture

and sanitary engineering reached a high degree of perfection in ancient Rome. With the decline of the Roman Empire, however, this branch of pottery fell into a state of decay from which it only emerged in the middle of the nineteenth century.

During the great migration of people in Europe in the fourth, fifth and sixth centuries, the pottery industry – together with most other forms of culture – was destroyed. Many centuries elapsed before the art of pottery returned to Europe via North Africa and Spain.

FAR EASTERN POTTERY

In the meantime, however, in the Far East the pottery art had reached a wonderful state of perfection. According to Chinese historians, the first pieces of pottery were made in the year 2698 B.C. under the Emperor Hoang-Ti. During the reign of this emperor the discovery of the compass, the preparation of the calendar, the invention of ships, the foundation of the sciences of astronomy, geometry and arithmetic, are also recorded. However, although the first pieces of pottery were thus reputed to have been made in the twenty-sixth–twenty-seventh century B.C., those discovered during excavations and investigations do not go back farther than the fifth century B.C. These are fired ceramic pots of a primitive nature, made on the potter's wheel and covered with a glaze. Fired bricks, with stamps and inscriptions indicating the same date of origin, have also been found.

Vessels excavated in the province of Shensi are assumed to have been made later on in the time of the Han Dynasty between 185 B.C. and 80 B.C. They exhibit a greater degree of artistry and craftsmanship and are a kind of stoneware, with brown, bluish-green and cream-coloured glazes. In many books these pots are described as the first 'porcelain' articles made, in which case Chinese porcelain was sixteen centuries ahead of European porcelain. Other authors, however, point out that these pieces were something between stoneware and porcelain, since they are not white and translucent enough to be termed porcelain.

No further progress of a spectacular nature in the art of pottery is reported in Chinese manuscripts in the following five or six centuries. Improvements in pottery were gradual, but, patronized by successive emperors, the art increased in perfection and beauty.

In the time of the Sui Dynasty (A.D. 581 to 617) and at the beginning of the following Tang Dynasty (A.D. 618 to 906), very remarkable translucent ceramic products were made. At that time skilful Chinese workmen were trying to imitate glass articles which had found their way to China from India. Using kaolin and other local raw materials they succeeded in making an opaque, glassy material which was most probably the first real china ever made.

The Tang Dynasty witnessed a great advance in all arts, but in painting, poetry and the ceramic art particularly. Stoneware sculptures, some bisque (without glaze) and others with yellowish white glazes, of great artistic value, were also made. The tea-drinking habit first reported in the middle of the eighth century favoured the manufacture of translucent porcelain cups and created new ceramic requirements.

Ceramic art flourished under the succeeding Sung Dynasty (A.D. 960 to 1290), the porcelain bodies becoming finer and more translucent, and yellow and green decorating colours being added to the blue. The first 'Flambé' vases and the development of the famous Nanking pottery both date from this period. Of all Chinese pottery, that of the Sung period is the purest, the most dignified and the most expressive.

Under the Ming Dynasty (1368 to 1643), Chinese pottery acquired the high technical perfection which made it so famous. Blue and white porcelain were decorated with overglaze enamels, and coloured glazes were also lavishly employed. Although the richness in palette tended to a certain over-embellishment, the widening of the colour range was accompanied by simplification in form, and the general impression is always harmonious. One never feels confused or embarrassed with this ware as one does when looking at certain over-decorated specimens of modern pottery 'inspired' by old Chinese examples.

After the Ming period comes the period of the Emperor K'ang-Hi or K'ang-Hsi (1662–1722). Ceramic technique and craftsmanship made further progress and reached a state of highest virtuosity. The most wonderful glazes, underglaze colours and on-glaze enamels were employed. Many glazes are of great beauty and richness and from the technical point of view unsurpassable. We, who nowadays have scientific laboratories and the recorded work of ceramic scientists at our disposal, are unable to reproduce some of the effects apparently so easily attained by Chinese potters in that period.

Among the glazes, the 'ox-blood', and the 'peach bloom', turquoise blue and aubergine purple, golden brown, black and celadon green, may be mentioned. Under-glaze colours – cobalt blue and copper red – were painted or sprayed on the bisque ware and covered with translucent and coloured glazes. Enamel on-glaze decoration was used, not only on white glazed porcelain but also on a blue and black ground. This enamel decoration was very often done in 'five-colour' painting (green, red, blue, yellow, purple).

The Chinese 'Potteries'. – The main Chinese pottery town was King-Te-Chin. From a description by Père d'Entrecolles, a Jesuit who visited this town in A.D. 1712, we learn that it bore comparison with the largest and most popular cities in China. There were more than a million souls, and the pottery materials, even the wood for the furnaces, had to be brought to the town from great distances. The cost of living was very high, yet numerous poor families found employment and were able to exist. 'The young and the old, the lame and the blind, all find work at which they can earn a livelihood by grinding colours or otherwise. Formerly there were only 300 furnaces, now there are nearly 3,000.'[1]

The Yung Chen and K'ang-Hsi Periods. – After the K'ang-Hsi
    1. See: Chaffers, *The Keramic Gallery.*

period come the Yung Chen and Chien Lung periods (1723 to 1795).

The artistic standard in these periods was also very high, the material being treated with the greatest virtuosity both from the artistic and technical points of view. Wonderful glazes, several of which are impossible to imitate, were used and the vases, dishes, bowls and cups were modelled in a style which equals the finest achievements of modern studio potters.

Porcelain manufacturing technique in China in those days was based on the principle of mixing a plastic refractory material which would *not* fuse during the firing with a material which *would* fuse during the firing. The plastic and refractory material was kaolin (Pain-go or Ngo-T'u in old China). The fusible material was Petuntse, a material very similar to our Cornish stone. The body preparation was carried out in a similar way as in the western part of the globe in the days of our grandfathers.

The main difference between the Chinese technique and ours was in the mould making, the glaze composition and the glazing. The Chinese made their moulds from clay. They then fired them in order to give them strength and in the firing they became almost dense (we use porous plaster of Paris moulds). Next, the plastic paste was pressed into the moulds. The articles were left in the moulds for a certain time and were then removed from the moulds for drying and glazing before firing (we harden porcelain articles by firing *before* glazing). They used a one-fire process, whereas nowadays for fine china-ware we use a two-fire process.

The glaze contained much greater amounts of calcium compounds, such as lime, than our glazes which contain more felspar. This accounts for the greenish shade of Chinese glazes. Vegetable ashes such as rice straw ash, weed ash, bracken ash, which are very often rich in lime and in phosphorus were admixed to the kaolin and petuntse (the material containing felspar-clay-sand mentioned above.)

The articles were placed in saggers (refractory containers)

as in present-day practice, placed in the oven and fired very slowly. Firing took about ten days and cooling about the same. Wood was used as fuel.

Chinese pottery has been deliberately dealt with at some length in this chapter. It will be seen that mass production and artistic design are not antagonistic. Chinese pottery manufacture is an example of an industry which gave employment to thousands of people through many centuries because it always maintained the highest standard of craftsmanship and artistic culture.

Japan. – Our information as to the origin of Japanese ceramic ware is very scanty. It is believed that the first porcelain vases and statuettes were made in the first century A.D. The story goes that progress in pottery manufacture was very slow until in the thirteenth century A.D. a Japanese potter, named Kato-siro, went to China to study the secret processes of porcelain making. After his return to Japan he is said to have made great improvements in porcelain manufacture.

The Japanese ceramic industry developed slowly but surely in the course of the centuries and became, in certain technical details, superior to the Chinese ware. Particularly famous is the Japanese 'egg shell', so named because it is very thin and translucent. The Japanese became remarkably skilful at producing very large translucent vases and plates of thin section. In addition to porcelain, they also made faience, common pottery and stoneware, very often having a translucent glaze and under-glaze decoration.

Japanese common pottery-ware fired at a low temperature and covered with a soft lead borax glaze is called Raku ware. 'The word "raku" ranges in meaning from ease, comfort, or enjoyment, to happiness, and comes from the ideograph engraved on a gold seal given in 1598 by the Taiko, who was an enthusiastic patron of the tea-ceremony, to Chojiro, son of Ameya, a Korean who settled in Kyoto in 1525 and who is said to have been the first to make this ware.' (*A Potter's Book*, Bernard Leach.)

POTTERY IN CONTINENTAL EUROPE

Spain. – After the decline of the Roman Empire the ceramic art, dormant in Europe for several centuries, came to life again in Spain. Lustred Majolica was first made by the Arabs and Saracens at a very early period, and they manufactured it wherever they gained new territories.

The glaze employed by the Arabs had an opaque, milky white appearance. This was due to the use of tin oxide, a practice known to the ancient Babylonians. The Arabs and the Saracens most probably acquired this knowledge from them and introduced it into Europe during their conquest of Spain in the eighth century.

Tiles and vases were made of porous material covered with a white opaque glaze, decorated with blue enamel and distinguished by a golden lustre. Particularly richly decorated tiles and vases were made on the Isle of Majorca. (The name Majolica is a corruption of the name Majorca.) The pottery made in Majorca was exported all over the world, but in particular to Italy. Another centre for the production of Majolica was Malaga where, amongst other elaborately decorated pottery articles, the finest specimen of Moorish faience – the celebrated vase of the Alhambra – was manufactured.

Italy. – For many centuries the Italians copied the ware imported from Spain. From the fifteenth century however, they developed their own style, and Italian pottery kept in step with the wonderful development of other Italian art of the period.

One of the greatest ceramic artists was Luca della Robbia, born at Florence, A.D. 1400. He covered his sculptures with an opaque tin glaze in order to render them impervious. His principal works are statues or groups made of a porous biscuit ware covered with a glaze of uniform colour, white, blue, green, or yellow. One of his most outstanding works is a medallion in high relief 10 ft. 7 ins. in diameter, the relief being decorated in various colours. Luca was succeeded by his nephew Andrea who had several sons. They were all distinguished ceramists and continued to make the same type of coloured reliefs and wonderful altar pieces.

One of the most ancient pottery towns in Italy was Faenza. This town gave to the French the name faïence, which is the word they use for their glazed porous pottery, just as Spain gave to the Italians the name Majolica. (It is interesting to note in this connexion that the celebrated glazed pottery of Delft gave the name to pottery of the same type manufactured in England in the seventeenth century.)

Another famous Italian ceramist was Giorgio Andreoli of Pavia who worked in Gubbio. He possessed the secret of the ruby and yellow metallic lustre with which he not only embellished his own products, but also enriched the work of other artists.

Ginori of Doccia must certainly be mentioned. His family played a part in Italy similar to that of the Wedgwood family in this country.

Apart from the places already named, Pesaro, Venice, Naples, Urbino, and Castel Durante were also famous for the manufacture of pottery of high artistic standing.

French Faience. – Faience was made in France from the twelfth century onwards. Glazed bricks, paving tiles, vases and bowls were produced in factories in Troyes, Dijon, Paris and Beauvais. In Paris, many manufacturers were potters and goldsmiths at the same time. They often made a design first in enamelled pottery and then they reproduced it in precious metal. The form and style of their pottery showed the characteristic features of goldsmiths' work.

One of the most remarkable potters in the France of the sixteenth century was Bernard Palissy. After many years of research carried out under most trying circumstances and frequently hampered by lack of means (he once burnt his table and chairs to heat his furnace), he finally succeeded in producing a glaze which he considered suitable for the decoration of his work. It was a matt glaze containing tin, resembling the Italian faience glazes. His rustic pottery and other works of art such as vases, statues, plates, candlesticks, inkpots, were soon highly appreciated and he then rapidly acquired a great fortune. Being a Protestant he was persecuted after the edict of 1559 and only escaped the massacre of St. Bartholomew's night because of the protection of Catherine de Medici. Later on, after the death of his protectress, he was put into prison for his belief and died there at the age of eighty.

Many factories for the production of faience were established in France, after the death of Palissy, in the seventeenth and eighteenth centuries. The technique was borrowed from the Italians but the style was French. The great centres of French faience manufacture were Nevers, Rouen, and Strasburg.

In the second half of the eighteenth century the manufacture of faience in France began to decline. Many works closed and others had to struggle very hard to compete with porcelain (from factories established at that time in France), with imported china and with imported English earthenware.

French Porcelain. – Many attempts made in France in the seventeenth century to produce real porcelain proved unsuccessful. However, they resulted in the manufacture of a new type of porcelain, very often called 'soft porcelain', first made by Chicaneau in 1693. This type of soft vitreous porcelain was, strictly speaking, not porcelain at all. It was made of pieces of glass (frit), finely broken, then ground, and made plastic by the addition of a small amount of clay. It was very difficult to form and even more difficult to fire. The French gave it the name of 'soft artificial paste' or *'porcelaine de Réaumur'*. Several factories were established for the manufacture of this type of porcelain, one of them being at Vincennes, near Paris. This factory was purchased by Louis XV and transferred to Sèvres.

In spite of considerable improvements in the manufacture of Sèvres soft porcelain the factory, in 1761, purchased the 'secret' of the manufacture of hard porcelain from a Frenchman who had acquired this knowledge in a German porcelain factory in Frankenthal. It was not possible, however, to use this formula in France until several years after, when the excellent kaolin beds near Limoges were discovered. Both the hard and soft types of porcelain were made at Sèvres until 1804, when the director, M. Brongniart, discontinued the manufacture of soft porcelain.

During the following years, in and near Limoges, a great number of factories were established for the manufacture of hard porcelain, thus forming the centre of the French industry.

The porcelain produced there not only supplies the requirements of the home market, but owing to its fine quality, it is also appreciated in many other countries. One of the best known private firms in Limoges is Messrs. Haviland.

Dutch Faience. – At the end of the sixteenth century in the town of Delft, was founded a faience factory which made Holland famous for its pottery. Under the supervision of the Guild of St. Luke the Delft faience manufacture became very important, both as regards turnover and quality.

A century later when this industry reached its greatest prosperity, there were about thirty potters in Delft. No one was allowed to establish a factory unless he obtained a licence from the Guild. A multitude of articles was produced, including imitations of porcelain, from Japan in particular, but also from other places as far apart as Saxony and China. The export of Delft faience to England was for some time very considerable. By the middle of the eighteenth century, however, owing to the competition of English pottery, the Delft industry began to decline.

German Stoneware and Faience. – With the availability of very plastic refractory clays on the lower Rhine, in the Westerwald and in Franconia, stoneware manufacture started in Germany as far back as the twelfth century. The ware of these factories had a dense and very hard yellowish body, covered with dark brown or blue glazes. Salt glazing was used in Aix-la-Chapelle and near Cologne in those early days. The stoneware from the Cologne district became very famous. It was greyish or bluish and decorated richly with blue and brown on-glaze colours and was exported to England and to the Low Countries in great quantities. Vases and jugs were decorated in relief depicting scenes of hunting or dancing. Stoneware potteries also existed at Siegburg, near Bonn, and at Höhr and other places.

Pottery of the faience or majolica type was manufactured in Germany in the Middle Ages, particularly in Nuremberg. The celebrated ceramist, Veit Hirschvogel of Nuremberg (1441 to 1525), studied the art of majolica making in Italy and after his return brought it to a high state of perfection in Germany. In the sixteenth century Nuremberg also became famous for the fine faience stoves used for domestic heating in Germany.

Other celebrated German faience factories were at Ansbach, Höchst-am-Main and Frankenthal.

German Porcelain. – The first pieces of Chinese porcelain to reach Europe were brought by the Arabs in the twelfth century. Their place of origin, however, was not known until Marco Polo, the Venetian, returning from his voyages, brought with him porcelain which he had acquired while in India, but which he knew to have been made in China.

In the middle of the sixteenth century regular supplies arrived from the Far East and so the trade was intensified.

During the reign of the Chinese Emperor K'ang-Hi, A.D. 1662–1722, the production of porcelain and china increased enormously and considerable shipments reached Europe. The wonderful pieces were much admired and eagerly bought by the numerous European princes who were in power at that time. Chinese porcelain came greatly into vogue and in the castles of the various princes secret experiments were carried out in an endeavour to imitate the Chinese art.

The first man in Europe to succeed in his aim of making white translucent hard porcelain was Böttcher. He first worked for William I of Prussia as an alchemist, a position rather midway between a witch doctor and chemist. Böttcher's own story, in later life, was that he left William to work for Augustus II, Elector of Saxony, because he was annoyed at the unbearable supervision to which he was subjected whilst in William's employ. The true story probably is that Böttcher himself became doubtful whether the stuff which he turned out really was gold and decided to get away, while the going was good, before the Prussians found him out. He got away only just in time. In fact, as soon as he reached the first town in Saxony, he was arrested at the request of his late employer, William, who asked for his extradition to Prussia. However, the Elector of Saxony needed a man who could make gold, and so he was detained as a prisoner, first at the fortress of Königstein, then in the castle of Albrechtsburg, near Dresden, where the supervision turned out to be no less unbearable! Böttcher continued his gold-making experiments but at the same time carried out experiments to reproduce the Chinese porcelain which in his opinion would be an indirect but better way for him to make gold for the Elector. In 1706 he succeeded in producing a fine red stoneware. This ware was not glazed, but was cut and then polished. He followed this up in 1708 by finding a white kaolin which made possible the manufacture of true porcelain – a white translucent pottery. The Elector subsequently established a great factory at Meissen, near Dresden, of which Böttcher was appointed director. The first porcelain body was perfect from the technical point of view, but it took some time until the decoration reached the same standard.

From 1731 to 1753, Kändler, a great sculptor, was in charge of the artistic side of the works.

This period is the most brilliant in the history of 'Royal Dresden'. Beautiful ware, however, was also made under the administration of Marcolini who became director in 1796. 'Royal Dresden' is a misnomer, in general use in English-speaking countries. In Dresden cheap pottery only was produced by small private firms. The proper term is 'Royal Meissen'.

The strictest control was employed in Meissen. The penalty for betrayal of any secrets connected with porcelain was life imprisonment or death. In spite of this, two workmen escaped to Vienna and contributed their knowledge towards the manufacture of porcelain at a newly-founded factory there. It was not easy for the founders of the Viennese factory to engage these two men. First of all they had to proceed secretly to Meissen and make their acquaintance in a coffee house. Then they had to make them directors at a yearly salary of 1,000 dollars (1,000 Thaler) with a carriage at their disposal – stiff terms for those days. The factory was established in 1718 and run first as a private firm until 1744 when it was bought by the Empress Maria Theresa at a price of 45,000 guilders.

The imperial factory was very successful at first and famous artists were engaged. A celebrated chemist prepared the colours and a high state of perfection was reached, particularly in the gilding. Later on, however, from the financial point of view the venture was not a success, and in 1864 the Imperial factory in Vienna was sold for other purposes and work discontinued.

The Royal Berlin porcelain factory was founded in 1751 by Wegely, an excellent ceramist. However, he suffered severe financial losses and so he sold the works to Gottskowski, a wealthy banker. The latter was more successful and twelve years later – in 1763 – he sold the works and 'secrets' to the king for 225,000 thaler.

King Frederick the Great took a personal interest in this factory and frequently used its products as generous gifts to princes and other influential personalities all over the world. When he occupied Dresden in the Seven Years' War he 'transferred' many of the best technicians and artists, and also a great part of the valuable collection from there to Berlin.

Frederick inaugurated a highly efficient selling organization. He permitted Jews to marry only if they could produce a certificate, signed by the managing director of the factory, stating that they had purchased a certain amount of porcelain. (Incidentally the right to sell porcelain – thrust upon the Jews by Frederick 'the Great' – was taken away by his most recent and most unsuccessful successor – Hitler). Frederick's scheme

B

was as great a success as Hitler's was a failure. The Jews disposed of their purchases more readily than the general dealer. As a result, in 1776, 700 workpeople were employed by the royal factory.

Other well-known porcelain factories established in Germany in the eighteenth century include those in Nymphenburg, near Munich, Frankenthal (in Palatinate), Höchst-on-Main, Fürstenberg (Thuringia), and Ludwigsburg (in Württemberg).

From the beginning of the twentieth century the porcelain industry in Germany grew rapidly. The number of people employed in it before the Second World War exceeded that in any other country. The main centres were Thuringia, Silesia, and Upper Franconia (a district in Bavaria). The first two centres are now in eastern Germany and the last-named in western Germany. The largest privately owned firms were Porz. Fabrik Kahla, Porz. Fabrik Rosenthal, and Porz. Fabrik Hutschenreuther, the two latter being in western Germany.

BRITISH POTTERY

Medieval Pottery. – The oldest ceramic ware found in excavations in Britain is of Roman origin. It is the same type of ware as that found in those other parts of the world occupied by the Romans in the first centuries A.D.

Distinctive native ware made earlier than the thirteenth century has not been found. The oldest native pieces were coarse earthenware jugs, covered with a green or yellow glaze, of sturdy shape and simple beauty, just fit for their purpose. This green or yellow glazed ware was improved upon in the fourteenth and fifteenth centuries by simple decorations in a different coloured glaze.

In the sixteenth century we find the 'Cistercian ware', coarse faience, in most cases glazed black or dark brown. The body is frequently decorated under the glaze with different coloured clay. The ware is so called because it is believed to have been made mainly by the Cistercian monks of those days.

Slip ware. – In the seventeenth century the manufacture of English slip ware reached a state of perfection never equalled elsewhere on the Continent. The earthenware body is of a coarse character and the decoration is applied by trailing a pattern over the surface with different coloured clay slips. (A 'slip' is a clay diluted to the consistency of thick cream.) The colours of these slips were orange, white, and red. Very often the orange formed the ground and the white and red the design. In other cases the design was in white on black under a transparent amber glaze. The best slip ware was made by Staffordshire potters.

The most prominent potters practising this type of art were the Toft brothers. Their large plates and oven dishes are masterpieces, both from the artistic and technical points of view, and superb in their restraint of colour and sureness of design. Very remarkable slip ware was also made by George Richardson and Nicholas Hubble at Wrotham, Kent.

Majolica ware. – Just at the time that Staffordshire slip ware was reaching its highest peak (in the middle of the seventeenth century) the manufacture of Majolica was started in Lambeth.

Until this type of manufacture started over here, much Delft majolica was imported from Holland. About the year 1650, some Dutch potters began to establish themselves in Lambeth. The industry developed quickly and soon about twenty manufacturers were making glazed pottery and tiles. The character was similar to the native Dutch. A fine glaze, made white and opaque by the addition of tin oxide, completely covered a paste of dingy colour. The pottery was decorated with blue landscapes and other ornamentation.

The industry flourished until the end of the eighteenth century, when the competition of the Staffordshire earthenware beat the Lambeth majolica out of the field.

A similar type of majolica was also made in Liverpool between 1716 and 1756.

Stoneware. – In the sixteenth and seventeenth centuries

stone-ware was imported from Holland and Germany in great quantities.

The first known successful English imitation of Continental stoneware was made by John Dwight. He established a factory in Fulham where he started the manufacture of salt glazed stoneware. The ware which he turned out was very good indeed and soon surpassed the German original. The paste was white or greyish white, and the ware very dense, extremely hard, and where thin, slightly translucent. It is consequently, technically speaking, salt glazed porcelain.

The First European Porcelain. – Dwight also carried out experiments to develop a soft frit porcelain. He succeeded about 1670 and applied for a patent in 1671. The granting of this patent is of great interest considering the fact that in many books dealing with the invention of porcelain Böttcher is described as the first to make European porcelain, in 1708.

The first paragraph of this patent reads as follows:

'Charles the Second, by the grace of God &c., to all to whome theise presents shall come, greeting.

'Whereas wee have been informed by the humble peticion of John Dwight, Gentl. that he had discovered "The Mistery of Transparent Earthenware, comonly Knowne by the names of Porcelaine or China, and Persian ware as alsoe the Misterie of the Stone Ware vulgarly called Cologne ware; and that he designed to introduce a Manufacture of the said wares into our Kingdome of England, where they have not hitherto been wrought or made" &c.'

Unfortunately further experiments with soft porcelain were disappointing. Dwight was very much annoyed and destroyed everything which reminded him of its manufacture. He thereafter concentrated on the production of his white salt glazed stoneware.

However, Dwight turned out a great variety of objects and was a great ceramist.

It is assumed that he employed some excellent sculptors at Fulham and he himself may have been the one who modelled the finest works of art produced there. Certainly the figures, busts and groups made in Fulham between 1671 and 1737 are among the finest pieces of pottery ever produced.

The Ehlers Brothers and Stoneware. – In 1693 Dwight brought a lawsuit against the brothers Ehlers and others for infringement of his patents.

The Ehlers brothers originally started a factory for the manufacture of stoneware in London, but later moved to Staffordshire, where the conditions were more favourable. They were of German-Dutch origin. Their father was a nobleman from Saxony, their mother the daughter of a Burgomaster of Amsterdam. Although the brothers were originally silversmiths, they also studied the manufacture of salt glazed stoneware in Cologne. One of the brothers, John, was also a clever chemist. He was most probably the first to mix Staffordshire clays after carefully washing, levigating and sifting them. This made possible the manufacture of a dense ware having a very fine grain size and a smooth surface.

The Ehlers were outstandingly successful in the manufacture of red stoneware in competition with Dwight's 'red porcelain', particularly in the case of teapots, bowls, etc. These were ornamented in relief on the inside by means of copper moulds in which the designs were engraved. They were then turned on the lathe to finish the outsides. Since the body used was tough and hard, it was possible by this method to produce very thin walled articles.

The Ehlers brothers opened a new field in Staffordshire pottery, and their brown salt glazed ware was imitated by many potters. From the brown to the white salt glazed stoneware was only a step. Not a very easy step, however, in those days, i.e. the turn of the seventeenth to eighteenth centuries.

Early in the eighteenth century, Astbury of Shelton succeeded in making white salt glazed stoneware. It is said that he got his knowledge of the Ehlers' secret 'formula' by getting a job at their factory. After having obtained their secret he started a business of his own. (Incidentally the first use of china clay as a raw material for giving greater whiteness to an earthenware paste is attributed to his son who noted by chance the whiteness of Cornish clay powder used by a veterinary surgeon.)

The manufacture of white salt glazed stoneware reached the height of perfection in Staffordshire in the middle of the eighteenth century. Very tastefully decorated stoneware was made in those days, the beautiful white glaze lending itself marvellously to decoration by painting.

Transfer printing was also used for decoration. This was done very sparingly and artistically.

Charmingly primitive and stylish figures were also produced, and the best of these are thought to have been made by Aaron Wood, who was previously an apprentice of Thomas Wedgwood, Josiah Wedgwood's father.

Brown and white salt glazed stoneware was also manufactured in Nottingham.

In no other countries in the world has such high quality ware of this type been manufactured as in England in the first half of the eighteenth century. It is surprising that, in the manufacture of artistic and household pottery on an industrial scale, salt glazed white stoneware has completely disappeared all over the world.

Earthenware. – The use of china clay in earthenware manufacture (introduced by Astbury as mentioned above) was a great success. The body became whiter, much stronger (when properly blended with plastic clays), and lent itself to mass production. Numerous new factories were established, using this new development and various other new processes associated with it, such as the employment of porous plaster moulds, a method imported from France. The use of moulds made it possible to produce exact copies in great quantities. The production costs decreased and the purchase of pottery was made available to a much wider public.

The Wedgwood Family. – Factories for quantity production were established in, amongst other places, Burslem, Hanley, Leeds, and Liverpool. At first the ware made in these towns was not of outstanding quality. It was, however, brought to a high degree of perfection by Josiah Wedgwood, the most celebrated English ceramist and one of the outstanding potters of all ages. He was, at the same time, an excellent ceramist, a business man, an engineer and an artist, qualities very rarely found in one person.

The Wedgwood family was engaged in the pottery trade for several generations before Josiah's birth at Burslem (1730). He was the youngest of thirteen children and served as an apprentice in the factory of his brother Thomas. After working with various partners, he established a factory, on his own account, at Burslem in 1757. Here he made a fine ivory-coloured earthenware which was a great success.

His first endeavour was to improve the white body. After carrying out a long series of systematic experiments he succeeded. Similarly, he perfected the ivory body which he was able to supply in various shades from light ivory to light yellow. He also improved the glaze which consisted of flint glass, zinc oxide and sand. (The flint glass was the equivalent of what we now know as 'frit'.) The new shapes were designed by Wedgwood himself in these early days. Later on he relegated this task to sculptors or modellers.

In 1765 Queen Charlotte ordered a tea and coffee set of Wedgwood ivory ware, decorated with green and gold. This order was executed in such an excellent way that he obtained many orders for this ware (famous afterwards under the name 'Queen's Ware') and for other similar table ware.

Wedgwood organized his work into two completely separate departments. Articles like Queen's ware were produced in the 'useful' department. A red stoneware and a black stoneware (called 'Black Egyptian' and made of a mixture of 80% various clays, 10% iron oxide and 10% manganese oxide) were manufactured in the 'ornament' branch under the supervision of his partner, Thomas Bentley, who specialised in the manufacture of reproductions of antiques such as vases, cameos, etc. Both the products of the 'useful' and 'ornament' branch were of the highest standard and were produced at a price which attracted vast business. To meet this increasing demand, a new factory was established at Etruria in 1769 where, generally speaking, the same types of ware were manufactured.

In 1776 the manufacture of another new type of ware, the Jasper ware (a stoneware body containing barium sulphate, barium carbonate, and felspar and stained with different metal oxides for various colours) was introduced.

A very important invention which facilitated mass production of decorated ware was made in 1752 in Liverpool by John Sadler and Guy Green. They invented and developed the method of transferring prints from engraved copper plates to pottery. Wedgwood employed this new method of decoration in his work and also sent weekly earthenware consignments to Messrs. Sadler and Green for decoration.

Wedgwood's prices were very cheap considering the quality of his products. In many cases he was satisfied with a very small profit. The average price, for example, of his Greek vases was only between one and two guineas each. When he accepted orders for ware which did not fall within his standard range, but had to be made to special specifications, he did not even make a small profit, but charged his actual costs! For instance, in 1773 he accepted an order for a 952 piece dinner-set from Catherine, Empress of Russia. Each piece had to be decorated with an individual picture of English landscapes, castles, country houses, and the like. The price of this dinner service was £3,000. It can be seen from the correspondence which Wedgwood had with his partner Bentley that this price just covered the actual prime cost. To offset this, however, the dinner service was on view in London for two months and this exhibition was, of course, enormous publicity for Wedgwood.

By the end of the eighteenth century English fine earthenware (characterized by a white or ivory paste covered with a translucent glaze) had completely supplanted faience and majolica (which employs a muddy coloured paste covered by an opaque white glaze).

At the beginning of the nineteenth century the art of earthenware manufacture spread from England to the various Continental countries where this ware was called English earthenware (just as a century ago faience of the Dutch type, made in England, was called Delft).

EARLY ENGLISH PORCELAIN

Any history of English porcelains, however short, should first of all explain that three different types of porcelain have been manufactured to date in this country. They are:

1. Hard Porcelain.
2. Soft Porcelain.
3. Bone China.

(Later on in this book, the characteristics of all three types will be discussed at some length and so at this stage the technical references will be as brief as possible.)

1. Hard Porcelain is characterized by two factors:

(a) It is fired at a high temperature – about 1300° to 1400° C. – already covered with a glaze, which fuses at the same temperature at which the paste matures.

(b) There is usually no bisque fire (firing in the unglazed state) or only a very easy bisque fire.

The reader will remember that earlier on in this chapter it was explained that the Chinese, the Japanese and most of the Continental Porcelains are 'hard' porcelains.

2. Soft porcelain is fired 100°–200° C. lower than hard porcelain, i.e. somewhere between 1200° and 1300° C.

Unlike the hard porcelain mentioned above, the soft porcelain body contains glass or 'frit' (a specially-prepared glass) and is always fired twice.

(a) It is first fired in an unglazed state at the temperature mentioned above, namely 1200° to 1300° C. This is called bisque firing.

Frenchman, Nicolas Spremont, was in charge of it. In those years the factory was hardly able to execute all the orders which it received from the royal family and especially from the aristocracy. Statuettes and bird figures were made in large quantities. Table ware was very tastefully designed and very often decorated with paintings of fruit and flowers, with butterflies and insects.

In 1769 the factory was bought by Dewsbury of Derby. He carried on manufacture in Chelsea until 1784. He then closed the works and transferred material, equipment and most of the workpeople to Derby, where some years previously he had acquired a porcelain factory.

(Incidentally, soft porcelain was first made in Derby, by a Frenchman, André Planché. He made a ten years' agreement with a Mr. Heath, who provided the capital, and with Mr. Dewsbury, by which the three of them undertook to co-operate in the manufacture of porcelain. Planché seems to have come out worst eventually, because by the time his agreement expired, his two partners knew all the 'tricks of the trade', were no longer in need of his services, and so named the firm Dewsbury and Heath.) In 1786 Dewsbury's son William entered the firm as a partner. The name of the firm changed into W. Dewsbury & Son.

The Chelsea–Derby table ware is of a very fine quality. The porcelain is very translucent and is decorated with colours both lively and delicate. About 1815 Robert Bloor took over the works. They were closed in 1848.

The factory at Worcester is one of the very few early porcelain factories still in operation, and at the same time flourishing as one of the leading factories in England. It was established in 1751 by Wall, an artist and chemist. Very early on, he introduced printing on the fired, unglazed ware (biscuit). His main collaborator in this field was Hancock, a very skilful craftsman and artist. They used an ingenious method of transfer printing. In transfer printing an engraved copper plate is employed (the design is engraved in the plate). In other processes it is usual to smear the copper plate with the desired colour, but at Worcester it was covered with a sticky oil. They then proceeded as follows:

They removed the oil from the plain surfaces of the plate and left oil only in the engraved spots. Glue bats were then pressed on the plate, from which they received an oily copy of the engraved pattern. The glue bats were next pressed on the biscuit china ware, which received the oily pattern on its surface. The china was then dusted with the desired colour. The colour could easily be blown off the clean surface, but remained on the oily pattern. The biscuit ware, complete with coloured pattern, was then ready for firing.

This method is still used to a very great extent in Continental porcelain factories, the glue bat being replaced by rubber sheets or rollers. (Lots of glue bats can be made from only one copper plate.)

The porcelain made at Worcester between 1760 and 1770 was of a particularly fine quality. The patterns were usually influenced by Japanese work, and gilding played a very important part in the decoration. In 1785 the works were purchased by Thomas Flight and later on named Flight & Barr. In 1840 the firm was amalgamated with Messrs Chamberlain (a firm established in Worcester since 1786). The new firm was named Chamberlain & Co, and manufactured very fine table services. Their speciality was the manufacture of very elaborate and richly-decorated porcelain. Very high prices were obtained and for very richly decorated table services prices as high as £4,000 were charged in the middle nineteenth century.

Bone China. – Bone china was perfected by Josiah Spode about the year 1805. Bone ash took the place of the glassy ingredients of soft paste porcelain. This new type of porcelain was something midway between hard porcelain and soft porcelain. It was easier and cheaper to manufacture than fritted soft porcelain. It was more translucent and more suitable for decoration with brilliant underglaze colours than hard porcelain. England obtained a great reputation as the only country manufacturing this beautiful type of porcelain.

MODERN CERAMICS

This brief summary of ceramic history has brought us to the nineteenth century. Secret formulas are slowly but surely replaced by scientific principles. The potters to-day are still wonderful craftsmen but the processes have been speeded up by mass production which makes ceramic ware inexpensive and thus more and more people are able to buy it.

As regards design and decoration, the transition period to mass production was not an easy one. Tradition had developed shapes and designs which were not intended for mass production. New industries (like the plastic industry) did not have such a transition period. " Plastic " articles were, from the beginning, designed and shaped for mass production. The public like them and although the material is much inferior to ceramic materials for many household applications from kitchen to lounge, their design and vivid colouring appeal to the buying public. Fortunately, many leading pottery manufacturers also have proved that mass production and good design are not incompatible.

It is true to say that those works which employed the best (and the most highly paid) artists were always more successful than those which did not like expensive artists but were more generous in the amount of gilding and colouring which they splashed over their otherwise very beautiful pottery.

Generally speaking, it can be said that the pottery industry has made much progress in recent years, not only as regards manufacturing methods, but also as regards design.

After the interruption of the war years, industrialists and artists alike are now ready to meet the market both at home and abroad with pottery of tasteful shapes and patterns. These are based on tradition but take into account the requirements of mass production and the changed and improved taste of the ultimate customers.

MECHANIZATION IN THE POTTERY INDUSTRY

Some non-technically-minded people pine for the days of the individual craftsman and view with dismay all mechanization and mass production in industry. This is all very well, but in this connexion it may not be out of place to give an illuminating example of the cost of producing the necessary power by using a man and alternatively a machine, thus demonstrating how replacement of man hours by kilowatt hours reduces cost of production. Electrical power is sold by the unit, or kilowatt hour. Mechanical work is usually expressed in horse power. One horse is assumed to do the work of seven men and three kilowatts are roughly equal to four horse power. It is a very simple calculation to show, therefore, that one k.w.h. (or electrical unit) costing, say, one penny, is equivalent to nine men working for one hour, each getting say two shillings per hour. On this basis man hours are over two hundred times as expensive as kilowatt hours. The price of k.w.h.'s will go down and the price of man hours go up, as years go by.

Mechanization in the ceramic industry has been carried out to a lesser extent than in many other industries. The following are the main reasons:

1. The materials used in the ceramic industry do not lend themselves so easily to mechanization as do, for instance, metals, plastics, and the like.

2. The ceramic factories usually manufacture a greater variety of individual articles than other industries (exceptions are, of course, the brick, tile and refractories works).

3. The ceramic industry employs fewer engineers, particularly in the leading positions, than the younger industries. However, the general trend in the ceramic industry is, as in most progressive industries, towards mechanization. Automatic machines are being increasingly introduced for the various shaping and other processes.

However, as mentioned above, not all shaping processes lend themselves readily to mechanization and many difficulties have still to be overcome, particularly in the case of high quality pottery. Close collaboration between the practical potter and the ceramic engineer will certainly solve many still outstanding problems.

Transport of raw materials, of prepared bodies, of semi-finished products is being mechanized more and more. Firing is mechanized by the use of continuous tunnel kilns. Whether one likes it or not the craftsmanship of the individual potter, which in the past was decisive as regards the success or failure of individual firms, will require more and more the partnership of the ingenious engineer who plans and co-ordinates automatic machinery and mechanical devices.

REFERENCES

The Keramic Gallery, William Chaffers, Gibbins & Co, London.
Grundriss der Keramik, Friedrich Jaenicke, Stuttgart.
A Treatise on Ceramic Industries, E. Bourry, Scott Greenwood, London.
The Potter's Book, B. Leach, London.
English Pottery and Porcelain, Cecilia Sempill, Collins, London.
A Guide to the Collection of Tiles, Arthur Lane, Victoria & Albert Museum.
The Art of the Potter, W. B. Honey, Faber & Faber, London.
Chinesisches Porzellan, Ernst Zimmermann, Leipzig.

CHAPTER II

What are Ceramics?

By the term 'ceramic' is implied a material made of clay or similar substance formed in a plastic state and then dried and fired at a temperature high enough to give the necessary strength.

The word 'Ceramics' is of Greek origin. In ancient Hellas the potter was called 'Kerameus', and 'Keramos' meant both the product of the potter and also the raw plastic clay material used in pottery. Nowadays, we understand by 'ceramics' not only the manufacture of pottery articles, but also the manufacture of all those in which clay or similar plastic raw material is used and which, after having been shaped and dried, are subjected to a firing process to give the desired mechanical strength. Furthermore, we understand by ceramics that branch of technology which deals with the manufacture of ceramic articles, their technical characteristics and the raw materials used.

Ceramic products supply the needs of man in the construction and decoration of buildings (bricks and tiles); they are used in the manufacture of metals (refractory materials), as insulators in the electrical industry (porcelain and steatite), in the manufacture of chemical products (stoneware and porcelain), in sanitation (earthenware and vitreous china), in drainage of water and sewage (stonewares). The pottery branch of the ceramic industry supplies the various domestic requirements from the kitchen to the dining-room (porcelain, china, earthenware). In the production of art ware practically all types of ceramic materials are used from terra cotta to fine china.

THE SUB-DIVISION OF CERAMICS

Although the number of individual types of ceramic materials in commercial production throughout the world runs into hundreds, they can be broadly classified under two headings, the 'heavy clay' products and the 'pottery' products.

A – *Heavy Clay Products*. 'Heavy clay' products are broadly those which consist mainly of clay with only very small additions of other raw materials. They are used principally in structural work and for general industrial purposes. Industrial refractory materials, however, also come under this heading although large additions of raw materials other than clay are very often employed.

The following list contains the more important members of the 'heavy clay' products group.

1. Common bricks
2. Fine bricks
3. Paving bricks
4. Hollow tiles
5. Conduits
6. Roofing tiles
7. Drain tiles
8. Sewer pipes
9. Stoneware for industrial purposes
10. Refractories

B – *Pottery Products*. 'Pottery' products are those made of terra cotta, majolica, faience, earthenware, vitreous china, porcelain, and bone china. Technical and structural ware made of earthenware, like wall tiles, and electrical insulators, made of porcelain or other ceramic insulating materials, also come under the term 'pottery'.

The Board of Trade returns list under the heading 'Pottery':
A. Tiles:
    Glazed wall and hearth tiles.
    All other sorts of tiles.
B. Sanitary ware.
C. China, including translucent pottery and all pottery known as china or porcelain.
D. Electrical ware (including insulators).
E. Earthenware of all other descriptions.
F. Refractory goods.

ALTERNATIVE CLASSIFICATION

A more technical classification is to separate ceramic products into permeable and impermeable ware. (This distinction is only applicable to the body, since glazes are always impermeable.) Permeable ceramic ware absorbs water, impermeable pottery absorbs very little or none. Whether the ware is permeable (porous) or impermeable (dense and vitrified) depends firstly on the composition of the body, and secondly on the temperature at which the firing is carried out. For example, a body which is porous when fired at, say, 1200° C. may be dense when fired at, say, 1400° C.

Again, in the case of two different bodies, one containing additions which melt at a *low* temperature and the other containing additions which melt at a *high* temperature, the former may become dense, while the latter is still porous, at the same temperature.

Both the porous and the dense type of ceramic ware may be glazed or unglazed.

A – *Permeable Ware*. Permeable (porous) pottery shows a rough fracture and sticks to the tongue when tested in this fashion. Permeable ware is sub-divided into:

1. Heavy clay ware.
2. Refractory ware.
3. Terra cotta.
4. Earthenware, faience, majolica.

(1) Heavy clay ware has already been defined.

(2) Refractory ware is composed in such a way that it may be subjected to very high temperatures without suffering damage or deformation.

(3) Terra cotta comprises all porous pottery ware which is not covered with a glaze. It is fired at a lower temperature than earthenware and is consequently softer and more porous. It can be scratched by a hard steel. Its colour varies from light yellow to red, reddish brown, and brown.

(4) Earthenware on the other hand is white or ivory and coated with a glaze. It is harder than terra cotta, being fired at a higher temperature.

Faience is a name given to tin-enamelled earthenware, and in France is applied to glazed earthenware generally.

Majolica is a name given to tin-enamelled pottery, particularly to Italian tin-enamelled earthenware.

B – *Impermeable Ware*. Dense, non-porous (vitrified) ceramic ware is sub-divided into:
1. Stoneware.
2. Vitreous china.
3. China and Porcelain.

(1) Stoneware is ceramic ware with a slightly coloured greyish or brownish body. It is dense (non-porous but not translucent).

(2) Vitreous china is very similar to stoneware. It is dense, or practically dense, but unlike stoneware its colour is white.

(3) Porcelain (and china) is pottery with a white translucent and impermeable body.

(Very often the term 'pottery' is used by laymen for earthenware and terra cotta as distinct from porcelain and china. In technical books on ceramics, however, the term 'pottery' includes china and porcelain.)

WHITE WARE

In the U.S.A. the term 'White Ware' is used for pottery and includes:

Porcelain.
Bone China.
Vitreous Sanitary Ware.
Vitreous Floor Tiles.

Electrical Insulators made of porcelain and steatite.
Semi-vitreous table ware.
Earthenware.
Wall tiles.

CERAMICS IN A WIDER SENSE

Articles made from ceramic raw materials and which are made plastic by other means than by the use of clay, are nowadays also classified as ceramics, provided that, after shaping, they are subjected to a firing process. For instance, in the preparation of alumina bodies for the manufacture of sparking plugs, the alumina is made plastic by treatment with acids.

Again in the manufacture of certain high-grade refractory materials cements are often used as binders. Numerous bodies of this nature have been developed in recent years and articles made of such bodies, after being subjected to high temperatures, are called ceramic articles. Ceramics in a wider sense are therefore the products of 'High temperature chemistry of non-metallic materials'.

CHAPTER III

Clay

WHAT IS CLAY?[1]

IN Chapter II the question 'What are Ceramics?' was answered by the statement that by the term 'Ceramic' is meant a material made of clay, formed in a plastic state, and then dried and fired. The next question to arise therefore is 'What is clay?'

Clay is a product of the decomposition of the mineral feldspar and so before we can answer the question 'What is clay?' we had better first deal with feldspar.[2]

Feldspar is the most abundant mineral found in crystalline rocks, the commonest of which are granite and gneiss. Three fourths of the known surface of the earth is formed of granite and gneiss containing 60% to 90% feldspar.

Granite is an unstratified, granular rock, whereas gneiss is a laminated rock, i.e. arranged in layers. Both are composed of the minerals quartz, feldspar and mica which are mingled without regular arrangement of the crystals. As already mentioned they are the most abundant of the igneous crystalline rocks which were formed by volcanic agency from the molten magma, one of the supposed fluid layers under the earth's crust. The magma is slowly cooled, deep down in the bowels of the earth, under the enormous pressures of 5 to 10 tons per square inch. Such 'plutonic' rocks only stay in equilibrium under these conditions deep down in the earth. When, by subsequent erosion, the rock is exposed to the influence of air and water, it is no longer stable. The rock breaks down to a greater or lesser extent dependent on the size of the

1. The word comes from an old English word 'claeg', Dutch and German klei, from 'kli' – 'to stick to', in German 'kleben'.

2. Feldspar comes from the German feldspat, feld meaning 'Field' and spat 'a spar'.

crystals. The break up is due to two causes, mechanical disintegration and chemical decay.

Although feldspar occurs principally in the form and manner just described, i.e. as small crystals in granite and gneiss, there are also deposits of practically pure feldspars of larger crystal size.

The quantity of deposits of such purer feldspars is small compared with the amount of feldspar embodied in igneous rocks; but for commercial uses of feldspar the purer deposits are used.

Formation of Clay

We may now return to our original subject. Under the influence of carbonic acid and water (particularly if the rocks are covered by marshes and bog earth developing humic acid) and if the access of atmospheric oxygen is prevented, the feldspar is decomposed and clay is formed.

Potassium feldspar, which is the main constituent of these rocks, is a combination of potash (K_2O) and alumina (Al_2O_3) with silicic acid (SiO_2). It has the formula $K_2O.Al_2O_3. 6SiO_2$ and contains 16.9% potash, 18.3% alumina and 64.8% silicic acid. (Apart from potassium feldspar there are other types of feldspar. These and their characteristics will be discussed later on. At present we will confine our attention to the decomposition of feldspar and the formation of clay.)

The decomposition of feldspar is a process in which potash and a part of the silica is dissolved by water under the conditions described above, while at the same time the remnants of the decomposition attract water and combine with it. This process takes place in the following way:

	SiO_2	Al_2O_3	K_2O	H_2O
100 parts potassium feldspar . . .	64.63	18.49	16.88	— %
Dissolved and taken away . . .	— 43.05	–	— 16.88	— %
Added . . .	–	–	–	+6.47%

	SiO_2	Al_2O_3	K_2O	H_2O
Clay formed (46.5 parts)	21.58	18.49	–	6.47%
Converted into percentage figures . .	46.3	39.8	–	13.9%

The dissolved potash and silica are washed away and clay remains. Small feldspar crystals are more easily decomposed than the large crystals found in pure feldspar or pegmatite deposits. (Pegmatite is a feldspatic rock containing feldspar and quartz.) This has been demonstrated by the following experiment. Pieces of pegmatite and granite are covered by vegetable earth, rich in humus, in a hothouse for a year or so. At the end of this period the granite shows clearly the beginning of disintegration whereas pegmatite does not.

We have seen above that, theoretically, the end-product of the chemical process described above has the following composition:

$$46.3 \ SiO_2 \quad 39.8 \ Al_2O_3 \quad 13.9 \ H_2O,$$

the chemical formula being

$$Al_2O_3 \quad _2SiO_2 \quad 2H_2O.$$

This is pure clay or kaolin. But a clay of such pureness does not exist in nature. The ceramists call it 'clay-substance'. All natural clays and kaolins contain impurities.

Kaolin (or China Clay)

The name kaolin is assumed to come from the Chinese word 'Kao-ling' which means 'high ridge'. It is believed to refer to the district in China from which the kaolin or china clay was originally obtained.

It is very interesting to observe how nature transforms the non-plastic rock mineral feldspar into a plastic material clay. (A 'plastic' material is one which can be deformed under mechanical stress without losing its cohesion and which is able to keep the new form given to it.)

It will be remembered from a previous page that granite is a heterogeneous mixture of feldspar, quartz, etc. The feldspar is decomposed by chemical action. Other substances, such as the quartz, are not attacked and remain unaltered. The mixture is a substance of white greyish or brownish tint and is called 'raw kaolin'.

Raw kaolin consists mainly of three substances.

1. True clay particles (which the ceramist refers to as 'clay substance').
2. Quartz grains of various sizes.
3. Undecomposed feldspar.

Of course, many of the impurities found in the original stone such as mica, titanium and iron compounds, and other constituents in small quantities, still remain in the raw kaolin.

If the raw kaolin has been formed by the decomposition of fairly pure feldspar beds (which is not very often the case), the decomposition product is a kaolin which contains only small amounts of impurities. The compositions of the original rocks, however, differ considerably and this explains the considerable variations in the composition of primary clays or kaolins.

'Primary' clays or kaolins are clays which are still on or near the place where they were originally formed.

If the clay is carried away by water, those materials in it which are of small grain size are kept in suspension. They are jostled, tossed and milled en route until the speed of the water is reduced. They are then deposited, and form beds of a material consisting of exceedingly small particles of clay and other materials. These particles have been reduced on the way to very small grain sizes. The heavier and larger stones have already been dropped upstream. Clays collected in this way are called secondary 'clays' and if they are very pure and white, secondary 'kaolins'.

It has been explained that most of the clays – whether primary or secondary – found in nature contain admixtures – in various amounts – such as sand, feldspar, mica and so on. When speaking about clay, clay ware, and so on, we do not imply pure clay but we refer to a mixture of clay with other materials.

WHY IS CLAY PLASTIC AND SAND NON-PLASTIC?

Clays, as we know them, always contain water. The amount of water which they already contain, or the amount of water we add to them, affects the degree of plasticity. Plasticity in the presence of water is a typical characteristic of all materials which contain clay-substance. It is dependent not only on the amount of clay-substance present in the material, but also on the physical properties of the clay-substance itself. Although the chemical composition of two clays may be identical, the plasticity may be different. The plasticity of clay is due to two factors.

1. The sheet-like structure of the clay mineral.
2. The minute size of the clay crystal.

The plasticity of a clay is the greater, the smaller the size of its particles. The particle size of kaolins is greater than that of secondary clays, and so the latter are more plastic. Very plastic clays contain particles so small that it is impossible to recognize their crystalline shape even with a powerful optical microscope. Fortunately, X-ray analyses and electronic microscopes prove that even those minute colloidal particles are in reality of a crystalline nature. Because ball clays consist of smaller particles than china clays (kaolins), the former are more plastic than the latter. The particle size of kaolins is less than 0.01 mm. diameter, and ball clays are even smaller.

Ceramists usually consider clay particle sizes in terms of 'sieves'. Commercial kaolin material has to pass a 200 mesh sieve, but most of the particles of a plastic clay are much finer and of ultra-microscopic size.

To get some idea of the extremely minute crystal size of plastic clays, it is instructive to compare them with the size of a hydrogen molecule on the one hand and with the particle size of a non-plastic material, ground so finely that it passes through the finest available sieve, on the other hand. This comparison was recently published by Marcus Francis and D. G. Beech of the British Pottery Research Association.

Table I gives the relative diameter of typical particles in terms of the hydrogen molecule as unit diameter.

Table I

	Typical Relative Size
Hydrogen molecule	1
Starch molecule	50
Bentonite (an ultra-plastic type of clay) .	1,000
Clay (kaolin)	10,000
800-mesh barytes (a non-plastic mineral) .	250,000
Limit of vision with unaided eye . .	500,000

That very small grain size is conducive to plasticity is not peculiar to clays. All minerals acquire a certain degree of plasticity by very fine grinding. For instance, if sand is milled in a jar mill for many days and thus reduced to a powder of minute grain size, the addition of a suitable amount of water will develop a certain amount of plasticity, but nothing comparable with the plasticity of clay. The structural unit of sand and of all other non-plastic materials possesses a three-dimensional lattice. In these, each unit is attached to the next, in three dimensions, by valency forces. (The resulting crystal is of three-dimensional nature.)

The much greater plasticity of clays over other minerals of minute grain size is due to the lamellar or sheet-like structure of the clay crystal. The unit clay crystals are attached to one another by valency forces in two dimensions only, namely in the planes of the sheets, so continuous layers are formed one crystal unit thick. The crystals are almost of two-dimensional nature. In the dry state even the most plastic clay is a non-plastic substance, but if water is added, the material becomes plastic and molecular attraction increases, the smaller the particles. The sheet-like form of the crystals makes this attraction still more powerful. Layers of clay crystals are stacked, one above the other, with layers of water molecules between them. There is, of course, no chemical bond between them (as in the case of the polymerized organic plastic materials).

The bond is looser and of an electrical and gravitational nature.

This structure of the clay-crystal-water system explains the extraordinary sensitiveness of plastic pastes to the addition of a few drops of an alkaline solution such as sodium carbonate or sodium silicate. The following description of a very simple experiment illustrates the complex and singular nature of clay.

WHY A FEW DROPS OF ALKALINE SOLUTION TURN A STIFF CLAY PASTE INTO A LIQUID SLIP

If we prepare a stiff plastic clay paste by kneading or stirring clay and water, and add to this paste a few drops of an alkaline solution such as a sodium carbonate solution and continue kneading or stirring it, the plastic paste is converted into a liquid slip of cream-like consistency. If we add more and more sodium carbonate solution, the liquid slip turns back again into a stiff and sticky paste. If we now add some drops of an acid (for instance acetic acid) the stiff paste is again converted into a slip, and if we add still more acid the slip will return to stiff paste consistency. With suitable clay only 0.2% of alkali is required to make a liquid slip out of a stiff plastic paste. How is all this possible? The alkaline sodium carbonate or sodium silicate solution contains free OH ions (hydroxyl ions) negatively charged. They repel the negatively charged clay crystals and counteract the mutual electrical attraction of the clay crystals (mentioned above). The greatest slip fluidity is obtained when the number of free ions from the alkaline solution saturates the free ions of the clay crystals. If too many ions are put to work (that is if too much alkali is used) they begin to cause mutual attraction of the clay particles, which can no longer move about freely in the water and consequently form a stiff paste again.

The quantities of alkali required to give the best possible viscosity to the slip depend entirely on the nature of the clay. For several very plastic clays only 0.2% sodium carbonate is required; for others the addition of 0.4% gives better results. Many kaolins require as much as 1%. Many clays already contain alkali in the form of impalpably powdered feldspar or mica. Such clays need smaller additions of sodium carbonate to convert them into slips.

As will be described later on in the book, clay is used in slip form in the process of casting pottery. The discovery that small amounts of alkalis, without additional water, will turn a plastic clay liquid, has made it possible to use the casting process for mass production.

The electrostatic forces of repulsion in an alkaline clay slip are so great that an enormous number of clay particles per pint of water are kept in suspension for a very long period without settling. They even keep non-plastic admixtures in suspension (for instance ground sand and feldspar), which would settle down at once, were it not for the clay particles present in such abundance. Clay particles are so small that, even without the addition of an alkali, clay will remain in suspension, if added to and thoroughly shaken with water. The more plastic the clay the more readily it will keep in suspension, the reason being that the more plastic a clay the smaller its particle size. Use of this property of clays is made, e.g. in the mixing of glazes. A small amount of clay added to the non-plastic glaze materials will keep them in suspension and prevent settling.

Amount of Water Required for Different Consistencies

Since clay in a completely dry state is non-plastic, water has to be added to give it the requisite plasticity and consistency to suit the method of shaping a particular design. Various consistencies are, of course, used.

For the consistencies mentioned hereunder, different quantities of water have to be used. The smaller percentage figure given in each case is for an open body containing more open china clays. The higher percentage in each case is for very plastic bodies containing more plastic ball clays.

	Water in per cent
'Dry' body	7–18
Stiff or semi-dry	10–20
Semi-stiff or stiff plastic body . .	12–25
Plastic body (normal consistency for jolly-ing)	15–30
Oversoft body	17–35
Liquid body	20–50

The water which is added to give a body the required
consistency is called the 'water of formation'. It evaporates
gradually if the body is left in a dry atmosphere, but by careful
application of warm air the drying process can be accelerated.
Apart from the water of formation, the clay also contains, as
previously mentioned, water chemically combined with the
clay. This water forms an integral part of the clay substance
and amounts to 14 per cent. If the material is heated to between 450° and 500° C., the clay crystal breaks down and the
water of combination disappears.

PURIFYING CLAYS

The property of clay particles of remaining in suspension provides the key to the method of purifying raw clays and kaolins.
The raw clays or kaolins together with water are put into a
container (called a blunger) in which arms or propellers break
up the large lumps of clay and mix them thoroughly with the
water. The mix is run into a basin where the heavier particles,
such as sand, feldspar and so on, settle, while the lighter clay
particles remain in suspension and are poured off with the
water. This method is called washing of clays.

Elutriation Method

An alternative method is to carry the lighter particles away,
in suspension, in a stream of water, whereas the heavier particles sink to the bottom on their way. This method, very often
called 'elutriation', is used by nature herself to a very large
extent.

It has been described previously how clay, owing to its physical nature, also keeps a certain amount of non-plastic particles in suspension with it. The washing and levigation processes therefore (whether applied by man or by nature), will not separate clay from all the admixed impurities. It will only leave behind the coarser impurities. The lighter ones (for instance finely divided feldspar, mica, sand, and so on) will be carried away with the clay, and they will all settle together later on in basins provided by nature, or by man, as the case may be.

Whereas man takes every possible precaution to prevent other materials from falling into the slip, on its way from the blunger to the settling basin, with nature conditions are often very different. The river or stream carrying the clay may meet and combine with others bearing sand, lime, or mud of various kinds, or may pick up sand or chalk from the bed over which it passes. The mixture of materials so formed is carried by water currents of varying speeds, and is deposited when the velocity of the water is reduced by the shape and nature of its path. Beds of various compositions are then formed, sometimes simultaneously and sometimes by a series of separations, according to the speed and other characteristics of the water current. In this way are formed beds of varied types, plastic and lean, containing refractory, vitrifiable, fusible clays, and so on. The qualities of all these various types of clays will be described later. It will, however, be easier for the reader to understand how the various ingredients admixed to the clay – either by nature or by man – influence the characteristics of these clays, if first the behaviour of pure clay during drying and firing is discussed.

WHY DO PLASTIC CLAYS HARDEN IN DRYING?

The practical potter as a rule does not bother to ask why his clays or his pastes set hard during the drying process. He knows by experience that articles made of plastic clay become harder and stronger mechanically than those made of less plastic clays or those made of plastic clay to which a lot of unplastic sand is admixed. He also knows that if he made a cup by using a slip of calcined clay instead of an earthenware slip, it would be so brittle, after drying, that it would break at once when gripped by hand.

The ability of clays to become hard and mechanically strong during drying is due to the shape of the clay crystal. When the clay is mixed with water, the latter acts as a kind of lubricant. The sheet-like crystals can move in the direction of the crystal plane without losing the cohesion which is maintained by the electrical forces of the ions present in the watery solution. Because of this, the plastic paste can be shaped and will keep the form given to it. As the water evaporates during drying, the lubricant between the crystal sheets disappears and they come in direct contact with one another.

Everybody knows how difficult it is to separate two clean glass plates which have been placed one on top of the other. The dry clay crystal sheets stick together in a similar way In contrast to the sheet-like crystals of the plastic clay materials, crystals of non-plastic material are of three-dimensional nature and are more or less in point contact with each other. To give an example, it is not difficult to separate two glass balls which touch each other, in contrast to the two glass plates mentioned above. In the same way the cohesion between the dry particles of a non-plastic powder is much less than the cohesion between dry clay particles.

Not all the crystal sheets in a plastic clay paste lie parallel to one another. The number of crystals in direct contact with each other in a given space is obviously the greater, the smaller the size of individual crystals and the more tightly they are packed in that space. In dried articles made of a plastic type of clay more particles are in direct contact than in those made of non-plastic clays. It is therefore obvious that the mechanical strength of dry articles made of plastic clay is greater than those made of non-plastic clays or kaolins. To give an example:

Type of Clay	Modulus of rupture lb./sq. inch.
Ball clay	650
Plastic fireclay	225
China clay	75

Elimination of the water (i.e. the drying) takes place in two phases. The first phase is the evaporation of the water which surrounds the clay particles in the form of a thin skin. The clay particles then approach closer to each other and the body shrinks. If the arrangement of the crystals in the paste was quite homogeneous, the body would continue shrinking until all water is evaporated, but the arrangement is never quite homogeneous. This means that the clay crystals never lie all parallel. At certain points the crystals and their intermediate water layers are not stacked together in an orderly manner and pockets are formed where there is only point-to-point contact between the crystals. These pockets are filled with water so long as the layers between the crystals are sealed off by other water. When all the water between the crystal layers and between the point contacts of crystals is removed, no further shrinkage can take place as the drying process proceeds. The water which fills the minute pockets between the clay particles evaporates and pockets filled with air are formed. To give an example: A cylinder made of plastic clay, say 1.5 ins. in diameter and 8 ins. long, is made by mixing 75% dry clay and 25% water. The test piece is dried at room temperature, the loss of water and the shrinkage being ascertained twice daily. We note that the body gradually loses water and continues to shrink until after, say, 60 hours drying. It has now lost 14% of its water and has shrunk by 8%. After the 60th hour it continues to lose water but no longer shrinks. The evaporating water causes pores until after about 150 hours all the water (with the exception, of course, of the chemically combined water) has evaporated. No further shrinkage takes place during the last 90 hours, the total shrinkage being still 8%. This example is for a medium plastic clay. Very plastic clays need more water in order to form a plastic paste. Their shrinkage is greater and so is the amount of pores formed during drying. When the clay which we have just considered above is mixed with 25% water it has a very plastic consistency. In this state it is most suitable for jollying or jiggering.

When the paste has been allowed to dry for a time and has lost the greater part, say 14%, of its water, it is called 'leather hard' or 'in the green state'. It is then particularly suitable for turning and will not continue to shrink as the drying is continued. This property is very welcome when two pieces have to be joined by sticking them together. (The joint would break if one piece shrinks and the other does not.) If the drying process is continued still further, until the water filling the pores evaporates, the body turns white and becomes quite hard. Turning in the 'white state' is employed for precision work in insulator manufacture.

To illustrate the relationship of plasticity, shrinkage, water of formation required, and drying time, details are given of three clays of different plasticity as follows:

Test cylinders made of	Water of formation required	Drying time at room temperature in hours	Shrinkage in %
Lean clay . .	16	120	18
Clay of medium plasticity . . .	21	140	22
Clay of high plasticity	27	180	26

Equivalent test pieces of china clay would require a drying time shorter than that given for a lean clay and they would shrink less.

If we made test cylinders of a non-plastic material, such as a sand or powdered feldspar, they would dry very rapidly – the more so the coarser the particles – and they would not shrink at all. Mixtures of clay and non-plastic materials develop varying characteristics depending upon the proportion of plastic and non-plastic materials present in the mixture. The non-plastic materials facilitate drying and reduce shrinkage and are called 'opening materials'. They also reduce the dry strength.

VERSATILITY OF CLAY

We may digress here for a moment to draw the reader's attention to the singular and extremely interesting position which clay occupies amongst the various materials available to manufacturers. It can be used in a slip form for casting, in a soft plastic state for jollying, in a medium or very hard state for turning. For pressing, clay is also used in plastic state, but in the form of a powder, wet, semi-dry and dry, and all this at room temperature. Metals are also shaped in various states, but the difference here is that, apart from machining and similar operations, and cold forging, metals have to be heated above melting point for casting, and above softening point for all operations requiring a certain plasticity. Organic plastic materials are also shaped in different states which again are dependent on the temperature maintained during the shaping process.

BEHAVIOUR OF CLAY
WHEN HEATED ABOVE ROOM TEMPERATURE

When a pure clay or kaolin is heated above room temperature, after the water of formation has dried out, certain chemical processes take place as the temperature increases.

1. The chemically combined water is almost completely evaporated at 450° to 500° C. and meta kaolin ($Al_2O_3.2SiO_2$) is formed.

2. Between 800° and 830° C. meta kaolinite is decomposed.

3. Between 850° and 910° C. the decomposition continues and alumina (Al_2O_3) is formed.

4. Between 910° and 975° sillimanite is formed ($Al_2O_3.SiO_2$).

5. At 975° C. the formation of mullite commences (3 $Al_2O_3.$ 2 SiO_2).

Pure kaolins and clays fired at about 600° C. have a whitish or yellowish colour. At this temperature they have a certain mechanical strength, although the fusing of the particles has not yet commenced and the bodies are still very porous and water-absorbent. With increasing firing temperature there is an increase in shrinkage and mechanical strength with a corresponding decrease in porosity until the shrinkage has reached its maximum value. The temperature at which this maximum shrinkage value is reached is dependent upon the nature of the clay or kaolin. When we discussed the drying of clay we noticed that the drying shrinkage is caused by the evaporation of the water of formation which separates the individual clay particles. The further shrinkage which takes place when clay is heated above room temperature is made possible by the fact that the surfaces of the clay particles soften as the firing temperature rises. The clay particles are drawn together and the size of the enclosed air pockets becomes smaller. When the clay substance becomes quite soft owing to the high temperature, the pores are completely filled and the body becomes dense. If we increase the temperature still further we approach the melting point of clay. Clays have no definite melting point. By the term 'melting point of clay' the ceramist understands the temperature at which a cone formed of any clay under test completely collapses, so that its apex leans over and touches its base. A cone made of pure kaolin collapses in this way at a temperature of about 1770° C. (when the temperature is raised at the rate of 100° C. per hour).

Firing Shrinkage of Clay

Firing shrinkage is dependent:

(1) On the chemical composition.

    (*a*) Fluxes like feldspar, mica, iron compounds, lime, etc., increase the shrinkage.

    (*b*) Refractory materials like alumina reduce the shrinkage.

(2) On the grain size of the clay particles and grain size of the admixed impurities. (For instance, a kaolin having very small particle size may shrink 12% when heated from dry state to 1400° C. Another of the same chemical composition but consisting of larger particles may shrink only 8% under the same firing conditions.) The smaller the particles, therefore,

the greater the shrinkage. This is due to the fact that the total surface area per unit volume increases with decreasing particle size. The greater the surface area the stronger becomes the chemical and physical interaction between the individual particles.

(3) On the firing temperature: the higher the temperature, the greater the shrinkage.

(4) On the duration of the firing and the rate of temperature increase.

If the temperature is increased slowly and sufficient time is available at any given temperature for the heat to perform its work, the greater will be the shrinkage. For example, a clay cylinder heated in twelve hours to 1250° C. may shrink 8%. When the temperature is raised more slowly and 1250° C. is reached in fourteen hours, a cylinder made of the same type of clay may shrink 9%.[1]

The drying shrinkage of a pure kaolin, or china clay of medium plasticity, from the plastic state to the white dry state is about 12 %.

The firing shrinkage from the white dry state to 1200° C. is about 7.5%, and when fired to 1400° C. about 10%.

To give an example: a cylinder made of pure plastic clay may have a length of 10 cm. After drying its length is then 8.8 cm. When this cylinder is fired up to a temperature of 1400° C. its length decreases to 7.8 cm. (Total shrinkage 22%.)

NOTES ON MATERIALS FOUND WITH CLAY

In nature, clay is as a rule mixed with feldspar, mica, lime, magnesia, iron compounds, titanium dioxide and sand in vary-

---

1. It can be seen from this example that in ceramic work it is often more important to register the work done by heat than the temperature as such. The work done by heat is very often recorded by using cones made of different ceramic mixtures. The individual cones will soften and bend over after having been subjected to different temperatures for a definite length of time. The use of such cones for measuring the work done by heat was introduced by the German ceramist, Seger, and they are therefore known as Seger Cones (S.C). They are more fully described later in the book.

ing amounts. The presence of any of these materials in the clay mixture reduces the drying shrinkage : mica, iron compounds and lime reduce to a lesser degree, and feldspar and sand to a higher degree. The materials which reduce the plasticity, open the body up and decrease drying shrinkage and are called 'opening materials'.

The first-mentioned four materials lower the vitrification temperature of clay and increase the firing shrinkage. They are therefore called fusible materials or fluxes.

1. *Feldspar*

It was pointed out earlier in the book that clay is a decomposition product of feldspar and that most clays still contain some remnants of undecomposed feldspar. The principal feldspars are:

1. Potassium feldspar, termed 'Orthoclase' or 'Microline', depending on the crystalline form. Its chemical formula is $K_2O. Al_2O_3. 6SiO_2$.

Theoretical Composition of Potassium Feldspar

Contents	Formula	Per cent
Potash	K_2O	16.9
Alumina	Al_2O_3	18.3
Silica	$6SiO_2$	64.8
		100.0

2. Sodium feldspar (Albite). The chemical formula is $Na_2O. Al_2O_3. 6SiO_2$.

Theoretical Composition of Sodium Feldspar

Contents	Formula	Per cent
Soda	Na_2O	11.8
Alumina	Al_2O_3	19.5
Silica	$6SiO_2$	68.7

Feldspar is the most important ceramic flux and is used in most types of ceramic ware.

Soda feldspars have a lower fusing temperature than potash

feldspars and the fluxing power of the former is greater. None of the feldspar minerals in the various feldspar groups occurs pure.

Potash feldspars are more abundant and always contain some sodium feldspar. Similarly, sodium feldspars always contain some potash feldspar.

Some feldspars fuse as low as S.C.3 (1140° C.) and others as high as S.C.9 (1280° C.), the average fusing point being round about S.C.7 and 8 (1230° and 1250° C.).

Feldspar has a large temperature range between softening point and melting point. Fused feldspar is very viscous. A cone of feldspar has to be heated approximately 100° C. above vitrification temperature before it is sufficiently soft for the cone to collapse and the apex to touch the base. It has to be heated a further 100° C. in order to make it fluid. On this extreme viscosity and the large temperature range between softening and melting point its usefulness in the manufacture of porcelain depends. To give some examples:

A mixture of 50% clay and 50% feldspar is

Vitrified at	1200° C.
Translucent at	1250° C.
Fuses at	1400° C.

A mixture of 50% clay, 25% silica, and 25% feldspar is

Vitrified at	1300° C.
Translucent at	1400° C.
Fuses at	1550° C.

A mixture of 50% clay, 30% silica and 20% feldspar is

Dense at	1350° C.
Translucent at	1450° C.
Fuses at	1600° C.

Sometimes vitrification is not required and only point-to-point welding of particles is needed (i.e. 'sintering'), in order to give the material the required mechanical strength (e.g. wall tiles, earthenware, etc.). For such materials depending upon the composition of the body (which frequently may contain other fluxes) and the particular firing temperature, only 5% to 20% feldspar is required.

There are clays which already contain up to 20% feldspar, but in most cases feldspar is added to the body. This can be done in two ways, either by the addition of pure feldspar or by using minerals rich in feldspar such as pegmatite or Cornish stone. Both are feldspatic rocks containing 3% to 20% clay, 30% to 60% silica and 30% to 60% feldspar. In Great Britain feldspar is usually introduced into ceramic bodies by using Cornish stone, since pure feldspar is not found here. The purest feldspar deposits in Europe are those in Norway, Sweden and Russia. There are also very pure feldspar deposits in the United States.

2. *Lime*

Lime (calcium oxide, CaO) is used as a flux in ceramic mixtures. It is introduced into the body either by the addition of chalk (calcium carbonate), or dolomite (calcium carbonate and magnesium carbonate), all finely ground, or calcium compounds may already be contained in the clay. If the clay contains chalk it has to be carefully disintegrated, since even small pieces of chalk, if not combined chemically with the clay substance during firing, would swell and spoil the ware when exposed to humid air.

Brick clays very often contain finely divided chalk.

Chalk is a strong flux and combines with clay, forming calcium-aluminium silicates. The addition of only 1% chalk has the same fluxing power as 10% feldspar, at temperatures above 1100° C. The addition of 2% CaO to a clay body reduces the vitrification temperature by at least 30° C. If more than 10% chalk is used, fusing temperature and densification temperature are almost identical. This means the firing range is too small. Such mixtures are not a practical proposition.

The most fusible mixture, the mixture with the lowest

melting point (the 'eutectic'), of the chalk-silica-clay system has the formula 2.9 CaO. Al_2O_3. 7.2SiO_2.

In preparing ceramic mixtures one must always bear in mind that pure chalk – (calcium carbonate) is a combination of lime and carbonic acid in the proportion of 56 parts to 44 parts.

3. *Magnesia*

Magnesia is present in many clays in the form of magnesite or dolomite powders, but only in very small proportions. It is also a flux and acts in clay mixtures in a similar way to lime. Certain compounds of magnesium, particularly magnesite and dolomite, are very important raw materials in the manufacture of high-grade refractories. Talc, a magnesium silicate, is an important raw material in the manufacture of low-loss electrical insulating materials. These will be discussed in more detail in the chapters dealing with refractories and electrical insulating materials.

4. *Iron Compounds*

Iron compounds are present in most clays, as a rule in a very finely divided form. If the clays are fired in an oxidizing atmosphere (if there is an excess of air), the iron compounds – depending on their amount – give to the clay a colour ranging from cream to red. White burning clays contain less than 1% iron oxide, ivory and yellow burning clays contain 1% to 4%, and red burning ones between 4% and 7%.

If fired in a reducing atmosphere, iron compounds in small quantities give the body a light greyish colour. If present in larger quantities (more than 4%) they give the body a dark grey or blue colour, particularly in the presence of other fluxes. Ferrous oxide (FeO) gives a grey or blue colour, and Ferric oxide (Fe_2O_3) gives cream to red colours in oxidizing atmosphere.

Iron compounds also act as fluxes and reduce the vitrification temperature, particularly in the presence of other fusible materials.

5. *Silica*

Silica occurs abundantly in the form of quartz (rock crystal) in volcanic rocks and consequently also in clays, the decomposition product of volcanic rocks, in sand, sand-stone, and flint. It is a very important ingredient in many ceramic bodies. It will be sufficient if we deal here with those characteristics of the various silica formations which are most important to the manufacturer of clay ware, namely with the thermal expansion of the various modifications and the volume changes which take place when one silica modification is transformed into another by heat treatment. The following are the most important crystal modifications of silica:

∝ quartz   β quartz
∝ tridymite   β tridymite
∝ cristobalite   β cristobalite

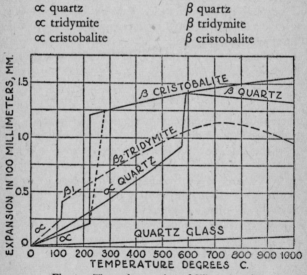

Fig. 1.   Thermal expansion of Silica-minerals.

Fig. 1 illustrates the expansion of the silica minerals quartz, tridymite and cristobalite, when heated from freezing point to 1000° C. It will be seen that at a temperature of between 220° and 250° C. a sudden expansion takes place. This is caused by a conversion of the silica crystal (∝. cristobalite) into another crystal (β. cristobalite) having, of course, the same chemical composition but a larger volume (a smaller density). Another important conversion takes place at 600°. Conversions occur slowly if the temperature rise or fall takes place slowly. If large silica grains are contained in the body and particularly if the temperature changes take place abruptly, the volume changes of the silica grains cause strains in the body. This increase in volume leads to cracks and to the destruction of the article. The large thermal expansion of cristobalite is of great importance to the ceramic industry. If silica is heated at approximately 1200° C., most of it is transformed into β-cristobalite, which has a larger thermal expansion than other silica crystals. Firing at higher temperatures than 1200° C. make certain ceramic articles 'craze proof' – that is, it prevents the formation of fine cracks in the glaze. Because of its larger thermal expansion, caused by the formation of cristobalite, clay ware fired at temperatures above 1200° C. will give a better 'glaze fit' with low temperature glazes, most of which have a large thermal expansion.

Silica is used in the ceramic industry in the form of sand, sandstone, quartz and pebble-flint. The term 'flint' is frequently used for silica by potters generally, but strictly speaking 'flint' refers to pebbles. These consist of pure silica and are found on chalky ground. The earthenware and china manufacturers of North Staffordshire prefer to introduce silica into their bodies in the form of calcined flint, whereas abroad, quartz or sand is used for this purpose. These materials give practically the same results. Before the first world war flint had to be of French or Belgian origin. English flint pebbles were not considered suitable. During the war, however, the import of pebbles from France and Belgium was impossible, and so pebbles from the mouth of the Thames and from other rivers were used by the millers, and the potter did not find any difference. Sand – which is available in profusion – could be used instead. If its iron content is too high, it can be cleaned. Sand has then to be ground to the fineness of calcined flint, and will do the job. Transport of the pebbles from the south coast to the Potteries, and also the calcining (fuel plus labour), could thus be saved. The refractory industry uses silica preferably in the form of sand. If the sand is rich in feldspar or mica it has to be washed, in those cases where the incorporation of these fluxes in the body would be undesirable.

Clayey sand is an excellent opening material, and is used in the brick industry and the refractory industry. Ganister is a clayey sand found at the base of coal seams, and this is also used in the refractory industry.

Generally speaking, potters regard silica (flint) as a refractory material. This, however, is correct only if silica replaces other stronger fluxes. If silica is mixed with pure clay substance, the fusing temperature of the mixture decreases with increasing silica addition until the silica represents 80% of the silica clay mixture. Silica is in this case a 'flux'. Further silica additions above 80%, however, raise the melting point.

Pure clay fuses at 1770° C. (S.C. 35).

Pure silica fuses at 1685° C. (S.C. 31).

A mixture of 80% silica and 20% clay fuses at 1610° C. (S.C. 27).

Fused silica (quartz glass) is extensively used in the manufacture of those articles where very great resistance to sudden temperature changes is essential, e.g. laboratory ware. This resistance to temperature changes is due to the very low thermal expansion of fused silica. It is the lowest of all known materials, namely 0.5×10^{-6} per $C°$. Quartz in crystal form, on the other hand, has a very high thermal expansion. Parallel to the axis it is 8×10^{-6} and perpendicular to the axis it is 5.4×10^{-6}. Consequently, if the particles are lying at random, the average expansion is about fifteen times greater than that of fused quartz. It will be appreciated from these figures why, during the firing process, the thermal expansion of ceramic mixtures is greatly reduced when part of the flint or sand content fuses and forms a glass rich in silica.

The coefficient of thermal expansion of glasses and ceramic glazes is the smaller the greater their silica content. The effect on the melting point is just the opposite. The greater the silica content, the higher is the melting temperature. It is interesting to note the increasing silica content from Seger cone 021 (650° C.) to Seger cone 27 (1610° C.), each cone containing slightly more silica than the previous one. Cone 021 contains 31% and cone 27, 85%. It is obvious from the foregoing that glazes suitable for porcelain and other low expansion ceramics must be rich in silica and must have high firing temperatures. (The same is true for glasses. Glasses, such as Pyrex, which are very resistant to sudden temperature changes, have a high silica content and consequently need high temperatures.)

After having discussed the nature of the clay substance and the characteristics of the foreign substances mixed with 'true clay' it is easier to form an idea as to the properties of the numerous varieties of clays occurring in nature. No single clay has exactly the same property as another clay found in another locality. This fact, of course, tends to complicate pottery-making and clay-working, but it also contributes to its fascination and general interest. Unfortunately at the same time it reduces the value and accuracy of recipes which, in other branches of industry, are so reliable and important.

It is extremely difficult to classify clays and to draw lines of demarcation between various classes of clays. The varieties of clay available for the service of man form a continuous series from the hypothetical 'clay substance' to the very complex substances in which clay is contained only in small proportions. A real demarcation line exists only between the two groups of primary and secondary clays.

PRIMARY CLAYS

Primary clays are found in the location where they were formed, usually in the midst of, or near to, granites, gneiss, or pegmatites. The most important primary clays are the kaolins (china clays). These natural substances are not used as found but have always first of all to be brought to a high degree of purity by washing. Kaolins are used in the manufacture of porcelain, earthenware, vitreous china, and sanitary ware. Outside the pottery industry kaolins are also used, for example in the manufacture of paper and paint. The chief china clay deposits in England are in Devon and Cornwall. On the Continent the best kaolins are found near Zettlitz (Czechoslovakia). They are white burning and more plastic than English china clays – as a matter of fact more plastic than any other primary kaolins – and have great dry strength. In France the more important kaolin deposits are found near Limoges. They are extremely pure and of very good quality. Other French kaolin deposits are in Brittany and in the granite mountains of the Pyrenees. In Germany, kaolins, very suitable for porcelain manufacture, are found in Saxony, near Meissen and near Halle (in the Prussian province of Saxony). These are both in the Russian-occupied territory. Russia also possesses very large and useful kaolin deposits, particularly in the Ukraine. In the Unites States primary sedimentary kaolins of very good quality are found, among other places, in South Carolina, Georgia, and Alabama.

There are primary clays which contain a considerable amount of silica, in the form of so fine a powder that it is difficult to separate it from the clay by washing. This non-separable silica may amount to 30%. Such kaolins are used as additions to other kaolins and to ball clays in the manufacture of porcelain and earthenware and also to refractory clays in the manufacture of refractory ware.

SECONDARY CLAYS

Clays washed away by rain or streams from the place where they were originally found, and deposited elsewhere, are called secondary clays.

The variety of secondary clays is enormous. According to the fusing or softening temperature they can be divided into three classes:

1. Refractory clays.
2. Vitrifiable clays.
3. Fusible clays.

Secondary clays are, as a rule, not purified by washing, since the impurities are in most cases so finely divided that it would not be possible to separate them from the clay. Clays containing coarser impurities are made homogeneous by passing through crushers and mills. The impurities, crushed and ground, are left in the clay.

1. Refractory clays, when formed to test cones, do not bend before reaching S.C. 35 (1770° C.). As their name would suggest they are used in the manufacture of refractory materials.

Silicious refractory clays, which may contain up to 50% free silica, can also be used in the manufacture of refractory materials, but only if the alkali, iron and lime contents are very small. Refractory clays of this type are found in Stourbridge, Northumberland, Durham, Yorkshire, Lancashire, Wales and Scotland. Most of the coal-bearing areas are rich in fireclays.

Pure secondary clays are used in the manufacture of earthenware, technical porcelain and, in small amounts, in the manufacture of table-ware porcelain. Of particular interest are the so-called ball clays. They are found in Devon and are the most plastic clays known. They occur in beds of great purity and uniformity, sometimes covered by lignite and sometimes with considerable amounts of lignite scattered through the clay itself. Although ball clays have a dark colour (owing to the carbonaceous matter they contain) they burn as light as or even lighter than any other highly plastic clay. Secondary china clays such as Californian secondary kaolins, and Czechoslovakian clays of the type found near Wildstein, are in many respects similar to English ball clays. In the U.S.A. there are also clays similar to the English ball clays, but all the published figures on dry strengths show that they are not quite equal to the English ones.

2. Vitrifiable clays contain a higher proportion of fluxes, and are used in the manufacture of stone ware, sanitary ware,

paving tiles, terra cotta, and vitrified bricks. They become vitrified – without the addition of fluxes – at temperatures between 1200° and 1350° C., dependent on the nature and amount of fluxes present. The colour after firing varies from red to black.

3. Fusible clays contain more and stronger fluxes than vitrifiable clays. They lose their shape at temperatures at which vitrifiable clays become vitrified, and are fired at temperatures as low as 1000° C. This is due to their lime content which, as previously mentioned, acts as a very powerful flux. This type of clay is used in the manufacture of bricks, very often mixed with more refractory clays. Fusible clays are widely distributed and are found in practically all countries.

CHAPTER IV

Composition of Bodies

THE term 'body' is used in the pottery industry to describe the material from which the article is formed. The name is used for the material both before it is fired and after it is fired. It may consist of a single clay, of a mixture of clays, or of a mixture of clays and other materials.

PREPARATION OF RAW MATERIALS

The raw materials as found have to be broken up and disintegrated in such a way that the resultant particles can easily be mixed with other materials and a body of a desired consistency prepared.

Raw materials can be disintegrated in different ways.

1. Weathering, the oldest method – the one used by nature – is chiefly applied to clays. Clays are left in the open air and are exposed to sun, rain, and frost. They expand, contract and break up. Mechanical means of crushing (see 3 below) replace weathering to a certain extent, but many clay workers still believe in the beneficial effect of weathering. By using the de-airing pug mill (a fairly recent development used in combination with mechanical crushers) it is possible to dispense with ageing or weathering, where conditions make this desirable.

2. Calcination (heat treatment) is used to make flint more brittle and more easily crushable.

3. Mechanical crushing machinery. Stone crushers or jaw crushers are used for breaking up large pieces of hard materials. They are often employed as a first stage to produce pieces less than half an inch in diameter. These are subsequently reduced to finer sizes by treatment in pan mills, edge roller mills, dust mills, and Alsing cylinders (ball or pebble mills).

Edge runner mills are frequently used. They are suitable for crushing calcined flint, sand, glass, and frits. There are two types of edge runners. In the first type (chaser mill) the pan is stationary, and the rolls rotate around a vertical shaft. In the second type the pan rotates and the shaft and rolls are stationary.

Wet pan mixes are used for sand tempering, for the mixing and grinding of clay and the mixing of raw clay with calcined clay (grog) in the manufacture of refractory materials.

Crushing rolls are used in clay working for breaking up lumps of clay and for disintegrating hard materials embedded in the clay. These machines employ several rolls rotating at different speeds so that a rubbing action is added to the crushing action as the materials pass between the rollers.

The distance between them can be regulated and safety devices are employed to prevent damage in case pieces of exceptional hardness come between the rollers.

The machines mentioned above are suitable for disintegrating non-plastic dry and wet materials, and for mixing and grinding clays and clay mixtures in plastic and semi-plastic states. They are, therefore, extensively used in the manufacture of bricks, roofing tiles, refractory materials, and so on, where mixing is done in a semi-dry or in a plastic state, and where the mixing is not necessarily very intimate as in the case of earthenware, porcelain, and china.

For uniform and very thorough reduction of unplastic materials grinding cylinders, very often called Alsing cylinders, or ball mills are used. These consist of an iron or steel drum, the inside of which is lined with silica or porcelain. The cylinders (after the silica or porcelain lining has been cemented in) are filled with pebbles or porcelain balls. These pebbles or porcelain balls act as grinders, when the cylinder is set in motion. When the cylinder rotates, the pebbles, together with the raw materials to be ground, are first lifted and then dropped, the raw materials being crushed and ground by impact. Alsing cylinders are used for both wet and dry grinding. A suitable amount of the material to be ground, the grinding pebbles and, in most cases, a suitable amount of water are fed into the cylinder through an opening. The opening is then closed and the cylinder is rotated until the grinding is completed. As a matter of interest the time required for grinding calcined flint in an Alsing cylinder of average size is about twelve hours.

Hardinge conical mills consist of a grinding zone and conical drum, mounted on hollow trunnions, through which the material passes continuously to and from the grinding zone. The conical shape of the mill causes a natural automatic segregation both of the grinding balls and of the material being ground, according to their size. In those parts of the conical mill where the diameters are largest, the material is crushed by the largest pebbles with the greatest drop and with the highest peripheral speed. As the material travels towards the discharge end, the crushing force gradually decreases with decreasing pebble size and with lesser height of fall of the pebbles.

This type of mill produces very regular grain sizes. The material is automatically fed in at one end and is discharged at the other. This mill is used where control of grain size is important, for instance, in china, earthenware and porcelain manufacture. One man can supervise a considerable number of such mills, as all of them are fed and discharged automatically.

PREPARATION OF BODIES

After the raw materials have been broken up into small pieces and then purified (when necessary) the next stage is to mix them together. The proportions have to be so arranged as to give the fired body the properties required and also to give the clay mixture the right consistency for the particular shaping process which is to be employed. The operations therefore resolve themselves into:

1. Measuring the raw materials to suit the body composition.

2. Mixing the materials in various ways and degrees, according to requirements.

Amongst the various methods of mixing are the following:

1. The clay is manipulated in a plastic state, either soft or stiff.

2. The clay is mixed in a dry state with the water removed and the necessary water added after mixing.

3. Dissolving the clay in water, then mixing the clay slip with pulverized non-plastic materials, the latter being either dry or dissolved in water (in slip form) and removing the water in filter presses.

1. The use of plastic clay for the preparation of the mixture is obviously the least costly because the clay used in the mixing process has the right consistency for the shaping process. The water has not to be removed prior to mixing and added again after mixing, as in the case of method 2, nor has surplus water to be added before mixing and removed after mixing as is the case with method 3.

The limitation attaching to method 1 is that the use of clay in a plastic state makes it impossible to achieve a mixture as intimate and homogeneous as those obtained with methods 2 and 3. Method 1 is used in the manufacture of bricks, roofing tiles, refractories, and stoneware.

Method 2 is used in cases where a very intimate mixture and uniformity of the body are essential, particularly for dry and semi-dry bodies. Method 2 is used, e.g. in the manufacture (a) of high-grade refractory materials, (b) of high-grade stoneware, and (c) in dust pressing of materials such as talc, or when plastic clays are present only in small proportions.

Method 3 is also used where a fine texture and an intimate mixture are essential, for instance, in the manufacture of earthenware, porcelain, china, and so on.

1. *Body Preparation using Clay in Plastic State*

If the clays already have the right consistency they are placed in the mixing machine in the required proportions. Where necessary, sand is added. If the clay is too dry, water has to be added and thoroughly mixed with the clay. This process is called tempering. (It has already been explained that the plastic materials have to be reduced previous to tempering by edge runners or crushing rollers.) If the material is too moist it has to be mixed with dry powdered clay or non-plastic material. To carry out these processes edge runner mills are preferably used. Further quantities of water are added in trough mixers or pug mills which are used to mix the materials in plastic or semi-plastic state.

Pug Mills. – Pug mills are of either horizontal or vertical type. The vertical pug mill consists of a hollow cylinder which is either tapered at its base or provided with a horizontal outlet. In this cylinder rotates a vertical shaft provided with knives at different heights. The material is introduced at the top and moves downwards owing to its own weight. It is, moreover, simultaneously compressed by the rotating knives which are arranged spirally. The mixing is done by the knives, which may vary in shape from flat to curved.

Horizontal pug mills employ the same principle. Since, however, the clay does not gravitate towards the outlet, it tends to turn with the knives unless counter-knives are arranged to prevent this movement.

Trough Mixers. – Trough mixers work on the same principle as horizontal pug mills. Two shafts provided with helical knives rotate in opposite directions, the cake being pressed towards the exit and reduced on its way into a granular condition. The clay is moistened both in pug mills and in trough mixers by water introduced through an open pipe, a perforated pipe, a spray or a jet.

Modern pug mills are frequently provided with vacuum chambers in which the pugged clay is de-aired. De-airing is employed not only in connexion with pug mills but also in connexion with extrusion machines, filtering and slip casting, and will for this reason be described separately at the end of this chapter.

Feeding Machines. – In order to ensure a continuous supply of material to the grinding mills, pug mills, or other mixers, automatic proportioning and feeding machines are used.

Rotary and disc feeders are employed for this purpose.

2. *Body Preparation Using Dry Clay*

From the description of the mixers used in the mixing of clay in a plastic state, it has been seen that the mixing operation is performed by knives or blades which cut and compress the plastic paste. Even if the plastic clay has been mixed in edge rollers preparatory to being fed to the mixers, the mixing is not very intimate. This is because the plastic clay is sticky and the individual clay particles adhere together. If the plastic materials are first dried and crushed they can then be mixed much more thoroughly.

The drying of the clay can be done in various types of special clay dryers. There are rotary dryers consisting of long, slightly inclined rotating steel tubes, the clay being fed in at the elevated end, with hot air circulating through the tube from the lower end. Tunnel dryers are also used, the clay being placed in trays on rack cars, which enter the tunnel at the cold end and travel towards the hot end.

The grinding of the dried clay is done by the various machines already described. The ground material is sifted and the coarser particles which do not pass the sieve are returned to the mill for further grinding. (Closed circuit dry grinding.) The mixing of the various materials is done either in Alsing cylinders, dust mills, or in mixers consisting of rotating propellers contained in cylinders or arranged on pans. Mills used for dry mixing have, of course, to be enclosed in housings to prevent the dust from contaminating the air and getting into the gear and the bearings. When the mixing is completed the mixture is usually moistened to give it sufficient plasticity for subsequent pressing. If the body has to be jollied more water has, of course, to be added to give it greater softness.

3. *Body Preparation Using Clay Slips*

The most intimate mixture of materials is obtained when the clay is dissolved (blunged) in water. When the clay is stirred it gradually softens and very soon the clay particles are completely and uniformly dispersed in the water. If several clays are treated in this way the particles of the various clays are

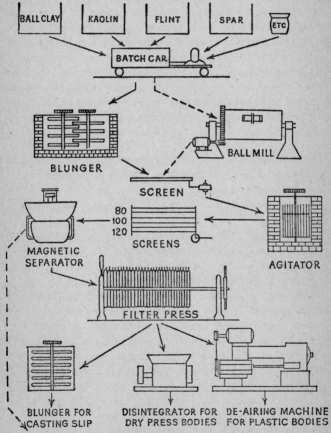

Fig. *2a*. Flow sheet of the body preparation steps used in the wet process – weighing dry materials.

most intimately mixed. When non-plastic materials of fine grain size are added to the cream-like liquid (called slip) they are kept in suspension by the stirring motion and by the colloidal nature of the clay (as previously described) and they are very evenly distributed in the liquid. In pottery works the clays are broken up and 'dissolved' in water in blungers. The various slips are mixed together in mixing arcs. Both blungers and mixing arcs consist of containers made of wood or metal, in each of which is a vertical rotating shaft on which two or more arms (or blades) are fixed. In the case of blungers the blades usually rotate more quickly than in the case of mixing arcs. If hard clays are to be broken up in blungers, this process needs considerable agitation and greater speeds. Propellers rotating at high speed are then used to great advantage. Non-plastic materials are introduced into the mixing arc either in the form of a slip or in the form of finely-ground dry powder.

Proportioning of Materials. – The proportioning of the materials to suit a given body recipe can be done in two different ways.

1. By weighing the various materials dry.
2. By measuring the volume of the various slips. See Figs. 2*a* and 2*b*.

In case (1) the materials are weighed in the dry state. The clays are then 'dissolved' in the blunger. The non-plastic raw materials, after being weighed, are either added to the mixing arc or they are put into an Alsing cylinder, together with a suitable amount of water (and very often with small amounts of clay). In this Alsing cylinder they are ground and mixed together and are then discharged into the mixing arc.

In case (2) each of the various ingredients is blunged in water and made into a slip. Each slip must conform to a certain definite weight in ounces per pint or in pounds per peck (16 pints). These different slips, each having its own proper weight per pint, are then mixed together in the mixing arc. This method is used in North Staffordshire for the manufacture of earthenware bodies, both in the table-ware and sanitaryware sections. A more accurate method of proportioning by measuring the volume of the slips is described in the chapter, 'A Visit to Josiah Wedgwood's Works in Barlaston.' Bone china manufacturers as a rule employ method 1. Insulator manufacturers use a cross between the two methods. In most Continental countries and in the U.S.A., method 1 is used. Both methods, of course, have their advantages and disadvantages. In the author's opinion, method 1 would be cheaper and more accurate if all the raw materials were either completely dry or if they always had the same water content. This requirement can be met with all ceramic ingredients including purified, filter-pressed china clay (if proper care is taken), but excepting plastic clays. Consequently the required proportions of all materials can be ascertained with great accuracy by dry weighing if the moisture content is taken into consideration. Plastic clays, owing to their varying water contents, must be treated differently. They are better blunged into a slip of definite weight per pint. A measured volume of this slip is added into the mixing arc to the other materials, the quantities of which have been ascertained by dry weighing.

Filter Presses. – From the mixing arc the slip is pumped into filter presses where the surplus water is removed. On the way to the filter presses it passes vibrating sieves, which retain the coarser particles, and through magnets, which remove iron particles (these iron particles would cause brown or black spots in the ware after firing). The filter press is the chief appliance nowadays used for turning the water slip into a plastic body. It usually consists of a number of recessed or unrecessed plates and frames (made of wood or iron) in each case forming a number of chambers. The two end faces of each chamber are covered by filter cloths, the cloths being pressed between the plates and the frames or between the edges of the recessed plates respectively.

The plates can be either round or square. Each plate and each filter cloth has a circular hole in the centre. The slip is pumped through this central aperture into the chamber. When the pressure in each chamber becomes sufficiently high the

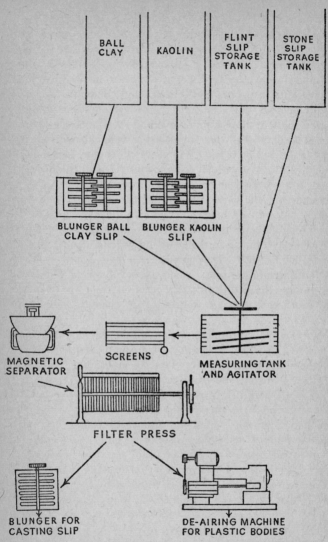

Fig. 2b. Flow sheet of the body preparation steps used in the method which is based on measuring the volume of the various slips.

slip water is forced through the cloths and runs out of the filter through recessed channels or grooves provided in the surface of each plate. Thus the solid parts of the slip remain behind and fill the individual chambers, forming plastic bodies called 'filter cakes' which can be removed in readiness for the next operation.

As can be seen from the description of filter presses, they work in an intermittent service. Emptying the press is an operation which does not lend itself easily to mechanization. Charging and discharging of the filter chambers take up a considerable number of man hours.

Two types of continuous filters have been developed in recent years and will probably find increasing use. One is the rotary vacuum filter. It consists basically of a cloth-covered drum suspended in a tank which contains the material to be filtered in slip form and in which the level of the slip is maintained at a certain height. The periphery of the drum is divided into a number of shallow compartments, each of which is connected through a common valve to a vacuum pump. The vacuum in each compartment can be regulated separately. As the drum rotates each compartment passes through the slip in the tank and sucks water through the cloth, forming a cake. The cake is discharged from the drum by a string which lifts the filter in a continuous sheet.

Continuous vacuum filters are manufactured by Filtration Engineers Inc. of Newark, New Jersey. They require very little supervision. For instance, in one large installation consisting of six rotary vacuum filters, only one man is required to supervise the whole slip house.

In this country L. A. Mitchell Ltd, of Manchester, have developed a continuous filter which consists of a steam-heated metal drum rotating in a slip tank. The hot drum surface picks up the dry materials out of the slip as it passes through it. The cakes are discharged continuously from the drum by a knife-like scraper. The water contents of the filter cake can be regulated by the speed of the rotation and the temperature of the surface.

De-airing of Clay. – De-airing of clay is one of the most important of recent inventions in the treatment of clay. The vacuum chamber, within the space of a few years, has become an important part of pug mills and extrusion machines.

Vacuum treatment considerably improves the plasticity and homogeneity of clay bodies. It was originally assumed that the removal of the air pockets by treatment under vacuum brought the clay particles in closer contact with each other, thereby considerably improving plasticity and workability. It has, however, been proved that the evaporation of water in vacuo exposes the clay particles to the action of a water vapour, thereby considerably increasing the plasticity. It has long been known that ageing (storing the plastic body for weeks or months) increases the plasticity and dry strength. It has been found that a short treatment in vacuo has the same effect on both dry strength and plasticity, as ageing for many weeks at a temperature of $90°$ C. Vacuum treatment, for instance, increases the modulus of rupture of clay specimens in the green state by 80% and in the fired state by between 15% and 20%.

De-airing Pug Mills. – De-airing pug mills are based on the following principle:

The clay, after being pugged, is pressed into a vacuum chamber. In the vacuum chamber the clay strings thus formed are shredded in order to increase the surface area of the clay exposed to the vacuum. The de-aired clay is finally compressed and extruded through the nozzle of the pug mill.

CHAPTER V

Shaping Processes

THERE are numerous individual-forming or shaping processes in use in the ceramic industries. Objects which have exactly the same shape may have been formed by one of several different processes. The physical properties of the finished articles vary considerably, depending upon the process used. The particular process employed depends on several factors, the most important of which are the shape of the article, the character of the raw materials and the desired properties of the finished product. The principal shaping methods are throwing, jollying, turning, pressing, extruding, and slip casting. In all these methods, with the exception only of the casting process, the plastic properties of clay are utilized. In shaping ceramic articles, similar principles are used in the various branches of the industry but the methods used vary greatly. For this reason the shaping methods will be described in more detail in the chapters dealing with the individual branches, such as brick-making, pottery, and so on. It is helpful, however, to consider now, very briefly, the main characteristics of the different shaping methods.

Throwing

Throwing is one of the oldest shaping methods and at one time most pottery articles were made in this way. At the present time this process is used mainly for forming special shapes. (The bulk of all clay ware is now made by mass production methods.) The term 'throwing' is not really accurately descriptive to the layman. 'Throwing' consists of shaping a mass of spinning clay between the thumbs, fingers and palms of the hands. The thrower places a lump of plastic clay on the wheel head and then sets the head in motion. He wets his two hands and, holding the spinning lump between them, he alternately squeezes and flattens it. He then gradually works the soft clay between his fingers, thumbs and palms to form the desired shape of the object.

Hand Moulding

Hand moulding is still used in the manufacture of clay products. Until fairly recent times all bricks were moulded by hand, but now only complicated shapes and special bodies are made by hand moulding. In some branches of the ceramic industry, for instance in the refractory section, a certain proportion of the output which does not lend itself to mechanization must be hand moulded. The simplest mould is that used for ordinary bricks. It consists of a wooden frame. When, however, articles are irregular in form, plaster of Paris moulds are used, either in one or more pieces. Plaster of Paris does not adhere to the soft clay body. It absorbs the water from the clay so that the clay can subsequently be easily removed from the mould.

Jollying

In jollying, the body is formed partly by a plaster of Paris mould and partly by means of a profile tool having a partial outline of the article to be made. The body is used in a plastic state. It is placed into or on a mould of plaster of Paris fixed on a rotating wheel (jolly) and pressed to shape by the profile. Part of the article is therefore produced by the plaster of Paris mould and part by the profile tool. For example, in the case of a cup, the outside is formed by the mould and the inside by the tool. In the case of a plate, the face of the plate is shaped by the plaster of Paris mould and the back of the plate by the profile tool. Automatic jollying machines for plate and cup making have been developed and will be described in more detail in the chapter dealing with earthenware and china manufacture.

Extrusion

In the extrusion process, the plastic paste is forced under pressure through a die or mouthpiece of the required shape.

Vertical and horizontal presses are used as well as convention-al and de-airing pug mills. The shape of the extrusion die corresponds to the cross-section of the rod, tube or bar to be extruded. After extrusion the material can be cut into pieces of suitable length. Extrusion is used in brick-making and, as previously mentioned, for rods, pipes, bars, etc., in porcelain, stoneware and refractory ceramics.

Pressing

Pressing in steel dies is used when large quantities are required. Pressing methods can be classified in various groups including:

(*a*) Wet pressing.
(*b*) Semi-dry pressing.
(*c*) Dry pressing.

In brick-making the following categories and nomenclature are used:

(*a*) Soft plastic (wire-cut process).
(*b*) The 'stiff plastic' process.
(*c*) The semi-plastic or semi-dry process.

Pressing, particularly semi-dry and dry pressing, lends it-self excellently to automatization. Automatic presses are des-cribed in the section dealing with brick-making and electrical insulators.

Turning

Turning is done on lathes similar to those used for metal or wood. Before a ceramic article can be *turned* it must be air-dried to a reasonably hard state. In the case of medium and large articles, the body is machined in what is called a semi-hard (green) state. Small articles, e.g. sparking plugs, are turned in a hard (white) state when all the water of formation is evaporated. In art pottery manufacture, turning is frequent-ly used after jollying or casting. For instance, grooves or undercut profiles are frequently turned in cups, pots and vases produced either by jollying or casting. In the manufacture of insulators and other technical porcelain, turning is used for producing grooves on cylindrical tubes, bushings and so on.

Slip Casting

This is carried out as follows.

First of all a dry plaster mould is filled with casting slip. After some time, the surplus liquid is poured out. The inside of the mould will now be found to be covered with a clay layer, a part of the water having been absorbed by the plaster. If one leaves this layer sufficiently long in the mould it becomes hard and can be removed. In this way an article can be formed, which reproduces exactly the negative of the form of the mould. The slip used for slip casting is prepared from plastic body by adding a small amount of sodium silicate (water-glass) or sodium carbonate, the free OH ions of the alkali depriving the clay particles of their plasticity and turning the plastic body liquid. Slip casting can only be used if the clay is not too plastic. Very plastic clays are too sticky and form an impermeable skin over the plaster of Paris mould, making it impossible for the plaster to absorb more water from the slip. Casting slips have to be extremely fine and must be carefully prepared. Very coarse particles would settle and the final body would not be homogeneous. Slip casting is used in pottery, earthenware and china manufacture for articles which, owing to the irregularity or special nature of their shape, would be difficult or impossible to produce by other means. It is also used to a great extent in the manufacture of technical porcelain and refractory material. Slip casting greatly simplifies mass production, but requires a very large number of moulds and consequently large factory space.

CHAPTER VI

Drying and Dryers

GENERAL

It has been explained in previous chapters that the various types of clay are made plastic and workable by the addition of water. It has also been explained that it is necessary to remove this water of formation by drying after the articles have been shaped, except where very little water has been used in the shaping, such as in dry or semi-dry pressing.

Clay ware is dried principally in order to harden it sufficiently for safe transportation to the next manufacturing stage, which is usually the placing of the articles into kilns or into saggers. It has further been mentioned that, during drying, the articles shrink, and that the shrinkage is the greater, the more plastic the raw materials used. On the other hand, the more open the bodies (this means the less plastic the clays used in their composition and/or the more non-plastic materials used in the preparation of the body), the more easily the drying process takes place. The water of formation contained in the body is evaporated into the surrounding air, particularly so if the air is warmer than the surface of the article and if it is not already saturated with vapour. It is obvious that the drying process will take place more quickly, the faster the surrounding air takes the moisture out of the body. Apart from the nature of the body used, the speed of drying is dependent on the following factors.

1. On the shape of the article.

Drying takes place more speedily, the greater the ratio of the surface area (that is in contact with the drying air) to the volume of the article. If various articles of different shapes, but all made of the same body and of equal weight, are considered, a spherical article would require the longest drying

D

time, whereas a suspended thin-walled tube would require the shortest drying time.

2. On the temperature of the surrounding air.

The higher the temperature of the air used for drying, the more water of formation is extracted and evaporated into the air in a given time.

A cubic metre of water-saturated air at:

$$20° C. \text{ contains } 17 \text{ gr. of water.}$$
$$40° C. \quad „ \quad 50 \text{ gr. } „ \quad „$$
$$60° C. \quad „ \quad 130 \text{ gr. } „ \quad „$$
$$80° C. \quad „ \quad 290 \text{ gr. } „ \quad „$$

A dry air-stream at 80° C. will dry about six times the number of articles which can be dried by a stream of air at 40° C. This is, of course, only an example and in practice it would seldom be advisable to employ dry air at 80° C.

3. On the velocity of the air circulation.

The speed of drying is also dependent upon the velocity at which air containing water evaporated from articles being dried is replaced by fresh warm air not containing vapour. Obviously the quicker moist air is replaced by fresh dry air, the quicker is the drying process.

4. On the humidity contents of the surrounding air.

If the surrounding air already contains water vapour, it is obviously unable to take as much moisture out of the ware as would dry air. Therefore it is possible to subject the ware to a stream of hot air of high humidity content, without depriving it of much water. Moreover, the interior and the exterior surfaces can thus be kept at almost the same temperature and drying of the surface at too quick a rate thus prevented. The dangerous time-lag between interior vapour pressure and surface vapour pressure is eliminated. It will be obvious, therefore, that by carefully controlling the temperature and humidity content of the air, internal stresses set up by too quick drying of the surface, with resultant unequal shrinkage, can be avoided. This consideration led to the development of humidity dryers, in which hot, damp air is used. The ware in the dryers is first treated with very humid hot air and then the humidity is gradually reduced, with the temperature unaltered. In continuous dryers, in which the warm air moves from the ware exit end to the ware entrance end (counterflow dryers), the same principle is employed. The kind of dryer used depends entirely on the type of ware to be dried and the layout of the factory.

Wherever possible, waste heat of the kilns, used for firing the ware, is employed for drying the ware before firing. If intermittent ovens are used, the waste heat is not always available, and additional steam usually has to be produced for drying. If, however, tunnel ovens are used for firing the ware, enough waste heat is usually available for operating the dryers, without providing extra heat. When planning a factory layout this point should never be forgotten.

TYPES OF DRYERS

The most important dryers used in drying clay ware can be classified as follows:

1. Intermittent dryers.
    (a) Lofts and hot floors.
    (b) Compartment and chamber dryers.
    (c) Humidity chamber dryers.
2. Semi-continuous dryers (dobbins and similar dryers).
3. Continuous dryers.
    (a) Tunnel dryers.
    (b) Mangles.

1. (a). Lofts and hot floors are extensively used in brick and refractories manufacture. Steam pipes are placed in sections under the floor, or the floor may be arranged over continuous kilns. This type of drying is, however, inefficient as far as labour is concerned and in new factories it is superseded by tunnel dryers.

(b) Compartment dryers are used in most branches of the ceramic industry, particularly in older factories. The ware has to be carried on shelves, trays, or rack dryer cars into the compartments, and has to be removed in the same way.

(*c*) Humidity chambers are an elaborate type of compartment dryers and are provided with accurate means of controlling the temperature and the humidity of the air. They are used for drying large and complicated articles such as big electrical insulators.

2. Semi-continuous dryers are chamber dryers which are provided with hand-operated means of transporting the ware through the drying chamber. One example will be quoted, namely the so-called dobbin which is a drying chamber in which shelves or boards loaded with ware are placed on horizontal arms fixed on a vertical spindle. The ware is moved through the stove by rotating the spindle. After one revolution of the spindle the drying process is completed and the ware is taken out of the drying chamber. Dobbins are very economical and used to a great extent in earthenware manufacture.

Continuous Dryers

3. Where potteries are scientifically laid out, there is an orderly flow of production from the raw materials to the finished product. Into such a layout continuous tunnel dryers fit well. A tunnel dryer consists of a long tunnel equipped with heating units, fans, and temperature and humidity controls. The heating units can be heated by flue gas, or the waste heat from the tunnel kilns can be led direct into the tunnel dryer. The ware is carried through the tunnel on cars, or by a conveyor belt or racks suspended from an overhead monorail. Tunnel dryers are used in most branches of the ceramic industry nowadays, particularly for heavy ware.

Mangle dryers are another type of continuous dryer in which shelves are suspended on endless chains and conveyed up and down through a chamber provided with baffles. As the ware travels up and down it passes, as a rule, from a moist hot atmosphere to a dry hot atmosphere. This type of dryer is widely used in the pottery industry for drying plates, cups, saucers, and other ware jollied in plaster moulds for

mould release. On one end of the dryer the mould containing the jollied article is placed. At the other end, the dried
article is removed from the mould. The latter travels on the
mangle back to the jollier.

Rapid drying is economically desirable but the speed is
limited by the danger of encouraging drying cracks or deformation of the ware. Generally speaking, heavy drying losses
are more likely to occur (*a*) when articles have an uneven
section, (*b*) when a body is used where the shrinkage is on the
high side, and (*c*) when articles of large dimensions are involved. Large insulators, sanitary ware, and large stoneware
articles require particularly careful drying. Large articles tend
to get drying cracks when the wall thickness is large, and they
tend to get deformed when they are thin walled.

Infra-red Drying

Infra-red drying has been used to an increasing extent in the
ceramic industry, particularly in recent years in the U.S.A.
Heat is delivered in most cases from a series of powerful bulbs,
placed in tunnels or over conveyors, near to the article to be
dried. Reflectors direct the infra-red heat rays on to the ware.

Successful use of infra-red drying is claimed in the following cases:

1. Drying bisque fired ware after glazing (dipping). The
drying time is reduced from five hours in the case of air drying,
to five minutes in the case of infra-red drying.

2. Drying of jollied cups and flat ware on plaster moulds
for rapid mould release in connexion with the use of automatic jollying machines. Very rapid drying makes it possible
to empty the plaster moulds after only a few minutes drying
time and thus reduces the number of moulds required.

3. Drying of large vitreous china tubs and other sanitary
ware.

High Frequency Drying

High frequency drying is a recent development. It is already used in the chemical industry, and it is rapidly becoming popular in the plastics industry. The principle is as follows:

Every electrical insulator, and particularly every bad electrical insulator (unfired clay ware is a bad electrical insulator), coming within the influence of an alternating electric field consumes a certain amount of electrical energy and transforms it into heat. The heat developed is the greater, the higher the voltage, the higher the frequency and the greater the 'power factor'[1] of the insulating material placed into the electric field. If one wishes to produce uniform heating throughout the article, the power factor must be uniform throughout. This is usually the case with synthetic plastic materials and because of this fact these materials lend themselves excellently to this drying process. In the case of drying clay ware, however, the heat produced within the article is not uniform throughout unless the water content is uniform. It is doubtful therefore whether high frequency drying will ever be used to a large extent for drying clay ware. Furthermore, at the time of writing, high frequency is an expensive source of energy.

1. The 'power factor' is a measure of the energy lost in an alternating field of an insulating material.

CHAPTER VII

Firing

THE action of heat on clays and mixtures of clays with other materials is really the basis of the ceramic industry. When treated at high temperatures, these materials acquire durability and many other favourable qualities seldom equalled by other substances. Certain methods of firing and corresponding kiln designs have been developed in the course of centuries, but the basic principles were little understood.

The advance of science and engineering has therefore been welcomed in the field occupied for centuries by the 'practical potter' and has revolutionized methods of firing and kiln design. Such important advances as the introduction of continuous tunnel kilns, intermittent car kilns, electric kilns, and so on are the outcome of ceramic research and engineering. The majority of clay ware is still fired in the kilns known as 'periodic kilns' which have been used for centuries with little fundamental change. At the time of writing, however (1953), the conventional type of intermittent coal-fired periodic kiln is completely out of favour for new plant construction and is only considered for extension of existing plant in very exceptional circumstances.

In existing factories there is, however, a great number of intermittent kilns in operation. In such particularly progressive branches of the ceramic industry, as the electrical insulator and sparking plug sections, both in this country and in the U.S.A., very few of the old-fashioned coal ovens are still in operation. In the U.S.A., in the china, earthenware and sanitary ware branches of the ceramic industry, intermittent coal ovens also are the exception rather than the rule. To compensate for the higher wages which the ceramic industry will have to pay in the future in order to make employment sufficiently attractive, it will be necessary to replace existing coal-fired intermittent ovens by kilns less wasteful in respect of labour and fuel.

CLASSIFICATION OF KILNS

In most brick and pottery kilns the heat is used direct. The flames and gases of combustion surround the ceramic articles or the refractory receptacles (called saggers) containing the ware. This type of kiln is called the 'open flame' kiln. It is used for firing goods which are not easily spoiled by contact with the flames or for firing ware which is placed and fired in saggers.

In another type of kiln called the 'muffle' type, the flames heat the outside of a refractory chamber containing the articles to be fired, but they do not enter the chamber. The muffle is heated directly and the ware inside the muffle indirectly by radiation from the muffle. Muffle kilns are used for firing delicate articles such as those with soft delicate glazes and colours.

In these two classes of kiln the firing may be intermittent or continuous. Intermittent ovens are characterized by the procedure that the ware is placed into the oven, which is then heated to the desired temperature and then cooled, and the ware removed after cooling. These ovens consist, as a rule, of one chamber. If they do contain several chambers, the chambers are fired simultaneously. A continuous oven is characterized by the fact that it consists either of a series of chambers which are fired one after the other or it consists of a tunnel through which the ware travels from the cold entrance end, through the firing zone to the cold exit end, on cars or conveyor belts, or on a moving refractory sole.

Intermittent Up-draught Kilns

These are usually circular in plan. Fireplaces are arranged at more or less regular intervals around the base circumference.

The flames from the fireplaces take two separate routes:

1. Directly upwards into the oven through flues in the walls and out through the 'bags' (fire brick structures which

prevent the flames from striking directly on to the ware or the saggers), to the dome and then out through the chimney.

2. Through flues beneath the sole and openings in the sole into the oven.

Dampers in the chimney and the dome make some sort of draught regulation possible. It is, however, difficult to draw as much heat towards the centre and bottom of the kiln, as is drawn from the fireplaces direct to the chimney. For this reason in large kilns a temperature difference not exceeding 120° C. at various points of the oven is quite an achievement. Intermittent up-draught kilns are used for firing various types of ceramics, including pottery, refractories, and so on.

Down-draught Intermittent Kilns

These are usually of two types.
1. Single chamber.
2. Two story.

They are used for firing pottery, stoneware, and refractory goods and are slightly better than the up-draught kiln, as regards fuel consumption and temperature distribution.

On the Continent, for firing porcelain and hardening clay ware, kilns with two chambers, one on top of the other, are frequently used. In the lower chamber glazed and unglazed porcelain articles are fired at 1400° C. In the upper chamber the clay ware is hardened at a temperature of between 900° and 1000° C.

The same fireplaces which provide heat for the lower chamber also serve the upper chamber. The flames from the lower chamber pass through holes in the sole and through flues into the upper chamber, thus heating the ware there to the desired temperature. The path of the flame in down-draught ovens from the fireplace to the chimney is as follows:

1. Fireplace.
2. Bag.
3. Firing chamber (interior of the kiln).
4. Crown of the firing chamber.

5. Down to the sole of the firing chamber.
6. Through the exit holes in the sole.
7. Through flues beneath the sole.
8. Through flues in outer wall.
9a. In the case of one-chamber kilns, into chimney.
9b. In the case of 2-story kilns, into upper story and chimney.

One-chamber kilns are used for ware which has to be fired only once, for instance, refractory ware, stoneware, etc. Two story intermittent kilns are used for ware which has to be fired twice at different temperatures.

Fuels. – The principal fuel used in intermittent kilns is coal. At the commencement of the firing, short-flame coal, or even coke, may be used to advantage. At the next stage in the firing, it may be mixed with a long-flame (fat) coal. During the last period of the firing, however, the use of long-flame coal is essential. The long flames produced carry the heat to the middle of the oven which would be extremely difficult to heat by radiation or convection.

In the case of both down-draught and up-draught kilns, the firing time could be much reduced if it were possible to heat the inner parts of the kiln as quickly as the outer parts. A proportion of the ware is, in fact, subjected to heat treatment much longer than is needed, owing to the necessity for bringing the inner part of the kiln to the required temperature at the final stages of the firing.

Lignite (brown coal) and lignite briquettes are used to a very great extent on the Continent for firing intermittent kilns, not only at the commencement, but also, in many cases, mixed with coal throughout the whole firing process. Its use is due to the fact that in several places on the Continent, particularly in Czechoslovakia, lignites of very high calorific value are available.

Disadvantages of Intermittent Kilns. – Intermittent kilns have two principal disadvantages :

1. The fuel consumption is very high, one reason being that the whole kiln (the sole, brickwork, chimney, etc.) has after firing to be allowed to cool down to a temperature which will permit workmen to enter the kiln and take out the saggers. After the next batch of saggers has been placed in position, the whole kiln has then to be heated up all over again, right from the very start. Intermittent operation of the kiln makes the use of recuperators and the use of waste heat almost impossible. The exception is the use of the waste heat during the last 600° C. of the cooling period, for drying other ware and for space heating generally.

2. The sagger consumption is very high, as a result of the considerable breakage.

The saggers filled with ware are hand-placed on top of each other, 10 to 20 saggers high, and are carried up ladders. After the firing, the same process is carried out in the reverse direction. Working space is restricted, to say the least, and conditions are frequently not too pleasant if emptying and filling are done when the kiln is still rather hot from the previous firing. Rough handling of the saggers cannot be avoided. Furthermore, in the case of large intermittent kilns, the weight of the saggers placed one on top of the other is considerable and consequently under the influence of heat and compression a certain percentage of the saggers becomes deformed. Another factor which shortens the life of the saggers is the fact that part of the lime, iron, etc., contained in the coal ash drawn with the flames inside the kiln, forms a kind of glaze on the surface of the saggers. This reduces their resistance to temperature changes.

The filling and emptying of kilns are very intricate and heavy jobs requiring great skill and physical strength on the part of the workpeople who have to carry the heavy filled saggers into the kiln and pile up high stacks of them. Work of this nature is very costly and expenses are increased by what one might call 'unavoidable' breakages of both saggers and ware.

Thermal Efficiency of Intermittent Kilns. – There are naturally wide variations in the thermal performances of different kilns for firing particular products, but the following table gives a rough idea of how the calorific value of the fuel is utilized in intermittent ovens:

Heating ware, saggers and supports . 10–12%
Heat taken up by kiln structure . . 30–40%
Heat lost by radiation from walls of kiln
or by conduction to the ground . 20–30%
Heat lost in waste gases . . . 20–30%

The problem of how to improve the low thermal efficiency of intermittent kilns and simultaneously of how to secure a better control of temperature distribution has occupied the minds of ceramic engineers for many years. Two parallel developments have taken place, the first being the continuous, or chamber type kiln, and the second the tunnel kiln.

Continuous Kiln for Bricks and Refractories

Potters have long been aware that a considerable saving can be obtained if one kiln can be heated from another. If gases are drawn from a kiln under fire, through a flue system, to one or more kilns the latter can, under appropriate conditions, be pre-heated with no expenditure of fuel. Such systems are used in the manufacture of bricks.

The modern 'ring' or 'chamber' type of continuous kiln is designed to utilize the heat absorbed by the cooling chamber and by the cooling ware. In these types of kilns the firing zone is advanced continually through a series of chambers, with a flue connexion to a chimney or fan at a constant distance ahead of that section of the kiln under fire. This makes it possible: (1) To utilize the heat of the waste flue gases from the zone under fire. (2) To pre-heat the ware between the fire zone and the chimney connexion. (3) To draw air through portions of the kiln in the process of cooling and thus make hot air available for combustion in the fire zone. Such kilns are being used in large numbers by the heavy clay industries all over the world.

They are called 'Hoffman kilns' and are shown in Figs. 3 and 4. A circular or oval burning chamber (A) has twelve doors (B), for filling and emptying, and is connected by twelve flues (C) with a main flue D1. This main flue D1 is connected with the chimney D. The flues C can be closed by valves F. The chambers are formed and can be completely shut off by movable dampers. Each chamber is enclosed between

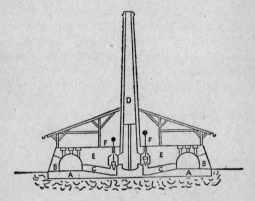

Fig. 3. Section of Circular Hoffman Kiln.

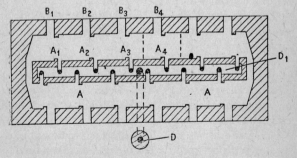

Fig. 4. Plan of Continuous Kiln.

two dampers and the brickwork of the walls (E), sole and cupola.

For small outputs, a different form of continuous kiln, the so-called zig-zag kiln, is used. Continuous kilns are considerably more economic in fuel consumption than intermittent ovens. They have, however, the following disadvantages:

1. The structure is continually heated and cooled, just as in intermittent ovens.

2. The ware has to be placed into the kiln and to be drawn out just as in intermittent kilns.

(This disadvantage has lately been overcome by a new type of kiln, which is a compromise between intermittent and chamber kilns on one hand and tunnel ovens on the other hand. Cars are loaded with ware outside the kiln and are pushed into the chamber for firing.)

3. The individual chambers are fired just as in intermittent kilns.

The heat distribution in a chamber of a continuous kiln is not much better than the heat distribution in an intermittent oven, but, as already mentioned, continuous kilns are much more economical in fuel consumption.

The most commonly used continuous kilns are:

1. The Hoffman kilns.
2. The 'Belgian' kilns.
3. The Staffordshire or Lancashire kilns.

Hoffman kilns (invented by Hoffman in 1863) are mainly used for the manufacture of building and facing bricks. The fuel (slack) is fed through a series of small holes in the kiln crown down amongst the bricks.

Side fired continuous kilns are known in Great Britain as Belgian kilns. They are similar to Hoffman kilns. The coal is, however, charged through the 'wicket' on to a grate extending across the chamber. The Belgian kiln is used for higher temperatures up to 1200° C.

The Staffordshire and Lancashire continuous kilns have division walls between the chambers and are top fired like the Hoffman kilns.

Continuous Tunnel Ovens

The name is more or less self-explanatory. The ware is carried through a tunnel on some moving medium. This may be a truck covered with a refractory lining, a moving refractory sole, or, in the case of temperatures below 1100° C., a belt conveyor made of heat-resisting metal. In this tunnel the temperature is greatest at the centre and the ware is gradually heated as it approaches the centre of the kiln (the firing zone). Here the final firing temperature is reached. During the passage through this zone the firing process is completed and the ware then gradually cools down as it travels towards the exit. When it reaches the exit the ware is sufficiently cooled for the truck to be removed from the kiln.

Much better use of the heating (calorific) value of the fuel is made by the tunnel oven than by either the intermittent oven or by the continuous chamber kiln. Once a tunnel oven is heated to the desired temperature it can be kept at this point by a comparatively small amount of fuel. We have seen that in the case of intermittent ovens as much as 30–40% of the heat produced is used to heat up the brickwork and structure generally. In the case of tunnel ovens, however, once the desired temperature is reached only the heat lost by radiation or convection has to be replaced, in order to keep the temperature of the kiln structure constant.

In most cases what is known as the 'counterflow system' is utilized. By this system the products of combustion developed in the high temperature zone are drawn towards the entrance end of the kiln giving up heat to the ware travelling towards the fire zone. As the ware passes through the cooling zone towards the exit end it is cooled by a stream of air which passes on to the high-firing zone, where it is utilized in fuel combustion. The use of this highly pre-heated secondary air results in considerable fuel economy. It is of great importance, particularly for high temperature kilns, and the benefit is far in excess of the actual quantity of B.T.U.s carried by the air.

For instance, at the temperature of 2300° F. (1260° C.) used for example for earthenware biscuit fire, a heat increase of 160% can be attained by using combustion air already heated to 1500° F. (820° C.). Again, where a fuel of low calorific value (such as producer gas) is employed, the use of hot air and pre-heated gas is even more essential on account of the low flame temperature.

In an intermittent kiln a temperature advance above cones 10 to 14 can only be achieved by hours of firing, and by the consumption of much extra fuel.

In a recuperative tunnel kiln, however, the higher firing temperature can be achieved with only a small increase in fuel consumption since the temperature of the combustion air becomes higher as the temperature in the firing zone of the kiln is raised. Philip Dressler, the well-known oven designer (who wrote the chapter on tunnel ovens in McNamara's book, *Ceramics*, The Pennsylvania State College), describes how, in tunnel kilns used for the firing of chrome super-refractories, the temperature is progressively raised from cone 16 to cone 30 or even higher, with an increase in fuel consumption of only approximately 33%. Without the benefits of 'recuperation', a temperature of cone 30 (if reached at all) could only be achieved by the expenditure of an almost infinite amount of fuel.

The advantages of tunnel kilns as compared with intermittent ovens and continuous kilns are:

1. The temperature is steady.

2. There is no loss of heat, or any wear and tear due to repeated temperature changes during heating and cooling of the kiln structure.

3. It is obviously easier to heat uniformly ovens of small cross section than those of large cross section. It is possible to design tunnel kilns of small cross section in order to secure uniform heat distribution.

4. Placing and drawing are done outside the kiln under conditions most suitable for obtaining a continuous flow of production in the factory.

History of Tunnel Kiln Development. – The difficulties in building and operating tunnel kilns proved very much greater than those encountered in the design of continuous chamber kilns. It was not until about 1910 that the tunnel kiln became a commercial success. At that time only very large tunnel kilns were built and so they were only suitable for factories which turned out ware on a very big scale.

Until recent years, potteries making high-grade ware did not have sufficient turnover to justify the use of such large tunnel ovens. For this reason a great deal of the early work on tunnel kilns was confined to plants making bricks, tiles, and other heavy products. As we shall see later on, the position has now completely changed. In recent years very small tunnel ovens have been built, both for high and low temperatures (for instance the former for the manufacture of alumina sparking plugs fired at 1900° C. and the latter for enamel kilns for pottery fired at only about 800° C.).

Incidentally, we now know that the problems involved in firing bricks, tiles, and other heavy clay products are on the whole more difficult than those encountered in firing fine china loaded in refractory saggers. Difficulties were caused by the oxidation of pyrites and carbonaceous matter from the heavy clay products and by the shrinkage of the whole kiln contents in the case of clay ware fired without refractory supports. These repeated failures of tunnel kiln installations quite naturally prejudiced the potters against tunnel kilns. This took many years to overcome, but is now past history.

One of the earliest builders of tunnel kilns was Otto Bock of Berlin. He built a great number of tunnel kilns in various German factories over a period of twenty years. (In 1880 he invented the sand seal, which has since been used to protect the metal parts of the car trucks from the heat of the tunnel.)

The earliest American inventor was Anderson of Chicago who took out patents in the early 1890's and carried out several installations for brick plants.

In Europe a number of kilns were installed by Dinz between 1900–10. In these installations coal was dropped through the top of the kiln arch on to the platforms of the kiln cars. (This follows the ordinary practice of the Hoffman ring chamber kiln in which slag coal is dropped among the stacks of bricks.)

One of these Dinz tunnel ovens, for the manufacture of sanitary ware, was still operating in France as late as 1926.

At the same time a French engineer, Faugeron, developed a producer-gas-fired tunnel kiln for general ware in France. This seems to have been the first commercially successful type of direct fired tunnel kiln placed on the market.

During the period 1908–10, Conrad Dressler was working on tunnel kilns in England. He developed a tunnel kiln in which the combustion gases were confined within a flue on each side of the kiln, in order to protect the ware from the direct impact of the flames. It was the first 'muffle' tunnel kiln.

In 1918 C. B. Harrop of Columbus started the development of tunnel kilns and in the 1920's he built a large number. These kilns were characterized by simplicity of construction. Moreover Harrop was the first to perceive that the oil and gas fuels available in the United States made possible radical alterations in the methods of tunnel kiln operation. By introducing fuel under pressure, mixed with a considerable proportion of air for combustion, it was possible to direct the flame to different parts of the setting on the kiln cars. At the same time it was possible to maintain a positive pressure in the high temperature zone. This permitted a better heat distribution than had previously been possible in open flame kilns operating under negative pressure. Until 1926 the majority of direct fired kilns used individual fire-boxes, similar to those used for firing coal, even in cases where oil or gas was used. These fire-boxes were placed along the firing zone of the kiln at distances from 8 ft. to 12 ft. There was thus a tendency for localization of heat opposite each fire-box, with a drop in temperature in between.

In this respect the open flame kilns gave less satisfactory results than the muffle kilns. In the latter the burners are arranged so as to draw the fuel stream within the centre of the muffle space, parallel to the length of the kiln.

In 1926 the Dressler tunnel kiln organization placed the multi-burner type of kiln on the market. In this design the individual fire-box is abandoned and replaced by a series of small port-holes in the side walls. These small port-holes are located above and below the ware setting in order to avoid direct impact of the flames on to the ware. Each port is connected by a flue to the interior of the kiln at the end of the cooling zone, adjacent to the firing zone. In this way each burner sucks in highly pre-heated air to the burners. Multi-burner kilns with as many as 120 burners have been built. These designs are applicable where both oil or gas fuels are available. Where coal is used, however, fire-boxes are still required.

For firing bricks, top-fired tunnel ovens are often used (Monnier kilns). The fuel is introduced through holes in the kiln crown in a similar way as in Hoffman kilns.

The reader will have gathered from the short history given that American industry has played a prominent part in the development of the tunnel oven.

It should, however, be pointed out that the manufacturers of tunnel ovens in this country have kept pace with their American and Continental counterparts, with the result that British designs are second to none.

The heat distribution in a modern tunnel kiln is very uniform, particularly in the firing zone. Where two tunnel kilns of different sizes are designed on the same principle, the one with the smaller cross section will have the more uniform heat distribution in the firing zone. As an example of heat uniformity it is interesting to note that, in the case of a multi-burner kiln of large cross section, for instance 5 ft. 8 ins. setting width and 5 ft. 2 ins. setting height, the heat variation is only one quarter of a cone (approximately 10° C.) at the peak temperature of Orton cone 13 (1350° C.).

In the pre-firing zone, however, the temperature at the top of the setting is, as a rule, about three cones (100° C.) higher than at the bottom of the setting. This disadvantage has been overcome lately by the introduction of a vertical heat circulation in the pre-heating zone. Fans soak hot air from the bottom of the setting space and press it through openings provided in the crown, thus producing a circulation of hot air in the pre-heating zone from the top to the bottom of the setting space. This arrangement not only improves the heat distribution in the pre-heating zone, but also allows a shortening of this zone and consequently of the whole kiln.

Various Types of Tunnel Kilns. – In the foregoing chapter the history of tunnel oven development was described briefly. To summarize, the types of tunnel kilns most widely used to-day are:

1. Open flame tunnel ovens of three types:
    (*a*) Fire-box type of tunnel kilns.
    (*b*) Top fired tunnel ovens.
    (*c*) Multi-burner type of tunnel kilns.
2. Muffle type tunnel ovens.

1. Open flame ovens are used in those cases where either the ware is protected from direct contact with the flame because it is placed in refractory receptacles (saggers) or where the ware to be fired is of such a nature as not to be affected detrimentally by contact with the open flame.

(*a*) The fire-box type of tunnel kilns is suitable when coal is used, and also when gas is used, if uniform heat distribution and uniform rise of temperature are not essential.

(*b*) 'Monnier' type of tunnel kilns are used in brick manufacture. Coal containing a certain proportion of pulverized dust is fed through holes in the kiln arch, the fine dust particles burn directly as they enter the kiln, while the heavier particles continue to burn as they fall to the car base. This gives complete combustion and relatively good heat distribution. Fig. 5.

(*c*) The multi-burner type of kilns is employed if gas or oil is used and where equal heat distribution and the use of a recuperating system are desired, either for fuel economy or for obtaining very high temperatures.

2. Muffle type kilns are used when the ware, or its glaze, is delicate and direct contact with the flame has to be avoided

or where open setting of glazed ware is preferred to the use of saggers. In the design of intermittent muffle kilns, the muffle is very often an integral part of the oven structure. In the Dressler muffle tunnel kiln, however, the muffle is built entirely separate from the structure of the kiln. It forms a tube or

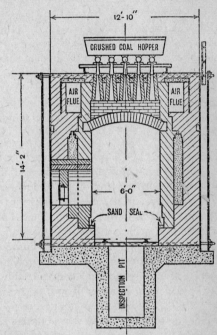

Fig. 5. Section through firing zone of patent tunnel kiln for building bricks.
(By courtesy of Gibbons Bros.)

flue on each side of the kiln, is supported on a bed of sand, and is thus free to expand or contract independently of the kiln structure. This is very important as the muffle gets much hotter than the kiln structure and the material of which the muffle is made often has a different coefficient of thermal expansion from that of the oven structure. Burners are let into the muffle and are each provided with a right-angle bend. The burning fuel is thus introduced into the centre of the muffle and the flames are directed parallel to the length of the kiln.

Any impingement of the flames on to the sides of the combustion chamber is in this way avoided.

Semi-muffle Type Kiln. – A smaller and less costly type of muffle kiln, the semi-muffle kiln, has recently been produced. In this the combustion chamber is not a complete muffle. It is bounded on the back, top and bottom by the masonry of the kiln. The front – facing the ware to be heated – is composed of a double-walled muffle tile resting upon a special bottom piece, with a thin wall on the fire side and open on the front side to radiate into the space beneath the ware platform. The burners are inserted into the muffle or combustion chamber through the brickwork of the kiln and are given a right-angle bend exactly as in the case of the standard muffle type described above.

Radiant Burners. – A very interesting relatively new development must be mentioned, viz. the use of radiant burners in connexion with gas-and-oil fired tunnel ovens. The design is such that uniform flameless combustion – around the surface of a ball-shaped burner – is obtained. The heat for firing the ware is thus achieved principally by radiation.

A great number of such radiant burners has to be used per kiln. For instance, in a gas-fired circular kiln for the manufacture of high-grade china constructed by Lennox Inc., Trenton, with a mean diameter of 40 ft. (corresponding to a straight kiln length of 125 ft. 8 ins.) 104 radiant burners are incorporated. The surface areas of these burners are very considerable and produce an effect similar to a muffle heated from outside by long, open flames. The advantage of this new design, however, is that a muffle is no longer necessary, since no flame enters the ware space and all the heat is radiated into the inside of the oven by the radiant burners. This type of oven is thus a compromise between an open flame and a muffle oven.

Fuel for Tunnel Ovens. – As mentioned previously, coal is used only in exceptional circumstances for firing tunnel ovens. The fuels most commonly employed are:

1. Town gas.
2. Producer gas.
3. Natural gas.
4. Oil.

In this country, town gas is used as a rule, but quite a number of ceramic plants employ producer gas. In the United States many potteries are favourably situated for supplies of natural gas and use it in the summer months and sometimes the whole year round. In winter there is often a scarcity of natural gas – owing to increased demand – and the price is increased during this period. For this reason many factories use natural gas in summer and oil in winter. For the switch-over from one fuel to another only the burners have to be changed.

The decision as to which fuel is the most economic depends principally on local considerations. Oil, of course, is used in places where town gas and natural gas are not available, or where it is cheaper than the last-mentioned two fuels. In this country, owing to the high price of oil, its use for tunnel oven firing is only an exception, but the coal and gas position in this country has induced pottery manufacturers to use oil fuel, odd as it may seem at first glance.

Producer gas is employed to a very great extent on the Continent, where large low-grade lignite formations, situated near important industrial centres, make its manufacture and use very economical. Factories using it have their own producer gas plants and also, in most cases, the necessary equipment for removing tar and other materials which might be detrimental to the working of the burners. In this country coke is the most important fuel for producer gas plants.

Electric Furnaces. – If the cost of electricity in, say, kilowatt hours per cwt. of pottery fired is compared with the cost of the number of cubic feet of gas burned per cwt. of pottery, it will usually be found the more expensive form of energy. Under certain circumstances, however, electricity may be cheaper than other fuels. There are cases where large hydro-electric power plants supply energy at a very low price, whereas the price of coal would be excessive owing to expensive transport (for instance in Switzerland and in Northern Italy).

The use of electricity for firing pottery has, however, many advantages which may outweigh its sometimes higher price.

1. The atmosphere in an electric furnace is cleaner than in any other type of kiln.

2. The ware does not have to be protected from the flames by muffles and saggers.

3. The weight of ware which can be placed in a cubic foot of setting space is greater than with any other furnace system (this derives naturally from 2).

4. The percentage of ware spoiled during the firing process is smaller.

Intermittent electric furnaces are, as a rule, only used in laboratories, where they are very handy and where the cost of the small amount of energy consumption is not decisive.

Electric tunnel ovens are used nowadays to a very great extent for firing on-glaze decorated pottery (decorating kilns or enamel kilns). The temperature required is only 700° to 800° C. Many colours are extremely sensitive to fumes and smoke and so conditions in electric kilns are ideal in this respect.

With regard to 'glost firing' of china and earthenware ('glost firing' means firing the glazes on ware which has been previously fired at a higher temperature) the same arguments apply and the advantage of a clean atmosphere may frequently outweigh the disadvantage of the higher price. The main difficulty with electric tunnel ovens for temperatures above 1150° C. has been for some time the question of electrical heating resistors. These difficulties have now been overcome. For temperatures up to 1200° C. nickel-chromium resistors are used. For temperatures up to 1300° C. special metal alloys (aluminium-iron alloys) are now manufactured. For temperatures from 1250° C. up to 1400° C. non-metallic heating elements are being used to a very great extent. The latter resistor consists mainly of silicon carbide ('Globar' resistors manufactured by the Carborundum Co., 'Gillil' by Siemens and Halske).

Electric tunnel ovens, for firing porcelain at a temperature of 1400° C. and single-fire vitreous sanitary ware at a temperature of 1200° C., have successfully operated for many years in Switzerland, Sweden and Italy. In this country electric tunnel ovens are used for china and earthenware glost fire by Messrs. Wedgwood in Barlaston and Messrs Wiltshaw and Robinson, Stoke-on-Trent. A description of the electric earthenware bisque and glost ovens is given in the chapter, 'A Visit to the All-Electric Works of Messrs Josiah Wedgwood & Son in Barlaston.'[1]

A very interesting electrical furnace has been developed by Brown-Boveri, Baden, Switzerland (Plate 12). It is particularly suitable for replacing old-fashioned bottle ovens, where the space is too small for tunnel ovens. The ware is placed on cars outside the firing chamber on 'batts' and 'props' (open setting) as illustrated in Plate 12. The car is then pushed into the oven which is still several hundred degrees hot from the previous fire. After firing to the desired temperature and cooling down to about 300° C., the car is removed from the kiln and pushed into a second chamber where the cooling is completed. (The second chamber is arranged so that heat energy can be tapped off, but this is not essential.)

Most Economical Dimensions of Tunnel Kilns. – It has already been mentioned that, in early days, the opinion was held that

1. Since writing the manuscript, numerous electric tunnel ovens have been put into operation in the North Stafford Pottery District and elsewhere, both for Glost Firing and for Enamel Firing (firing the decorations on the finished white ware). The conveyor belt type of electric tunnel ovens (such as the 'Birlec' and 'Bricesco' ovens) have become increasingly popular. The ware is put on to a moving conveyor belt made of heat resisting metal (for instance Nickel Chromium) at the entrance to the tunnel, and moves on it through the kiln, the cars covered with refractory brick work being no longer necessary, and the wattage per unit weight of ware considerably reduced. The life of the conveyor belt, which is continuously heated up to 1100° C. is of course limited, but a life of more than one year for Glost firing belts makes this type of oven a very interesting proposition, particularly for medium sized or small firms, since very small units of this type of oven are being built and give most satisfactory results.

very large units were the most economical ones. In particular, it was considered that small kilns did not compare favourably with large ones, particularly from the standpoint of fuel consumption. This opinion, however, has largely been abandoned within recent years. The tables on pp. 122–4 give details of dimensions of tunnel ovens built for ceramic plants in this country and in the U.S.A. during the last decade.

Three of the most vital factors are:

1. Cross-sectional area.
2. Lengths of various zones.
3. Speed of travel.

The larger the cross-sectional area of a tunnel kiln, the longer the time it naturally takes for the articles placed in the middle of the truck to reach a temperature approaching that of the ware at the sides of the truck, facing the burners. The speed of the trucks is therefore governed by the temperature of the ware at the centre and not by that at the sides. The trucks have to travel slowly enough to allow the centre ware, and particularly the lower part of the centre ware, to reach the same temperature as the hotter parts of the truck. If the cross-section of a tunnel oven is decreased, in order to improve the heat distribution, and if one wishes to retain the output associated with the larger cross-section, it is obvious that one would try to increase the speed of travel through the kiln. This has been done and it has been found, in many cases, that acceleration of the speed of travel – in kilns of small cross-section – does not detrimentally affect the characteristics of the ware, and that extremely rapid travel is possible, provided the ware does not emerge from the kiln in too hot a state. (The cooling zone has therefore to be long enough to offset the speed of travel.) These considerations explain why, in recent years, kilns possessing small cross-sectional areas and relatively great lengths have been increasingly installed, particularly for the manufacture of small- and medium-sized articles. Large articles, of course, require kilns of large cross-section.

Circular Tunnel Kilns. – A tunnel kiln may be designed either in the form of a straight line layout or in the form of a circular layout. Although a few circular tunnel ovens were built many years ago, this type is, generally speaking, a relatively recent development. The decision as to whether a circular tunnel kiln is preferable to a straight line kiln depends on the site conditions, e.g. the space available, the layout of the shaping and drying departments, etc.

The main difference between straight line and circular tunnel kilns is as follows:

In the straight line tunnel kiln the ware is carried on trucks through the oven, whereas in the circular tunnel kiln the ware is carried round on a rotating sole, or turn-table, lined with refractory brickwork.

Length and setting area of tunnel ovens built by leading British and American oven builders for firing different articles are given in the following tables.

Length and Setting Area of Various Tunnel Ovens
Swindell Dressler Corporation, Pittsburgh, Pa.

Name and location	Kiln length		Setting width	Setting height	Product fired
	ft	in.	ft. in.	ft. in.	
General Electrical, Schnectady	399	0	5 8	5 2	High-tension insulators
General Ceramics Keasbey, New J.	65	0	22	21	Steatite insulators
American Lava Corpn, Chattanooga, Tenn.	96	0	22	27	Steatite insulators
Dressler Thrift Muffle Kiln	110	6	30	24	–

Allied Engineering, Cleveland, Ohio

Name and location	Kiln length		Setting width		Setting height		Product fired
	ft.	in.	ft.	in.	ft.	in.	
Locke Insulator Corpn, Baltimore	265	0	5	8	5	8	High-tension insulators
Colonial Insulator Co., Akron, Ohio	130	0	4	2	4	1	Low- and high-tension insulators
Akron Porcelain Co., Ohio	140	0	4	4	4	4	Low-tension dry press porcelain
Bailey Walker China Co., Bedford, Ohio	40	0 (mean dia.) lengths = 140	5	5	4	5	Vitrified china
Victor Insulators Inc., Victor, N.Y.	200	0	5	3	4	4	High-tension insulators

Gibbons Bros., Ltd, Dudley

Name and location	Kiln length		Setting width		Setting height		Product fired
	ft.	in.	ft.	in.	ft.	in.	
Booths	240	0	3	8	4	3	Earthenware biscuit kiln
J. & G. Meakin	341	0	3	8	4	3	Earthenware biscuit kiln
J. & G. Meakin	210	0	2	2	3	1½	Earthenware glost kiln
Barker Bros.	130	0	3	8	3	10	Earthenware glost kiln

Name and location	Kiln length		Setting width		Setting height		Product fired
	ft.	*in.*	*ft.*	*in.*	*ft.*	*in.*	
A. Meakin	278	0	3	8	4	0	Earthenware glost kiln
T. C. Wild	130	0	3	0	3	0	China glost kiln
Gibbons Hinton	182	0	3	8	4	1½	Tile biscuit kiln
Pilkington	250	0	3	0	3	0	Tile kiln
Shanks	289	6	4	0	4	0	Sanitary earthenware kiln
Taylor Tunnicliff	118	6	1	10	1	9	Electrical Porcelain kiln
Colclough China	277	0	3	0	3	0	Bone china biscuit

Brown-Boveri Ltd (Electric Kiln)

Josiah Wedgwood	275	0	3	0	2	8	Earthenware bisque
	275	0	2	0	2	8	Earthenware glost

Birlec, Birmingham (Electric conveyor belt)

Floral China, Longton	70	0	3	0		10	China glost

A comparison of fuel consumption per ton of fired product in intermittent, continuous, and tunnel ovens is also of great interest.

TABLE I

Average fuel consumption per ton of fired product published by E. Rowden, British Refractories Research Association, Refractories Journal, October, 1946.

| Group | Coal Consumption Cwt. per Ton Product Kilns | |
	Intermittent	Continuous
1. Silica and Basic Refractories .	9.55	4.73
2. Fireclay Goods . . .	10.53	3.97
3. Salt-glazed Pipes . . .	13.81	–
4. Composite Works . .	9.84	1.94
5. Agricultural Pipes, Hollow Building Blocks, etc. . .	6.01	3.10
6. Roofing Tiles, Floor Quarries, etc.	7.33	–
7. Common Building Bricks .	3.24	1.48

TABLE II

Reproduced from Berichte der Deutschen Keramischen Gesellschaft

Average Fuel Consumption per ton of Fired Product

	Temperature	Intermittent Oven	Tunnel Oven
	°C	cwt.	cwt.
Porcelain table ware .	1410	70	30
Electrical insulator porcelain . . .	1410	60	24
Earthenware bisque .	1280	20	7
Glost earthenware .	1150	24	8.5
Sanitary earthenware bisque . . .	1280	30	10
Sanitary earthenware glost	1100	33	11

	Temperature	Intermittent Oven	Tunnel Oven
	°C	cwt.	cwt.
Wall tiles bisque . .	1280	10	2.5
Wall tiles glost . .	1060	8	–
Floor tiles . . .	1280	7	3.5

REFERENCES

A Treatise on Ceramic Industries, E. Bourry, Scott, Greenwood & Son.

Ceramic, Clay Products and Whiteware, Edward P. McNamara, The Pennsylvania State College.

Ceramic Whitewares, Rexford Newcomb, Pitman, New York.

Porcelain and Other Ceramic Insulating Materials, E. Rosenthal, Chapman & Hall, London.

CHAPTER VIII
Temperature Recording

TEMPERATURE control in ceramic kilns is carried out by various means. There are two fundamentally different methods.

1. The temperature is measured by pyrometers which indicate the exact temperature prevailing in the kiln at any given moment.

2. The effect of the heat is observed.

To appreciate the difference between the two methods one has to remember the following :

The work done by heat is dependent not only on the temperature to which the articles are subjected, but also on the time during which these articles are subjected to this temperature.

The following will illustrate this point. Take the case of a porcelain body covered with a glaze slip, ready for firing.

If the heat is increased slowly at a rate of 50° C. per hour to a final temperature of, say, 1300° C. the body will be properly vitrified and covered with a transparent glaze.

On the other hand, if the temperature is raised to the same temperature in steps of 500° C. per hour, the final body may be porous and the glaze still opaque.

In the first case a pyrometer will indicate 1300° C. after 26 hours, in the second case after about 2½ hours, and it will moreover, in both cases, not indicate whether or not the ware has become vitrified.

In some cases it may be of more value to record the work done by the heat. In other cases it may be more interesting, or at least adequate to record only the temperature as such.

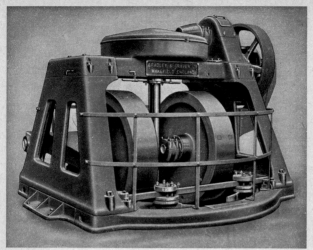

PLATE 1. Heavy duty grinder. This machine is used for crushing to powder form hard clay and shale used in the manufacture of bricks, tiles, hollow-ware, and firebricks. By courtesy of Bradley & Craven Ltd, Wakefield.

PLATE 2. Stiff plastic brickmaking machine. This machine produces 1,200 bricks an hour. By courtesy of Bradley & Craven Ltd, Wakefield.

PLATE 3. De-airing pug mill. By courtesy of Bradley & Craven Ltd, Wakefield.

PLATE 4. Automatic cutting table for cutting bricks. By courtesy of Bradley & Craven Ltd, Wakefield.

PLATE 5. Semi-plastic double re-press brickmaking machines. Stewartby Works, London Brick Company. By courtesy of *Picture Post*.

PLATE 6. Continuous car kiln consisting of eighty chambers. Stewartby Works, London Brick Company. By courtesy of *Picture Post*.

PLATE 7. Car loaded with bricks is pushed into the chamber of a continuous kiln. Stewartby Works, London Brick Company. By courtesy of *Picture Post*.

PLATE 8. Taking the pipe from pipe-making press. One of the processes in the manufacture of large stoneware pipes at the Doulton Works, Erith. By courtesy of the Royal Doulton Potteries, Lambeth.

PLATE 9. Large chemical ware in process room at Erith Works, May 1939. By courtesy of the Royal Doulton Potteries, Lambeth.

PLATE 10. Large chemical stoneware vessel in process of manufacture. By courtesy of the Royal Doulton Potteries, Lambeth.

PLATE 11. J. & G. Meakin – open flame kiln: first car – open setting, second car – ware placed in saggars. By courtesy of Gibbons Bros Ltd, Dudley.

PLATE 12. Electrically heated intermittent car chamber oven. By courtesy of Brown-Boveri Ltd.

PLATE 13. Gas-fired decorating kiln. By courtesy of Colclough China Ltd.

PLATE 14. Cup jolly. By courtesy of Josiah Wedgwood & Sons Ltd.

PLATE 15. Plate-making. By courtesy of Josiah Wedgwood & Sons Ltd.

PLATE 16. Throwing. By courtesy of Josiah Wedgwood & Sons Ltd.

PLATE 17. Hydraulic operated filter press producing four tons of filtered earthenware body per cycle. By courtesy of William Boulton Ltd, Burslem, Stoke-on-Trent.

PLATE 18. Eight-line automatic plate-making machine; each line produces twenty plates per minute. By courtesy of Miller Pottery Engineering Co., Pittsburgh, Pa.

PLATE 19. High-speed brushing machine for cleaning plates after bisque fire delivering these plates on to a conveyor belt on which they can be backstamped with the trade mark. By courtesy of Messrs William Boulton Ltd, Burslem, Stoke-on-Trent.

PLATE 20. Strasser cup-handling machine sticks handles on to 300 dozen cups per week with the assistance of two operators. By courtesy of Messrs Service (Engineers) Ltd, Stoke-on-Trent.

PLATE 21. Cars loaded with glazed earthenware ready to be pushed into the glost kiln. The plates are placed in pin cranks. By courtesy of Messrs J. Gimson & Co. (1919) Ltd, Fenton, Stoke-on-Trent.

PLATE 22. Machines for printing ceramic transfers. By courtesy of Rosenthal-Porzellan A.G., Selb, Bavaria.

PLATE 23. Multi-lining and pattern-banding machine. The decorated plates are placed into Buller's pillar cranks to move into the decorating kiln. By courtesy of Messrs F. Malkin & Co. Ltd, Longton, Stoke-on-Trent.

PLATE 24. A gold edge is painted by the use of a brush.

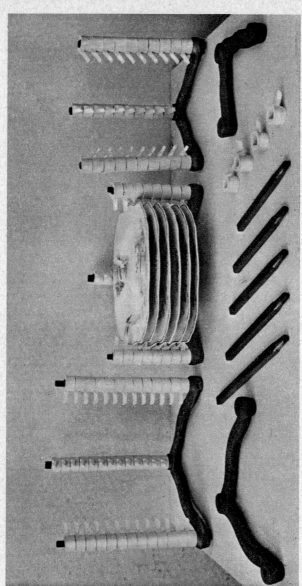

PLATE 25. Buller's iron cranks with ceramic pillar-rings used to a large extent for placing plates and saucers in the decorating kiln. This arrangement makes it possible to accommodate great numbers of plates in the kiln.

PLATE 26. Part of the colour previously sprayed by an aerograph is removed with a brush to give the required design. This method is used in hard porcelain manufacture for underglaze decoration.

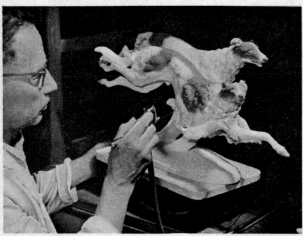

PLATE 27. Colour is sprayed on a porcelain figurine which is not yet glazed (underglaze decoration). By courtesy of Rosenthal-Porzellan A.G., Selb, Bavaria.

PLATE 28. Modern design of a coffee set made of porcelain, decorated simply with a black glaze. By courtesy of Rosenthal-Porzellan A.G., Selb, Bavaria.

PLATE 29. Simple modern shape, decorated by the American interior decorator F. Loewy. By courtesy of Rosenthal-Porzellan A.G., Selb, Bavaria.

PLATE 30. Porcelain table ware decorated with transfers, hand-painting, and printing – all on-glaze and fired afterwards at several different temperatures in the decorating kiln.

PLATE 31. Statuette made of hard porcelain decorated under-glaze.

PLATE 32. Transfer decorating on moving belt. By courtesy of Colclough China Ltd.

PLATE 33. The polisher. By courtesy of Josiah Wedgwood & Sons Ltd.

PLATE 34. Routine flash-over test on insulators for high tension lines of the British Electricity Authority.

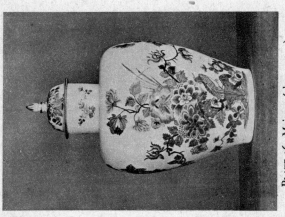

PLATE 36. Meissen (about 1725).

PLATE 35. Boettger's Red Stoneware (about 1710–15).

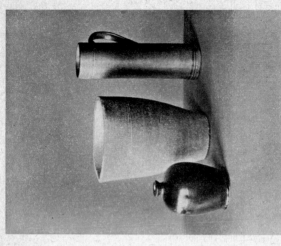

PLATE 37. Laboratory wares in hard-paste porcelain. Designed by T. H. Mott. Made by Doulton & Co. Ltd, Lambeth.

PLATE 38. Industrial stoneware, etc. Made by Doulton & Co. Ltd, Lambeth.

PLATE 40. Cream-coloured and green-glazed earthenware. Made by Josiah Wedgwood & Sons Ltd. Designs by Keith Murray.

PLATE 39. Vases made by the Royal Copenhagen Porcelain Co., and a bowl made by the Gustavsberg Pottery, Gustavsberg (Sweden).

PLATE 41. Hard Paste Porcelain. Made by the Royal Worcester Porcelain Company and Bullers Ltd.

PLATE 42. Earthenware table ware. Made by Josiah Wedgwood & Sons Ltd and by Johnson Bros Ltd, Hanley.

e itself, and not the work done by the tem-
e measured, pyrometers are used in the cera-
many other industries. If, for instance, the
e various parts of a tunnel kiln have to
olled and recorded, pyrometers are more

PLATE 43. Earthenware table wares made by Josiah Wedgwood & Sons Ltd and by Copeland and Sons.

PLATE 44. Earthenware dinner set 'Chinese Tree'. Made by Booths Ltd, Tunstall.

PLATE 45. 'Diana' Hard Porcelain figure. Rosenthal china.

PLATE 46. Hard Porcelain. Rosenthal china. Shape 'Helena'.

materials similar to those used in the preparation of bodies or glazes, they are ideally suited for reco work done by the heat to ceramic articles.

In this country Messrs Harrison & Son, Han

* 1. Seger Cone 13 (1380°C)	Orton Cone 13 (1	
„ „ 14 (1410°C)	„ „ 14 (1	
„ „ 15 (1435°C)	„ „ 15 (1	

The work done by heat may be controlled by observing the deformation of cones or bars, or by measuring the shrinkage of unfired ceramic rings caused by the heat.

Seger Cones

The use of cones made of different ceramic mixtures for heat recording was introduced by Seger (Staatliche Porzellan - Manufaktur, Berlin). These cones are called 'Seger cones'. They take the form of a three-sided pyramid, and depending upon their particular compositions, they become soft and bend over at different temperatures. The 'squatting' temperature of the cone is reached when its apex is level with its base. There is a complete range of these cones and their composition is chosen in such a way that the 'squatting' temperature of one cone is 20–30° C. lower than the 'squatting' temperature of the cone with the next higher number. Fig. 6 illustrates

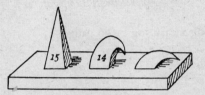

Fig. 6. Three subsequent Cones fired at 13/15[1].

three Seger cones numbered 13, 14, and 15,* which have been used to record the temperature of a porcelain kiln. No. 13 has collapsed completely, No. 14 is well on the way, and No. 15 remains impassive. Because Seger cones are made of ceramic

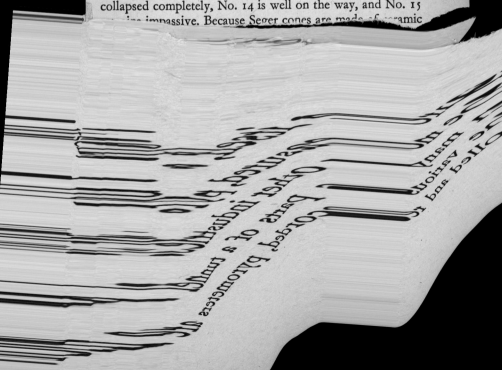

on-Trent, manufacture Staffordshire Seger cones. The cone numbers correspond to the temperatures given for Seger cones.

In the United States Seger cones have been modified and are called 'Orton' cones.

Buller's Rings

Buller's Firing Trial Rings indicate the work done by the heat by their radial contraction, which is dependent on the temperature. After firing and cooling the Buller's Ring is dropped into a gauge which registers temperature corresponding to the ring size. The gauge consists of a brass plate upon which is engraved a temperature scale and upon which the pointer or indicator is mounted.

The table below shows the temperatures corresponding to the various gauge readings.

Approximate Temperatures

						° C.
Ring measuring	1	on gauge	.	.		960
,,	,,	5	,,	,,	.	.	1,000
,,	,,	10	,,	,,	.	.	1,030
,,	,,	15	,,	,,	.	.	1,065
,,	,,	20	,,	,,	.	.	1,100
,,	,,	25	,,	,,	.	.	1,135
,,	,,	30	,,	,,	.	.	1,170
,,	,,	35	,,	,,	.	.	1,200
,,	,,	40	,,	,,	.	.	1,240
,,	,,	45	,,	,,	.	.	1,275

convenient than cones or rings. Various types are used including thermo-electric, optical and radiation pyrometers. Thermo-
electric pyrometers are generally employed when it is desired
to record the temperature graphically, and also for automatic
temperature control. The thermo-electric pyrometer utilizes
platinum-rhodium thermo-couples which generate an electric
current directly proportional to the temperature of the
kiln.

Various types of instruments have been developed which,
in conjunction with thermo-couples, automatically control
the air or gas supply, in the case of gas-fired kilns, or the voltage in the case of electric kilns. Modern electronic instruments permit precise and automatic temperature control 24
hours a day, with consequent elimination of temperature fluctuations and a reduction in labour costs.

CHAPTER IX

Setting or Placing the Ware in Kilns

STRONG porous goods, such as bricks and refractory ware which do not get soft during the firing, are placed into the oven, or on the tunnel cars, without the use of pre-fired refractory supports. They are piled one on top of the other and stacked as high as the dimensions of the ovens permit. Plates 6 and 7 illustrate bricks placed on oven cars.

Goods which soften during the fire, or which are too weak mechanically to be placed one on top of the other to an appreciable height, are placed in saggers. (Saggers are fireclay boxes shaped to hold the particular type of ware which has to undergo firing.) Saggers filled with ware are placed one on top of the other as high as the oven permits, but they must not be packed too tightly together as some space must be left between individual piles of saggers to allow the flames to circulate around them. Glazed ware has to be placed in saggers in such a way that the glazed surfaces cannot touch each other. Otherwise the contacting pieces would fuse and stick together. In those ovens, which during the firing of glazed ware are filled with smoky atmosphere, rolls of plastic fireclay ('wad clay') are placed between individual saggers in order to make them airtight and so prevent fumes from affecting the ware. The use of saggers for placing table ware and electrical porcelain is described in some detail in the chapters dealing with the manufacture of these types of goods.

Open Setting

Certain articles such as large sanitary ware and large electrical porcelain cannot be placed conveniently in saggers. Neither is it possible to pile one on top of the other because in the clay state they are too weak mechanically. Such large pieces are therefore set on open kiln cars, supported by refractory shelving. This shelving is known as 'kiln furniture'. It consists of large refractory slabs or trays with intervening posts strong enough to support heavy pieces at high temperature. Plate 11 show tunnel kiln cars with the ware placed in this fashion. Because of the severe conditions and high temperatures to which kiln furniture is subjected, it has to be made from highly refractory materials such as kyanite, silicon carbide and fused alumina. Open setting is preferable to sagger placing wherever the conditions permit. Every pound weight of sagger consumes approximately the same amount of heat as every pound of ware. It is therefore most important not to be extravagant in the dimensions and quantity of the kiln furniture used for placing the ware during firing. Certain types of ware which used to be fired in saggers, such as art ware, table ware, insulators, etc., are now often fired without saggers.

Through the use of muffle tunnel kilns, and as a result of improvements in the combustion of fuel providing cleaner kiln atmospheres, open setting is becoming more widely used. Provided the glaze is not too sensitive open setting is also made possible in open flame tunnel ovens.

The use of silicon carbide and fused alumina in the manufacture of kiln furniture gives it very high heat conductivity. This property and the great strengths of these materials make it possible to keep the supporting slabs and posts reasonably thin and so result in considerable saving in the dead weight carried on each car.

CHAPTER X
Glazes

GLAZES are vitreous (glassy) coatings which are used to cover ceramic bodies. In the case of porous bodies the glazes act as seals and prevent penetration of water. In the case of dense bodies they make the surface smoother and brilliant. The nature and composition of ceramic glazes is very similar to the nature and composition of glasses. Glass, however, is shaped by blowing or pressing in a hot liquid state as it comes from the melting pot. On the other hand, a glaze is formed on the surface of the shaped ceramic article during the firing. Before the firing, the glaze covers the surface of the ceramic article in the form of dry powder. When being formed, glass must be in an almost fluid state, otherwise it would be very difficult to shape into bottles, flasks, glasses, and so on, by conventional methods. However, a glaze on the surface of a ceramic article must not get too fluid. If it were fired to the degree of fluidity required for blowing a glass bottle, it would run off the ceramic article.

Glazes, like glasses, are the products of reaction between acidic and basic oxides. They are amorphous bodies and their molecules are not grouped in definite directions, as is the case with crystals. They are frozen or under-cooled liquids, the freezing or under-cooling process having taken place under conditions which did not allow the formation of crystals.

Acidic oxides used in the formation of glasses and glazes are:

1. Silica (SiO_2) introduced as sand, flint, feldspar or stone.
2. Boric acid (H_3BO_3) introduced as borax or as crystal boric acid.

The basic oxides used in the formation of glazes and glasses are firstly the alkalis (soda and potash) and lime. Other basic oxides used in the compounding of glaze batches are introduced by the addition of magnesium carbonate, barium carbonate, strontium carbonate, tin oxide, zinc oxide, antimony oxide, and lead oxide.

Alumina (Al_2O_3), which is an important constituent in ceramic glazes, is, theoretically, a basic oxide but in the computation of glazes it is considered by ceramists as neutral (neither basic nor acid).

The melting temperature of a glaze is the higher the greater its silica content. All the cones – from cone No. 021 (630° C.) to cone 27 (1600° C.) have a silica content which increases from cone to cone. In contrast to silica, boric acid, the other acidic oxide used in glaze manufacture, reduces the fusing point of glaze mixtures. This can be seen from the composition of the Seger cones fusing between 650° C. and 1200° C., which have a decreasing boric acid content from cone to cone.

A study of the composition of Seger cones is very interesting in giving information as to the softening temperatures of the various mixtures of the raw materials in common use for glaze composition. A Seger cone indicates a certain temperature by the fact that it becomes soft and the apex bends over and touches its base. The composition of this cone is such that at a temperature 3 or 4 cones higher it has the proper viscosity of a glaze. For instance, Seger cone 7, which gets soft at about 1230° C., becomes fluid enough to form a glaze at 1320° C. (Seger cone 11).[1] The same is true for the other cones. The molecular composition of the Seger cones consequently serves as a starting point to ceramists who wish to develop glazes for a certain firing temperature.

Glazes can be divided, according to the way in which they are prepared, into three types:

1. Raw Glazes prepared from materials which will not dissolve in water.

2. Frit Glazes. In these, certain materials which *would* dis-

	K_2O	C_aO	Al_2O_3	S_iO_2
1. Percentage Composition Sign Cone 7	5.05	7.0	12.75	75.38
,, ,, ,, 11	3.09	4.30	13.50	79.20

solve in water are first melted with silica in order to convert
them into *non-water-soluble* silicas, and are then mixed with
other materials not soluble in water.

3. Salt glazes. These are produced by throwing salt into
the fire mouth in the later stages of the firing. (Salt glazing is
used in the manufacture of stoneware and it is described in
the chapter 'Stoneware'.)

Frits

The preparation of a 'frit' is necessary for the composition of
glazes suitable for temperatures lower than 1200° C. All glazes
are applied to the surfaces of ceramic articles in the form
of finely-powdered particles suspended in water. Substances
dissolved in the water of the slip would not participate
in the formation of the glaze layer. Various fluxes which
are important for low temperature glazes are water-soluble, for instance, soda, potash, boric acid, and borax.
They have consequently to be converted into a non-water-
soluble substance, and this can be done by mixing them
with silica and heating the mixture at or above its melting
point.

Lead oxide, which, formerly, was much used as an addition
to raw glazes, is poisonous and must therefore not be used
directly in the glaze slip. It must first be added to the frit where
it takes part in the formation of a non-water-soluble silicate.

Most lead silicates are not dissolved by water and diluted
acids such as are produced in the human stomach. This is very
important, since lead compounds which are soluble in dilute
acid and which may pass through the mouth into the stomach
of a pottery worker have very dangerous properties. Lead-
bor-silicates are among the very few lead silicates which are
attacked by diluted acids. Lead should, therefore, never be
incorporated in frits which contain borax or boric acid. In
cases where frits containing boric acid are used, the lead should
be introduced into the glaze as a lead bi-silicate which is non-
water soluble and should be added together with the other

'mill materials' to the ground frit particles. 'Mill material' is the name given to the non-water-soluble materials which, together with the ground frit, form the glaze.

Action of the Glaze on the Ceramic Body

When glazes become soft in the glost fire they combine with the body material with which they are in contact. An intermediate layer is thus formed between the glaze and the body surface, uniting and welding them firmly together. It is very important that the thermal expansion of the glaze be practically the same as that of the body. In no circumstances whatever must it be larger than that of the body. If the glaze has a larger expansion than the body it will contract more and in the vain attempt to become smaller than the body will break when cooling down in the oven, since the tensile strength of the thin glaze layer is too small to resist such stresses indefinitely. This breakage of the glaze due to its larger thermal expansion causes numerous fine fissures and is called 'crazing'. The internal stresses, which exist in the glaze owing to its larger expansion, may not cause crazing when cooling down in the oven, but they may give rise to crazing at a later date, very often many weeks after manufacture. To ensure that no ware which may develop this fault leaves the factory, crazing tests are regularly carried out, either by heating articles in an autoclave under pressure, or by heating them to a temperature of say 160° C. and then immersing them in cold water. This temperature cycle is, as a rule, repeated three times.

If, on the contrary, the body has a larger expansion than the glaze and consequently contracts more during cooling, the surface area of the body will become smaller than the area of the glaze skin. There is, then, so to speak, not enough room on the surface of the ceramic article for the glaze and so it will peel off. The problem of obtaining perfect agreement between glaze and body is one of the most difficult in ceramics. In order to bring glaze and body into perfect agreement it is necessary to know the thermal expansion of both. Very often it is necessary to adjust the glaze to obtain a better fit and either to lower or to increase its thermal expansion. Many investigations have been carried out in recent years in order to find out how the various oxides present in glasses or glazes influence their thermal expansion. It is possible to calculate the thermal coefficient of a glass – at least approximately – if the chemical composition is known. It is first necessary to make a calculation, in order to establish the percentages of the various oxides present in the glass. This percentage figure is multiplied by a certain factor.

Much research work has been carried out to establish these factors. The most important investigations to establish this factor for the different oxides were made by Winkleman and Schott, *Ann. d. Phys. u. Chemik,* 51, pp. 730–46, 1894, Mayer & Havas, and English & Turner. Although these factors are established for glasses and not for glazes, they are also of interest to ceramists, particularly since nowadays glasses are often fused together with ceramic parts in the manufacture of electronic components. All investigators agree that silica reduces the thermal expansion of glazes. Since, as mentioned above, it also increases the melting point, it follows that high temperature glazes which are rich in silica have, generally speaking, a smaller thermal expansion than low temperature glazes. Boric acid, if present in quantities up to 15%, also lowers the thermal expansion of glasses and glazes. It is not quite accurate to use those factors for the calculation of the thermal expansion of glazes, since (1) the glaze formation does not advance to the same degree of fluidity, and (2) since chemical interaction between glaze and ceramic body changes the theoretical composition of the glaze.

It is most important that glaze and body are well matched and change their volumes at the same rate when heated or cooled. It is only natural that this can be most easily achieved with glazes having a composition very similar to that of the body. If this is the case, not only will the thermal behaviour of the glaze be similar to that of the body, but its softening point also will not be much lower than that of the body. It follows, therefore, that hard glazes (glazes having a high softening temperature) will, as a rule, fit better to the body than soft glazes. In hard porcelain manufacture both glaze and body are fired at the same temperature in the same fire. For this reason it is not difficult to obtain an extremely good glaze fit. Porcelain laboratory crucibles, for instance, can be heated above a Bunsen flame until they get white hot and can be cooled rapidly many times without any detrimental effect to glaze or body. (A description of glazes for hard porcelain is given in the chapter dealing with hard porcelain.)

It is much more difficult to obtain a good glaze fit if body and glaze have an entirely different composition, as is the case when the glaze is fired at a temperature much below the vitrification temperature of the body. Such conditions prevail in the manufacture of earthenware, bone china, and soft glaze feldspatic china. Some examples of earthenware and bone china glazes are given in the appropriate chapters.

Matt and Crystal Glazes

Whereas clear glazes are of an amorphous nature and are undercooled liquids, matt glazes are of a crystalline nature. The latter are obtained by using a composition which will favour the formation of a chemical compound which will tend to crystallize. Certain silicates have a tendency to form crystals, several of them small crystals, others large crystals. If large crystals are formed in a glaze it is called a 'crystal glaze'. Zinc oxide, magnesium oxide, and titanium dioxide, form large crystals under suitable conditions (slow cooling). Titanium dioxide is added in amounts from 8 to 12%, zinc oxide in amounts from 15% to 25%. Mixtures of both these oxides have a tendency to form well-defined crystals, particularly in the presence of calcium oxide. Calcium silicates form small crystals if no other crystal-forming silicates are present, and an addition of up to 50% of calcium oxide to an earthenware or porcelain glaze is suitable for the production of very pleasant matt glazes.

Matt glazes are semi-translucent. Completely non-translucent (opaque) glazes are formed by colloidal suspensions in the glaze.

The oldest opacifier is tin oxide (as mentioned in the chapter 'History'). More modern opacifiers include calcium phosphate (bone ash), zirconium oxide, and antimony oxide.

Coloured glazes can be obtained by the addition of colouring oxides. Such oxides may be dissolved in the glaze or be present as a colloidal suspension of the undissolved oxide or of a mixture of them. The same oxide may give different colours with different glazes. Chrome oxide, for instance, as a rule gives a brilliant green colour. If, however, zinc oxide is present, the colour will be brown. If no zinc oxide is present but large amounts of tin oxide, the colour will be pink. The same metal oxide may also give different colours when fired under different conditions. Copper oxide, for example, may form a brilliant green in oxidizing atmosphere, on the other hand it may be reduced and form a red glaze under reducing conditions (*sang de bœuf* or *rouge flambé*).

The following list contains some of the more common oxides and the colours they produce.

Ferric oxide – Yellow, red, brown and black.

Cobalt oxide – Various shades of blue, depending upon the concentration. Bluish green in the presence of chrome oxide.

Copper oxide – Green, blue-green, shades of green and red.

Manganese oxide – Violet, cream, brown, black.

Chrome oxide – Green, red, pink, brown.

Nickel oxide – Brown, violet.

Uranium oxide – Yellow.

Gold (colloidal) red and purple.

Tin oxide – (In colloidal suspension) white.

CHAPTER XI

Ceramic Colours and Decoration

CERAMIC colour pigments are metal oxides of various types. In the case of under-glaze decoration, the colours and the glaze fuse directly together. In the case of on-glaze decoration, they fuse together with the aid of a soft flux.

Under-glaze Colours

Under-glaze colours are applied to the 'bisque' (ware which has already undergone one firing) and the glaze is applied subsequently. The colours are prepared by first calcining colouring metal oxides with such materials as china clay, feldspar, alumina, and then by grinding the calcined mixture to an extremely fine powder. This powder is mixed with gum or oils and turpentine and applied to the bisque either with a brush or by spraying. In the case of china or porcelain the under-glaze decoration can be dried at room temperature. In the case of earthenware, however, it is necessary to fire it at about 600° C. (hardening-on-fire) in order to evaporate the heavy oils which are water-repellent and which would, for this reason, take less glaze than the porous body. The ware is next covered with the glaze either by dipping or spraying and is then fired in the glost oven. Although the glaze must react with the colour, it must not dissolve the colour. The latter would flow into the glaze and the contour of the decoration would be blurred. One of the advantages of under-glaze decoration is that it is completely covered and protected by the glaze from wear and tear.

On-Glaze Colours

On-glaze colours are applied on top of the glaze. They are prepared by mixing the colouring oxides with frits of low softening temperature. These frits are glasses consisting of lead-boro-silicates and potash or soda. The colouring oxides and the frit are mixed and fired together and ground to an impalpable powder. (As a rule, the potters do not make these powders themselves, but buy them from firms who specialize in colour preparations.) The powdered colour is mixed with oil and turpentine and is then applied to the glaze by the various methods described later on. The ware is then fired in the 'enamel kiln' at a temperature between 750° C. and 850° C. At this temperature the frits soften and envelop the metal-oxide-colour pigments, welding them firmly to the surface of the glaze.

On-glaze decoration is naturally not so resistant to wear and tear as the glaze itself, and unless it is well combined with the glaze the decoration will sometimes wear off. The more intimate therefore the combination of fluxes and glaze, the greater will be the resistance of the decoration to abrasion.

On-glaze decoration cannot compare with under-glaze decoration as regards durability. It does, however, afford a greater variety of colours in the enamel kiln, which is used for on-glaze decoration, as the temperature is sufficiently low for many colours to remain stable.

In the glost fire (1100° C.) used for firing under-glaze decoration, many of these colours would be dissolved and would be destroyed by the action of the molten glaze.

APPLICATION OF COLOURS TO POTTERY

The most important methods of applying colours are as follows:

1. Painting, (*a*) hand painting, (*b*) lining, banding.
2. Spraying.
3. Stencilling.
4. Stamping.
5. Printing and lithography.
6. Silk screen printing.

7. Ground-laying.
8. Sgraffito Decoration.
9. Gilding.
10. Relief Decoration.

1. Hand painting is the oldest method of decorating pottery. The painter uses a brush and applies the ceramic colour, which is mixed with oil and turpentine, to the ware. Hand painting with ceramic colours requires great skill and practice. The paints change colour during the firing and so the painter must know how his colours will look after the firing. To-day, hand painting is still used for the decoration of expensive art ware, but it is also used in mass production of pottery in combination with printing and lithography (5). The contours of patterns are often produced by printing and the areas within the printed lines are coloured by hand painting. Lithographs also are often perfected by brush work.

Lines and bands (thick lines) are made by means of a brush held at a slightly oblique angle to the article while it is revolving on a spinning-wheel. Nowadays mechanical devices are also used to an ever-increasing extent for producing bands and lines. As many as 1,000 dozen plates or saucers per day are lined, with an accuracy hardly obtainable by hand, on a single lining machine consisting of as many as sixteen rotating heads fitted to a revolving turn-table. Other types of banding machines incorporate holders with three brushes, their distances apart being adjustable. Each brush is connected with a separate colour container and in this way three bands of different colours can be made at the same time.

To produce gilded edges, the Ryckman edge-lining machine has become very popular in recent years. A golden line near or on the edge of a plate or cup dish is produced by a rubber roller covered with a tacky gold solution and pressed softly against the edge of the rotating plate. The machine applies also stippled bands and patterns to a great variety of pottery articles and the output from it amounts to several times that obtained from skilled hand operatives.

2 and 3. Spraying of colours is used to produce large

coloured areas. It is very often employed in combination with stencils, cut from paper or from thin copper sheet, if white designs on a coloured background are to be produced. These stencils are pressed against the surface of the article and the colour is then brushed, dabbed or sprayed over it. Positive or negative paper patterns may also be stuck (with an adhesive) to the surface of the ware, which may then either be dipped into a coloured glaze or may be sprayed over with colour. The paper is subsequently removed. A similar process is the use of 'wax resist'. Liquid wax is applied to the ware by means of a brush. After the article has been dipped or sprayed, the glaze or colour runs off the waxed surface.

4. In the stamping method, rubber stamps are used. They are charged with colours transferred from a pad previously covered with a layer of finely-ground sticky pigment. The stamps are made of india-rubber and the pattern which is limited to very fine lines is transferred to the ware by pressing the rubber stamp against the surface of the ware. Gold decorations are very often made in this way. Trade marks on pottery are usually made by this method, either on-glaze or underglaze.

5. In printing copper plates are used. The designs which are to be reproduced are engraved in the plates. A sticky mixture of the colouring material and linseed oil is spread over the engraved plate by means of a spatula. The excess colour is then taken off, the plate is covered with a sheet of thin paper and is then placed on a steam-heated printing table. The design is thus transferred to the paper. This paper is then cut into pieces, each containing the desired pattern. The paper pattern is then 'rubbed' on to the pottery by means of a roller. Next, the article is dipped in water and the paper is detached. The impression sticks firmly to the ware.

Lithograph printing is used if the design incorporates large coloured areas and several different colours. Lithography is the art of drawing upon and printing from stone. The lithographic stones at Kelheim, Bavaria, were the first to be used, and have proved particularly suitable. The stone is prepared as follows. The original design is traced on paper with special ink and is transferred to the stone. For each colour a separate copy is transferred to a separate stone. The contours thus produced are covered with ink. The surfaces of the stone are then treated with acidulated water. After this treatment, the pattern – which is protected by the ink – is slightly higher than the rest of the surface. The stone is then traversed by a leather roller from whose surface varnish is transferred to the parts covered with ink (since they are in slight relief). A sheet of paper is next spread over the stone and is passed through a printing machine from which the paper emerges decorated with varnish. The paper sheet is then dusted with colour-powder which sticks to the varnish and can be brushed off from those parts of the paper which are not varnished. The same sheet of paper is printed with varnish and dusted with colours several times, according to the number of colours employed in the design. Where the design is small it is reproduced many times on the same stone in order to make the best possible use of the surface available. The sheet is cut before being used so that each design can be transferred separately to the ware. The surface of the article to be decorated is covered with varnish and the 'transfer' is pressed on to the ware with a roller. After the varnish has hardened the paper is removed with a wet sponge and the design is left adhering to the ware. In mass production lithographing is highly mechanized. Continuous belts convey the ware to a drying chamber. The operators sit alongside the belts and attach the 'lithos' or 'transfers' to the ware as it passes. The lithos, as they emerge from the drying chamber, are then rubbed on to the ware which moves through water sprayers which wash the paper away, whereas the design sticks to the article (See Plate 13).

6. The silk screen printing process consists of rubbing or squeezing colour through a pattern, left free in a material of very fine mesh, for example a silk screen, on to the article to be decorated. With this silk screen process it is possible to print patterns on round surfaces, as well as on flat surfaces. Several colours may be printed one after the other, but each

colour must be allowed to dry before the succeeding one is applied. In carrying out this printing process the screen is supported somewhat above the article and the ceramic colour is forced through it by means of a rubber squeegee.

7. *Ground-laying*. To provide an even uniform colour over large areas, the ground-laying process is used in the fine china and earthenware industry. The glazed area which is to be coloured is covered with a sticky medium such as linseed oil and turpentine. Powder of ceramic onglaze colour is then dusted on to the sticky surface with a piece of cotton, and the excess dust blown off. Those parts of the article not to be covered by the colour are protected either by a stencil or a layer of solution of sugar or any other substance of such a nature that it can be washed off. The turpentine and the colour powder will stick to the china surface not treated with the sugar solution but will not stick to the surface of the article covered with the water soluble sugar solution.

8. *Sgraffito Decoration*. This is a process used in underglaze decoration. The green piece (in the case of hard porcelain the bisque-fired article) is covered with a thin layer of slip of a colour different from the body. After drying, the covering layer is scraped off to show the body where required. The article is then fired and glazed.

9. *Gilding*. Precious metals – gold, silver, and platinum can be applied to the ware as an overglaze decoration. There are two different processes for applying gold decorations; the one uses an oil soluble gold compound, the other metallic gold powder.

Liquid Gold Process. Gold salt soluble in certain oils is prepared by a complicated process and incorporated in a varnish and applied to the glazed article. On firing at a temperature of about 680° C., the gold compound is reduced to metallic gold and deposited on the glaze as a thin layer. There are also low melting fluxes incorporated in the solution (such as lead – borate – silicate) which cements the gold layer to the glaze. The gold laid down in this way is, however, very thin and wears off quite easily. This process is, therefore, mainly used for inexpensive ware. In the trade, this type of gold decoration is called 'bright gold'.

Burnished or coin gold. In this method, finely-powdered metallic gold is mixed with a flux of suitable oil-resin mixture applied to the glazed surface and fired at a temperature of about 680° C. After firing the gold decoration is brown and matt. In order to form a brilliant gold surface, the gold layer is burnished by rubbing with a smooth stone or, if less brilliant gold is required, with glass fibre. In the trade, this type of decoration is referred to as 'Burnished gold' or 'Best gold'.

Silver is not used for decoration, to a great extent, since it loses its bright finish under the influence of humid air. For white metal decoration, platinum is preferred to silver. For technical purposes, such as the manufacture of ceramic condensers, silver coatings are used to a great extent. Aluminium powder is also employed for producing white metal decorations.

10. *Relief decoration*. The earliest decorations of pottery were relief carving on the surface. At first, the ornament was simply scratched into the surface. Later sculptured reliefs were applied. Embossments can be produced on ceramic ware by attaching to the body preformed ornaments made of a paste similar to the body of the article. These ornaments may have another colour to give colour contrasts.

The Cameo ware, as made by Wedgwoods, is an example of ornamental decoration and described in chapter XVI.

'*Pâte-sur-Pâte*' *method*. This method was brought to a high degree of perfection in England and the European Continent in the nineteenth century. Each piece has to be made individually by the artist who builds up a relief in white porcelain slip on a ceramic background of the raw, 'green' body, or a coloured slip on a white body. This is done with a brush, and layer after layer built up until the relief is completed. After firing, the different degrees of translucency give a very delicate effect. The whole is covered by a translucent or coloured glaze.

CHAPTER XII
Bricks and Tiles

REFERENCE has already been made in the first chapter of this book dealing with the history of ceramics, to brick-making in Egypt, Babylonia and Rome. The first English bricks were manufactured by the Romans during their three and a half centuries of occupation. After the departure of the Romans, practically no bricks were made in England until the thirteenth century, when the manufacture of bricks and tiles was again started on a small scale. In the time of Henry VIII (1509 to 1547) brick-making flourished, influenced by Flemish technicians. The great fire of London in 1666 destroyed a wooden city. Buildings made of bricks replaced the wooden houses and because of this the brick industry expanded.

In the eighteenth century bricks were much the vogue with architects and builders. The fine old country houses scattered throughout England bear witness to the skill of the brick-makers of those days. The capacity of the brick-making industry had to be stepped up enormously in the nineteenth century to cope with the increase in house and factory building. Just prior to the Second World War the industry in Great Britain produced about 700,000,000 bricks per month. In 1953 the industry hopes to reach again the same figure.

MAIN TYPES OF WARE

The main types of ware under this heading comprise common bricks, facing bricks, engineering bricks, multi-coloured and blue bricks, rustic bricks, hollow building bricks; red, multi-coloured blue and sand-faced tiles, roofing tiles, paving bricks and floor tiles.

The products covered in this chapter consist of practically 100% clay, with only small additions of other raw materials, and are of relatively low unit price.

The raw materials used are very widely distributed and are consequently cheap. The principal items in the cost of most bricks and tiles are the cost of extracting the clay from the deposit and the cost of transporting it to the works. The usual practice is therefore to build the brick or tile works as near as possible to the clay bed with convenient transport facilities. As already explained in the chapter dealing with clay, each clay varies and requires its own individual treatment as regards preparation, shaping and firing.

BRICKS

Common Bricks. – According to British Standard Specification 657, the dimensions (see Fig. 7) should conform to one of the following types:

Type II – 8¾ in. × 4¼₆ in. × 2⅝ in.
Type III – 8¼ in. × 4⅜₆ in. × 2⅞ in.

The tolerances are ± ⅛ in. for the length (L) and ± ¹⁄₁₆ in. for the width (B) and depth (D).

Quality of Bricks. – Bricks have to be fired at a temperature high enough to provide the required mechanical strength and adequate resistance to atmospheric influences. During the firing the surfaces of the particles have to become sufficiently soft to fuse together. In the case of building bricks complete vitrification

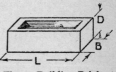

Fig. 7. Building Brick.

is not desirable, as a certain degree of porosity is necessary and improves the thermal insulating properties of the brick.

It has been found difficult to standardize the minimum qualities of clay building bricks for various types of exposures. They are not covered by British Standards Specifications owing to the complexity of the problem.

The compressive strength of building bricks varies between 1,500 lb. to sq. in. and 7,000 lb. to sq. in. according to specific requirements. (Bricks having higher compressive strengths than 7,000 lb. are termed engineering bricks.) The water absorption should not be less than 8%.

The American federal specification sub-divides common clay bricks into three grades, H (Hard), M (Medium), S (Soft). The compressive strength of grade H is 4,500 to 8,000 lb. to sq. in.

Grade M is 2,500 to 4,500 lb. to sq. in.

Grade S is 1,500 to 2,500 lb. to sq. in.

Average water absorption:

     H 10% or less.

     M 16%.

     S No limit.

Compressive strength and water absorption of engineering bricks are covered by British Standards Specifications, as follows:

Compressive Strength of Clay Engineering Bricks

Class of Brick

A . .	10,000 lb. to sq. in.
B . .	7,000 lb. to sq. in.

Average Water Absorption by Weight

Class of Brick

A . .	4.5%
B . .	7%

Manufacture of Common Bricks

Originally all bricks were made by hand-moulding processes. However, for the manufacture of standards, such as building bricks, the hand-making process is obviously slow and inefficient. The vast expansion of building and industry during the nineteenth century created a huge demand. This demand called for speedier processes to replace the time-honoured hand-moulding and to-day practically all bricks are made by machinery. The development from hand-making to fully automatic manufacture has passed through many stages during the last century. To-day the most important methods of making bricks

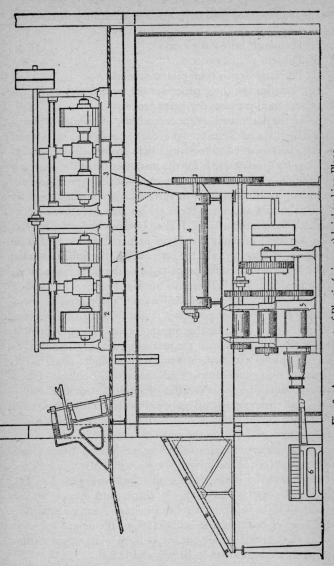

Fig. 8. Arrangement of Plastic (wire cut) brickmaking Plant. (By courtesy of Wm. Johnson & Son (Leeds) Ltd.)

can be sub-divided into three groups according to the state of the clay used.

1. The plastic wire-cut process.
2. The stiff plastic process.
3. The semi-dry or semi-plastic process.

(In America the three processes are termed soft-mud process, stiff-mud process, dry-press process.)

1. In the *plastic wire-cut* process a body of maximum plasticity is used, the moisture content being 15 to 20%. This method is especially adapted to forming bricks from the lower grades of clay. Its greatest use is for the manufacture of the common red building brick. The clay employed for this type of product is usually a surface clay. Most surface clays contain impurities such as stones and small rocks which may have been incorporated during the mining. It is an obvious and accepted fact that the more carefully the clay is prepared the easier will be the forming operation and the better will be the finished bricks. (The machinery used for preparation of the body is described in some detail elsewhere in this book.)

The fundamental difference between the plastic wire-cut process and the other processes is that in the former process no moulds are used for shaping the bricks. The principle of this method of forming is the extrusion of a continuous column of a plastic clay paste by a pug mill through a die. The die forms the outer dimensions of the product. The column is then cut into bricks by the taut wires of a cutting machine. Fig. 8 shows an arrangement of machinery for making bricks and tiles from a plastic clay. No. 1 is the hoist gear which hauls the wagons of clay from the pit to the plant, No. 2 and No. 3 show Edge Runner Plastic Grinding and Mixing Mills, where material is crushed and mixed, No. 4 is a Pug Mixer, where the crushed material is thoroughly mixed and pugged, No. 5 is the Brick-making Extrusion Machine, and No. 6 is the Cutting-Off Table, where the brick column is cut off into suitable sizes of bricks before being taken to the dryer.

On the Continent wire-cut bricks form a larger proportion of the total output than in Britain and U.S.A.

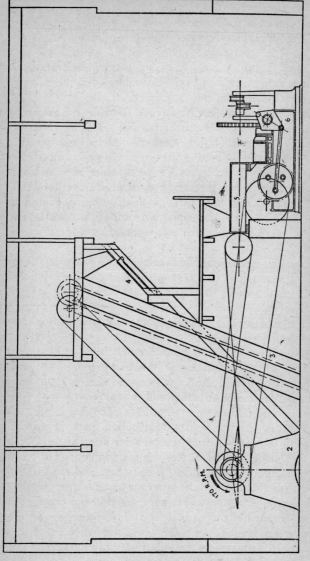

Fig. 9. Arrangement of stiff-plastic Brickmaking Plant.
(By courtesy of Wm. Johnson & Son (Leeds) Ltd.)

170 R.P.M.

In contrast to the plastic wire-cut process, in the stiff plastic and the semi-dry processes the bricks are moulded in a press.

2. *Stiff Plastic Process*. – In the stiff plastic process the water content varies from 10 to 15% depending upon the clay used and the type of product to be formed.

The raw materials are ground and mixed by the machinery described elsewhere in this book. The plastic body is then forced by a pug mill into a closed mould (clot box) and when the mould is full the body is discharged. This pre-formed piece of clay (clot) is then fed to the press. Modern presses very often consist of two eccentric presses which press the bricks alternately. Whilst one press is discharging, the other is exerting its pressure. In stiff plastic pressing it is important that the pressure is maintained on each brick for a considerable time.

Re-pressing. – When highly-finished bricks (for instance, facing bricks) are required, they are re-pressed in a follow press. The bricks coming from the first press are lifted into a position from which, by means of a pusher, they are accurately placed in the mould of the follow press, which is driven at the same speed as the first press.

The arrangement of the machinery in a brick-making plant using the stiff plastic process is illustrated in Fig. 9. The shale or marl is carried in small trucks on an endless chain hoist (1) to the perforated grinding mill (2), where the material is reduced to dust, lifted by an elevator (3), and discharged over a screen (4). Its meshes pass the required grade of material to the mixer, sending back the over-size material to the pan mill for further reduction. No. 5 is the double shafted mixer where a little water is added, if necessary, and the material thoroughly mixed. From the mixer the material drops into the brick-making machine which pugs, moulds and presses the bricks automatically. (For best facing bricks a repress is provided as described above.) The bricks are delivered on to a table ready for taking to the kiln, if the material is such that no intermediate drying is required.

3. *Semi-dry process – semi-plastic process.* – The semi-dry (or as it is very often called the 'semi-plastic') process uses, as the name implies, clay of a consistency midway between dry and plastic. The material employed is in the form of a damp powder containing between 5 and 9% water. Bonding of the clay particles is produced by the brick-making machine exerting a very high pressure (between 500 and 20,000 lb. to sq. in.) on the body. The drier (or less plastic) the material, the greater is the pressure required to give the necessary bonding of the particles. Semi-dry pressing and dry pressing are also used in other branches of the ceramic industry, for instance in wall tile and insulator manufacture. The conditions in the other branches are, however, different from those prevailing in brick pressing because the nature of the body and the type of article to be pressed influence both the design of press and the method of pressing. Consequently, only semi-dry pressing of bricks and tiles is considered in this chapter.

The semi-dry process is particularly suitable for pressing bricks from clays containing bituminous matter. The latter acts as a lubricant, making the addition of oil to the clay powder unnecessary (oil has to be added in the case of pressed porcelain insulators). For this reason in the Fletton and Bedfordshire districts, where the clay deposits are rich in bituminous matter, the semi-dry process is extensively employed. In a semi-dry brick-making machine the material, after having passed the perforated grinding mill and screen, falls in dust form, owing to gravity, down a canvas chute into the sliding carriage. This carriage moves forward over the empty mould, into which the damp dust falls. The sliding carriage then recedes to its original position. The damp dust which has fallen into the empty mould is pressed by two distinct pressures between the top and bottom pistons. The pressed brick is pushed on to the delivery table by the carriage, as it again moves forward to fill the empty mould. For re-pressing, an additional mould (the repress mould) is placed directly in front of the first mould. To this additional mould the brick is delivered automatically and pressed again. One of the main advantages of semi-dry pressing is the fact that the pressed bricks have not to be dried in special dryers but can go direct into the oven.

Drying. – Bricks can be dried in different ways, for example, in the open air, on indoor shelves, in ventilated drying sheds or in dryers heated by steam and/or waste heat from the kilns. On the Continent the drying sheds are arranged on the upper floors of multi-story buildings, the kilns being on the ground floor. Thus simple use is made of the fact that warm air tends to move upwards. Fuel consumption in brick dryers is considerable—2 cwt. of fuel for drying a thousand bricks is a good average. Labour costs for drying are also considerable. In a medium-size brickworks without mechanical driers, where eight man-hours are required for making a thousand bricks, one man-hour out of eight is needed for transport to and from the dryer. In order to reduce costs it is consequently essential to mechanize the drying process. Tunnel dryers – in which waste heat is used and in which wagons carry the bricks from the brick-making machine through the dryer to the kiln – permit a considerable saving in fuel and labour. If the moisture content of the clay is low enough and the body not too plastic, separate drying is not necessary and the ware can go direct from the press to the kiln, as in the case of the semi-plastic process, and very often in the case of the stiff plastic process. This means great saving in fuel and labour.

Firing Bricks. – The various types of kilns used for firing bricks have already been described. Continuous top-fired chamber kilns predominate. Where the output is small, say below 600,000 bricks per annum, intermittent ovens are used, since continuous chamber kilns are only economical for larger outputs. To date, continuous tunnel kilns have only been used to a small extent for brick and tile firing. Interest in them is, however, increasing. There is no doubt that the number of man-hours involved in tunnel kiln operation is smaller than the number of man-hours required by any other type of kiln.

This is a point which will become increasingly important. The workmen's demands have greatly increased and the jobs have to be improved to attract the best people. This means higher wages and consequently the amount of labour has to be reduced. Modern plans are based on placing the brick direct from the press on to the kiln car, drying the car loads in tunnel dryers and firing without re-loading. The success is dependent upon the bricks being stiff enough in the unfired state to withstand, without deformation, the heavy loads to which they are subjected.

The use of tunnel ovens is complicated in those cases where the carbonaceous matter of certain clays starts to burn in the pre-firing zone when a temperature of about 700° C. is reached, causing a sudden and dangerous increase in temperature. This fact has to be considered in the design of tunnel ovens for firing clay ware containing carbonaceous matter. No satisfactory design has so far been developed. For the time being the most economical type of kiln for firing clay ware containing much carbonaceous matter is probably the car kiln mentioned later on in connexion with the description of the Stewartby Works.

General Arrangement of Brick Works

Brick works can be divided into the following classes:

1. Works using hand moulding and firing in intermittent ovens.

2. Works using hand moulding and firing in continuous kilns.

3. Works shaping bricks by machinery and employing continuous kilns: (*a*) Using intermediate dryers and re-loading from the dryer to the kiln, and (*b*) Using intermediate dryers without re-loading.

4. Works shaping bricks by machinery in such a way that no intermediate dryers are required and firing in continuous kilns (or tunnel kilns).

A Visit to the Stewartby Works of the London Brick Co. – To give the reader some impression of a modern brickworks the

Stewartby Works, the largest and most modern in the world, will be briefly described.

The pre-war production was 11,750,000 bricks per week with a labour force of 1,900 operatives—the astounding figure of 6,000 bricks per week per man.

The raw material used throughout by the Company in all its works is a particular deposit of the Oxford clay which was formed probably in a stagnant shallow of the vast Jurassic sea which, many thousands of years ago, covered the whole of England east of a line from Yorkshire to the Dorset coasts. The beds worked lie around Peterborough, along the shallow valley south-west of Bedford in which Stewartby is situated and in small island form in Buckinghamshire and Oxfordshire. They are remarkably uniform in composition and are thus admirably suited to mechanical excavation. A further important economic feature of this particular clay is its content of bituminous fuel matter, the heat value of which is sufficient to supply the whole of the heat required in theory to burn the bricks, were there available a kiln of 100% efficiency. In the kilns employed by the Company it reduces the coal consumption to a little over 1 cwt. of coal per 1,000 bricks.

The Stewartby pit must provide 42,000 tons of clay per week to cope with the full output of bricks. This quantity is dug by one electric excavator. The clay is dropped by this one main excavator into a sorting machine which reduces the larger lumps and feeds the final material into wagons for conveyance to the works.

On arrival at the works these wagons (weighing 6 tons) are lifted bodily by tipplers (designed and made by the Company, as are other specialized items of machinery) and the contents are dumped into storage towers which automatically feed two lines of grinding mills. These reduce the clay to a fine powder which is sieved in revolving screens and distributed by a belt conveyor to the line of brick presses below. The presses mould the powdered clay into bricks between heated dies and under four progressively increasing pressures.

The 'green' bricks so produced are strong enough to be

loaded directly into the kiln without preliminary drying, thus saving time, handling and fuel.

The kilns in which the bricks are heat-treated or 'burnt' are a series of large ovens, each holding up to 48,000 bricks and inter-connected by a system of flues and dampers which enable the hot air from cooling bricks to be used to dry incoming 'green' bricks and so utilize the otherwise wasted heat.

In the older kilns the bricks are set into the chambers and withdrawn after burning by hand, but in the latest part of the works the bricks are pushed into the kilns standing upon the trucks upon which they have been loaded from the brick presses.

These kilns consist of eighty chambers. As explained, the bricks, as they come from the press, are loaded on kiln cars. Each car takes 3,000 bricks. The cars are pushed into the various chambers of the kiln. Each chamber accommodates twenty-four cars. Consequently, in each chamber 72,000 bricks are fired simultaneously—enough bricks to build twelve houses of average size. The oven is a continuous chamber kiln, the individual chamber being successively filled, burnt and unloaded. The drying and warming up of the ware is carried out very slowly by the warm air drawn from cooling chambers and the temperature is raised slowly to the point where the carbonaceous matter which is embodied in the clay starts to burn. The temperature now rises very quickly until all the carbonaceous matter is burnt away. The temperature reaches about 1000° C. without any additional fuel. The bricks are now allowed to soak at this temperature for a considerable time, no additional fuel being used until the temperature has dropped by about 200° C. Only then is coal used, being dropped through holes in the arch, as described previously. The firing temperature is about 1100° C. At the time of the author's visit the following bricks were being made at Stewartby:

Standard 'Phorpres' bricks (an all-purpose building brick), and 'Phorpres' sand-faced facing bricks (a facing brick which has a special sand-faced surface on one or more faces as required). Formerly this sanding was a hand operation, but it has now been completely mechanized in these works. Another type of facing brick has its face textured or 'rusticated' in a special machine before it is burnt, which, like the cook's forking of pastry, enables the heat to enter the texture and produces a pleasing variation in colour.

Hollow Clay Building Bricks

Hollow building bricks are blocks which, instead of being solid, have one or more hollow spaces running through them. The wall thickness is usually small compared with the size of the holes. They are consequently very much lighter than solid clay bricks per unit volume. At the same time they are quite strong from a structural point of view and their large size and light weight allows them to be loaded up in a wall easier and faster than solid bricks. They play a very important part in modern building structure as a back-up material, and have found many new uses in combination with structural steel frame-work and reinforcement. Hollow bricks are first formed by the plastic process and they are, in most cases, finished by the extrusion wire-cut process. Since a certain porosity is essential and the mechanical strength required is lower than that of common building brick, hollow bricks, if made of the same clay, are fired at a slightly lower temperature than the building bricks. If fired in the same kiln as the standard bricks they are placed on easier points in the kiln.

Hollow clay building bricks are, according to the British Standards Specification No. 1190, 1944, sub-divided as follows:

1. For use in internal walls (load bearing) and partitions.
2. For use in structural floors, roofs, mansards and so on.

Blocks covered by (1) comprise three types, namely (*a*) those with both faces keyed for plaster or rendering, (*b*) those with both faces smooth and suitable for use without plastering or rendering on either side, (*c*) those with one face keyed and one face smooth. The British Standards Specification quoted above covers, among other items, the dimensions and tolerances of hollow blocks, water absorption and crushing strength.

The crushing strength of blocks for use in internal walls (load bearing) should be at least 500 lb. to sq. in.: blocks for use in partitions 200 lb. to sq. in.

Facing Bricks

Facing bricks are the best type of building bricks. They are used for the exterior of buildings and other structures where the brick has to excel in colour, strength, resistance to weathering and uniformity of size and shape. They are produced in colours varying from the red of common brick to very light yellows and greys. The surface of the facing brick may be anything between a perfectly smooth finish and a very coarse rough texture.

The surfaces of rustic facing bricks are combed before firing. The area of surface accessible to oxygen during firing is thus increased and they acquire an attractive reddish-brown tone.

Sand-faced facing bricks have, as the name implies, one or more faces covered with sand. The sand is welded to the body during the firing to ensure permanence of cohesion of the sand layer.

It is naturally more expensive to produce facing bricks than common bricks, but their superiority in appearance justifies the extra cost. Various shades of bricks may be produced by blending two or more clays of different colour or, in some cases, by adding colour agents such as iron oxide or manganese dioxide which are used to darken the light burning clays. If the body is highly ferruginous dark bricks can be obtained, very often with a metallic sheen (metallic bricks, iron bricks, blue bricks).

Vitrified Bricks

Vitrified bricks are so hard that they cannot be scratched by iron and only with difficulty by steel. They are fired at temperatures at which vitrification begins, their colour ranging

F

from light to dark reddish-brown according to the iron and manganese contents. Vitrified bricks are used where great mechanical strength is required and are consequently called 'engineering bricks'. They are made by the same manufacturing methods as common bricks but the burning is carried out at a higher temperature. If they are manufactured from the same clay and fired in the same ovens as building bricks they are placed in those parts of the kiln which acquire the highest temperature during the firing. They are slightly darker than the common bricks fired in the same oven. The clay should contain slightly more fluxes than common bricks since the compressive strength increases with increasing vitrification.

On the Continent (for instance, in the Netherlands, Belgium, and in parts of Germany), and also in the United States, vitrified bricks are used for paving streets. In this country, paving bricks are used only to a small extent. A roadway surfaced with paving bricks laid on a suitable foundation is generally regarded as the most durable type. The individual bricks are almost indestructible under any ordinary traffic wear. The bricks are also not affected by weathering and may be used over again, if the road is to be reconstructed. The initial cost of brick paving is higher than most other materials used as a road surface. The longer life and lower upkeep of the bricks, however, justifies the additional expense.

TILES

Roofing Tiles

Roofing tiles are generally made by the plastic process. Rough blanks of stiff plastic clay are extruded by a pug mill through the die and are cut by wires in a similar way as in brick-making. These blanks are then re-pressed to give the tiles their final shape. The blanks are formed to the approximate size of the finished tile. This facilitates the pressing operations and results in better tiles than would be made if an unformed lump of clay was put into the press. Roofing tiles must be fired to such a degree that they have a porosity low enough to be practically impermeable to water, but they must not be too vitreous, in order to avoid 'sweating'. Roofing tiles must, of course, be resistant to weathering and frost since they are constantly exposed to the atmospheric action. Clay plain roofing tiles and fittings for roofing tiles are covered by B.S.S. 402: 1945. This specification is sub-divided in two parts.

Part I covers tiles and Part II covers the fittings. The size of a standardized tile must be 10½ in. × 6½ in. with a permissible plus or minus variation not exceeding ⅛ in. in the width and length. (See Fig. 10.) The thickness of the tile must be

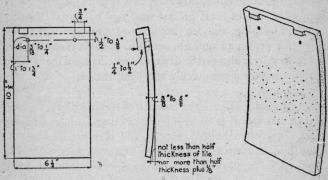

Fig. 10. Plain Tile.

not less than ⅜ in. and not more than ⅝ in. Two nail holes are to be provided and the sizes and the distance of these holes are described in this specification. The water absorption must not exceed 10.5%. Transverse strength must not be less than 175 lb. The tile fittings are also standardized and they are sub-divided into Eaves tiles, tile and a half-tile, Hip tiles, Valley tiles, Ridge tiles, and vertical angle tiles. A half-round ridge tile is illustrated in Fig. 11.

Drying of Tiles. – The drying has to be carried out very slowly. One might think that the drying of tiles would be carried out more quickly than that of bricks because tiles are much thinner and their surface per unit volume is greater, which simplifies

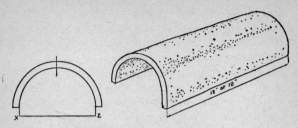

Fig. 11. Half round ridge tile.

the drying. In practice, however, tiles take as long to dry as bricks because of their greater tendency to warp. In order to avoid warping, wooden supports or frames are used which allow the drying air uniform access to both faces of each tile. If one face were allowed to dry more quickly than the other it would contract more quickly and bend the tile.

Firing of Roofing Tiles. – The burning of roofing tiles is effected in a similar way as in the firing of bricks, and similar kilns are used. Very often building bricks, and tiles are fired in the same kiln, the bricks forming the heating shafts which, in top-fired kilns, allow the fuel to burn when dropped down through the arch. When tiles exclusively are fired, however, the coal is better burnt on grates, or producer gas is used. The most economical kiln for roofing tiles is, however, the tunnel kiln. The same considerations hold good for tiles as those mentioned in the chapter dealing with brick firing.

Chimney and Drainage Pipes. – Porous clay pipes, shaped and fired in a similar way to hollow bricks, are used as chimney flue and drainage pipes. Plain pipes are extruded direct from the die and cut into the desired lengths by means of a wire-cutter. Pipes having a very large diameter are made on a sewer-pipe press. For firing purposes, pipes of equal diameter are placed vertically in the kiln, one on top of the other, and, as far as possible, pipes of smaller diameter are placed inside pipes of larger diameter, in order to make the best use of the kiln space. Drain pipes are required to be very porous but still have fairly high mechanical strength. The average porosity is about 20%. This type of drain pipe cannot be made of stoneware as it must be porous. (Sewerage pipes, however, and pipes for feeding water are made of stoneware which is practically impermeable. Glazed pipes used for sewerage are, of course, also made of stoneware and will be described later.)

*

Descriptions and illustrations of brickmaking machinery were supplied to the author by the following:

> Bradley and Craven, Ltd, Wakefield;
> Wm. Johnson and Sons, Leeds;
> Fawcett Ltd, Leeds;
> Richter and Pickis, Ltd, Southgate, London;
> Richard Scholefield, Leeds;
> C. Whittaker and Co., Accrington.

The author wishes to thank them for their helpful co-operation.

CHAPTER XIII
Refractories

A SECTION of the ceramic industry little known to the general public is that engaged in the production of refractories. The word 'refractory' means resistant to melting or fusion. Broadly speaking, wherever very high temperatures are involved, for example in furnaces, kilns and electrical heating apparatus, including resistances, the refractories industry provides the linings, supports and other fitments. So the refractories industry embodies those manufacturers who are engaged in the production of refractory bricks, special shapes, cements, hollowware and tubing for the construction and operation of a varied range of furnaces. The range of furnaces includes those for the melting and heat treatment of ferrous and non-ferrous metals, for smelting metals from the ores, for steam raising, etc. The range of kilns includes those for firing other ceramic products such as kiln furniture, for the manufacture of lime, cement and plaster, etc. In addition there is a multitude of other special types of furnaces for both the heavy and light industries.

The progress of this industry throughout the world has been marked by a high degree of co-operation between the producer and the user. Prior to the First World War England was behind in the production of refractory materials of the highest quality: Germany ranked first in Europe and America was ahead of both. The conditions changed in the inter-war period and before the outbreak of the Second World War England and the United States were both somewhat ahead of the German refractory industry.

A refractory material is not a perfect or permanent protection and it starts to wear away as soon as it is put into service. The operating life of refractory furnace walls depends upon the type of material which the furnace is called upon to handle. For instance, in the case of crucibles and tank walls used in the glass industry, the combination of certain alkalies in the glass and the impurities which exist in even the best fire-bricks, causes, in course of time, the entire destruction of the refractories. One of the principal concerns of the various refractories industries is therefore to improve the chemical compositions of their products by suitable admixtures so as to make them more and more resistant to the materials with which they come in contact. Continuous research is being carried out in this connexion.

Chemically, refractory materials can be classified as follows:

1. Acid products are those made of clay, of clay silica mixtures, and of pure silica. The more silica is used in a mixture the more acid are its properties.

2. Basic products are those which contain a large proportion of lime or magnesia or a mixture of these bases, or other metal oxides.

3. Neutral products are those formed of certain alumina silicates which contain more alumina than pure clay.

Substances like graphite, carborundum and so on are also termed neutral refractories.

FIRECLAY WARE

From the point of view of turnover – or quantities produced – the most important refractory materials are fireclay goods.

In the chapter dealing with clay it was explained that cones made of pure clay (clay substance $Al_2O_3 . 2SiO_2$) squat at $1770°$ C. (Seger Cone 35), and that additions of silica decrease the refractoriness (or resistance to heat) whereas an addition of alumina (bauxite) increases the refractoriness (see Fig. 12).

Silica is a mild flux compared with iron oxides, lime, or alkalies, which are present as impurities in most clays.

Fireclay goods are, as a rule, composed solely of fireclays or china clays with the addition, in the case of plastic clays, of

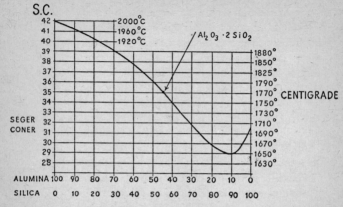

Fig. 12. Fusibility of mixtures of alumina and silica
in Seger Cones and centigrade.

some opening material such as grog or free silica. (Grog is a potter's term for broken granulated fired refractory clay and it is made from the rejects of fireclay works, broken saggers, crucibles, and so on. These broken pieces are ground and then sifted to obtain grains of various sizes.)

For very plastic clays, the proportion of opening materials may be as great as two parts by weight of grog to one part of clay. For opening up non-plastic clays, smaller amounts of grog have to be used. The use of silica as an opening agent changes the chemical composition and reduces the refractoriness. The addition of free silica introduces the following disadvantage:

Silica undergoes various volume modifications as it is being fired to high temperatures. The refractory body which contains silica is therefore liable to swell and even crumble.

For best fireclay goods it is usual to use only grog made of fireclay. To increase further the refractoriness of a fireclay body, kyanite, sillimanite, bauxite, fused alumina, or carborundum can be added instead of fireclay grog. These materials impart various advantages which will be briefly discussed later on.

The composition of fireclays varies considerably as the following table shows:

Content	Per cent
Silica	46 to 63
Alumina	32 to 45
Iron	0.7 to 2.5
Lime	0.1 to 0.6
Magnesia	Traces to 0.5
Alkali	Traces to 1.6

The influences which the various impurities impart to a clay have been described previously in this book.

Preparation of Fireclay Bodies. – Fireclay is usually dug some time before it is used. It is allowed to weather as long as possible in order to increase its plasticity. It has previously been mentioned that the weathering can be replaced by de-airing. Clay and grog are mixed in a pug mill and the desired proportion of water is added. In more modern factories clay powder and grogs of different grain size are stored in hoppers placed in an upper story so that they run down by gravity into the pug mill or other mixing machines. Mixing of dry clay with grog or other opening materials results in a more uniform and intimate mixture. The necessary water is, in this case, added after mixing. If the grog used in the body preparation has a large grain size, the resultant refractory goods are more resistant to sudden temperature changes.

If the grog has a very small grain size the final fireclay material is less porous and more resistant to chemical attacks. If a refractory has to be resistant both to temperature changes and to the chemical action of materials with which it may come in contact at high temperatures, a compromise is necessary. It will be realized, therefore, that the manufacture of refractories to meet various furnace conditions calls for skill and knowledge in blending, fabrication, and firing, to ensure a finished product of suitable quality.

Materials made from fireclay are in use in furnaces and kilns wherever production at a heat greater than a dull red heat is required. It is no exaggeration to say that modern industry could not carry on without fireclays (or other refractory materials).

Shaping of Fireclay Goods. – Fire-brick standards and special shapes are manufactured according to circumstances:

1. By hand moulding from plastic mixture.
2. By machine pressing from a coarse damp dust.
3. By extrusion through dies of a plastic mixture.
4. By tamping of damp dust or plastic clay by rammers into strongly-made moulds.
5. By casting.

These shaping processes yield fireclay refractories for boiler furnaces, blast furnaces, gas retort settings, lime kilns, cement kilns and metallurgical furnaces for melting, re-heating and heat treatment of iron, steel and non-ferrous metals.

Fireclay hollow-ware includes fireclay crucibles, large and small, for melting metals, enamels and glass; fireclay tubes and other small furnace chambers, and a multitude of specialized shapes for external heating by coke, gas, oil, and resistance winding. Methods employed for the manufacture of refractory hollow-ware include spinning, pressing, extrusion, tamping and slip casting. Slip casting used to be confined to porcelain and earthenware manufacture. It is, however, now being increasingly used in the manufacture of refractories owing to the fact that in liquid form the various ingredients can be very thoroughly mixed.

Fireclay Bricks. – Fireclay bricks are classified according to their alumina contents and refractoriness as follows:

Refractoriness		*Type of fireclay brick*
Cones 26 to 28	.	Moderate heat duty
Cones 28 ro 31	.	Intermediate heat duty
Cones 31 to 33	.	High duty fireclay
Cones 33 to 34	.	Super duty fireclay

Burning of Fireclay Goods. – The firing of fireclay goods is done in kilns of various sizes and shapes – down-draught intermittent ovens, continuous chamber kilns, tunnel kilns, and other types. The down-draught intermittent oven is the oldest but still the most widely used type of kiln for firing refractories, though continuous chamber ovens and tunnel kilns are used considerably where the outputs are large. The time required for firing fireclay goods usually varies from five to ten days according to the class of goods being burnt and the type of kiln in use. The temperature to which the goods are burnt also varies and may be between 1200° C. and 1400° C. Fireclay goods rich in alumina are in most cases fired to 1400° C. and even higher. The cooling process usually takes from seven to ten days according to the class of kiln in use. Cooling has to be carried out very carefully, particularly in the case of large articles, to avoid cracking of the ware owing to sudden reduction of temperature. The cooling process can, however, be speeded up if sudden falls in temperature are avoided and the curve in the cooling zone is a straight line. The most economical type of kiln for fireclay goods is a modern tunnel oven because it is possible to regulate heat increases and rate of cooling according to the job in hand.

ALUMINOUS REFRACTORY GOODS

The term 'aluminous refractory goods' embraces those which contain more than 45 % alumina. This amount is necessary to combine with all the silica present to form clay substance (alumina bi-silicate). Strictly speaking, only those goods which contain more alumina than pure clay (clay substance) can be called aluminous. Aluminous refractory bodies are consequently prepared by adding alumina in some form or another to a pure fireclay. Nature, however, also supplies some clays which contain a surplus of alumina. Bauxite is frequently used, to increase the alumina content and refractoriness of the fireclay. It is hydrated alumina ($Al_2O_3 . H_2O$) and has to be calcined and ground before being added to the body. The

alumina content of bauxite bricks is between 45 and 80%.
Bricks having an alumina content higher than 55% have to be
fired at temperatures higher than 1400° C.; bricks containing,
for instance, 78% alumina, 17.8% silica and about 3% iron,
require a firing temperature of 1500° C. to obtain the necessary
strength. Owing to the high price of calcined bauxite and the
high firing temperature required, bauxite bricks are consequently much more expensive to produce than fireclay bricks
and they are, therefore, used only in special situations, for
example where very high temperatures are experienced or
where resistance to basic slags is required.

SILICA BRICKS

Unlike fireclay bricks, silica bricks are not used as a general
refractory material as they fall to pieces if heated or cooled
rapidly. They do not contain clay and are, strictly speaking,
not ceramic materials. However, in a chapter dealing with
refractories they cannot be omitted, since they are widely
used by steel makers in the roofs of their furnaces where a very
high temperature (1650° C.) is common practice and advantage
is taken of the property of silica bricks to expand under heat.
Sir William Siemens first used silica bricks in the building of
furnaces. The outstanding behaviour of lime bonded silica
bricks under compressive load at high temperatures enables
the open hearth furnace to be operated at the temperature mentioned above.

Alumina or silicates of alumina having a higher alumina
content than pure clay are more refractory than silica. They
occur, however, only very rarely in the pure state in nature, but
beds of practically pure silica are very numerous. Silica bricks
have been made since 1822 at Dinas in South Wales, of sand
found in that district. The raw material most widely used for
silica brick manufacture is quartzite. This is a rock composed
of crystals of almost pure silica, bound together by a cement of
similar material in such a manner as to produce an almost
smooth surface. These rocks are reduced to a convenient size

by heavy jaw and rotary crushers. The material is then weighed into a definite charge and fed into heavy grinding mills containing rollers weighing four or five tons each. In this way the quartzite is reduced to a proper size for moulding. As the powder is charged into the mill, a quantity of water and lime (1 to 2%) is added. (The water makes the material slightly plastic and the lime acts in the firing process as a kind of cement, thus producing a solid brick.) The mixed charge is then formed to the desired shapes, which are then placed on plates and fixed in racks to dry. The drying arrangements are often elaborate and costly because the ware is extremely delicate at this stage.

Burning or firing of silica bricks is also a difficult and expensive process. Down-draught intermittent kilns and tunnel kilns are mainly used. Slow firing in the early stages drives off the moisture. As the temperature increases the lime, together with iron and other basic impurities in the quartzite, fuses, forming a solid mass binding the quartz particles together. During the final stages of burning the quartz is converted into crystobalite or tridymite. The conversions of the crystal structure of silica were discussed earlier in this book. At 1500° C. a volume expansion of about 5% takes place, the brick expanding in all directions. The temperature in the oven is maintained at 1500° C. for about twenty-four hours. The whole firing period is about twelve days. The cooling has to be done very slowly and takes about ten to twelve days.

Silica bricks contain 94 to 95% silica, 1 to 2% alumina, 0.4 to 1% iron, 2 to 2.5% lime. For firing silica bricks tunnel ovens are also used nowadays. Owing to the fact that firing and cooling have to be carried out very slowly, they take a very long time. For this reason the tunnel ovens for firing silica bricks are very long. The first tunnel kiln in the world designed for firing silica bricks was built in Germany about 1933 and has a length of 500 ft. and a burning zone 200 ft. long. When burning silica bricks in tunnel ovens the firing cycle is shorter than with intermittent ovens, and firing plus cooling can be carried out in ten days. Heavy duty silica bricks are a recent development in order to improve refractories; the silica used must be particularly pure.

SILLIMANITE AND KYANITE WARE

If refractory materials of greater refractoriness than silica bricks are required, or if the refractory material is subjected in practice to higher temperatures than fireclay would withstand, and if at the same time owing to the occurrence of temperature changes silica bricks are not advisable, sillimanite or kyanite refractories are frequently used. Sillimanite and kyanite have the same chemical composition ($Al_2O_3 . SiO_2$) but their crystal structure is different. The term sillimanite is very often used for both these minerals. Sillimanite has a melting point of $1810°$ C. and if admixed with only small amounts of clay it can be used for temperatures up to $1700°$ C. Sillimanite and kyanite are not plastic and in order to make them 'workable' they have to be mixed with clay. Sillimanite ware is manufactured in the following way:

The raw kyanite or sillimanite is calcined at $1500°$ C. for twenty-four hours, then ground in two stages by the methods described previously:

1. Crushed dry in suitable crushers.
2. Milled in cylinders after water has been added.

In the manufacture of larger articles such as bricks, sillimanite is used having a larger grain size than that used in the manufacture of smaller articles such as pyrometer tubes. Furthermore, if the fired material has to be porous, the average grain size of the granulated sillimanite has to be larger than that for the manufacture of dense articles.

The sillimanite slip (the watery suspension of ground sillimanite) passes through sieves into a mixer or blunger where it is mixed with clay. The amount of clay to be added depends on the refractoriness required. Clay is a much cheaper material than sillimanite. Consequently no more sillimanite is used in the mixture than is necessary for obtaining the required refractoriness. Ordinary sillimanite ware is made of a mixture varying between 40% and 66% sillimanite and 60% and 34%—fireclay. Special quality sillimanite ware contains more sillimanite and less fireclay (up to 95% sillimanite). Ordinary sillimanite ware is fired at about 1500 to 1600° C. whereas special quality sillimanite ware is fired at temperatures up to 1800° C.[1] Firing is done both in intermittent ovens and tunnel kilns. In order to obtain the very high temperatures required, in the most economical way, the combustion air has to be pre-heated as described in the section dealing with the design of tunnel ovens. The furnace has, of course, to be lined with special quality sillimanite bricks.

Sillimanite ware is shaped in the same way as other refractories, the method chosen varying according to the size, configuration and composition, for example, by tamping with pneumatic hammers, by pressing in hydraulic presses or hand-operated presses, by extrusion from de-airing pug mills or hydraulic presses, by casting into plaster moulds, or by jollying and turning.

MAGNESITE

Magnesite is used in industry in situations where a highly basic refractory is required. It is employed, for instance, in the manufacture of steel by the basic process in the lining of the furnaces and is also used in both brick form and in granular form in the furnace bottom. The granules are often mixed with ground dolomite and rammed into the furnace bottom as a concrete.

Where slags of a basic nature are formed, basic bricks such as magnesite bricks are successfully used. Magnesite bricks are also used in metallurgical furnaces since they resist the attack of metallic oxides, to a certain extent. The manufacture of magnesite bricks is a double process. In the first stage the carbon dioxide gas is driven off. (The gas represents over 50% of the weight of the magnesium carbonate.) The calcination

1. Sillimanite Refractories consisting of 100% Sillimanite can be made by mixing Sillimanite with Siliconester. This is a very interesting new development.

is then carried out at a very high temperature so that periclase, the stable form of magnesia, can be formed. (For certain purposes it is not necessary to produce this conversion.) The magnesite is calcined at about 1600° C. After cooling, the magnesia is crushed to a fine powder in machines of the type previously described, and bonding materials such as iron ore are added. If the calcination of the magnesite is carried out at a low temperature, the product is caustic magnesia which has the property of setting hard with water. Advantage of this property is taken to mix a small proportion of caustic magnesia with the other materials before pressing and to obtain a harder brick in the stage preparatory to burning. The prepared powder is pressed into bricks in hydraulic presses. A pressure of 5,000 lb. per sq. in. is usual.

Drying is done very slowly in a way similar to that described for silica bricks, and, after a period of several days, the bricks are loaded into kilns for burning. The firing process is again slow and costly. The magnesite bricks are not strong enough to stand any weight under load and in consequence they have to be loaded in sections supported by silica bricks in order to reduce the load to which they would be subjected. The silica has to be protected from the magnesia to avoid chemical reaction taking place between them during the firing, and it is usual to use chrome ore as a neutral between them.

The kiln temperature is slowly raised to 1500° C. and then the kiln is slowly cooled, the whole cycle taking about three to four weeks. (In the case of tunnel ovens the cycle is considerably reduced.) One disadvantage of magnesite bricks is their tendency to spall (split) when subjected to temperature changes. Attempts have therefore been made to improve the resistance to temperature changes without decreasing the refractoriness. Composite chrome-magnesite products are used in order to combine the merits of magnesite and chrome refractories. Suitably graded mixtures of chrome ore and magnesite give bricks of high refractoriness and good spalling resistance. Another method of improving spalling resistance of magnesite bricks is a small addition (2% to 4%) of alumina.

REFRACTORIES FOR THE STEEL INDUSTRY
EXTRACTED FROM SEA WATER

Before the Second World War most of the magnesite required by the industry was imported from Austria and Manchuria, but nowadays magnesia is recovered from sea water and dolomite. Pilot scale trials were commenced in 1937 in Hartlepool and these were followed by a plant designed to produce 10,000 tons per annum. The output of this plant was further increased in 1939, and in 1941 the Harrington Shore Works near Workington, Cumberland, were built on behalf of the Ministry of Aircraft Production to supply magnesia for magnesium metal production. When the demand for this metal fell at the end of the war Harrington was closed down, but was re-opened in 1951 to produce magnesia for the refractory industry, and many major plant improvements and extensions have been made at Hartlepool since then, giving corresponding increases in output.

The process worked at Hartlepool uses, apart from fuel, only two raw materials, namely sea water and dolomite. Sea water contains magnesium sulphate and chloride in solution and dolomite consists of magnesium carbonate and calcium carbonate. The extraction of magnesia from sea water depends on the reaction of the soluble magnesium salts with a base to form insoluble magnesium hydroxide, which will settle, be filtered and calcined. The base used is calcium hydroxide which is conveniently provided by dolomite.

The dolomite is first calcined to give a mixture of the oxides of calcium and magnesium. This calcined product is added to the sea water in which the calcium oxide is converted into the soluble hydroxide which subsequently precipitates the magnesium salts of the sea water in the form of magnesium hydroxide and goes into solution as a mixture of soluble salts (calcium sulphate and calcium chloride). The magnesia from the calcined dolomite remains unchanged and settles with the magnesia derived from the sea water.

The use of dolomite limes in the place of high calcium lime approximately doubles the yield of magnesia per unit volume of sea water. The magnesia precipitate passes in the form of a dilute slurry from the reactors to settling tanks having a size of up to 240 ft. in diameter. These are equipped with mechanisms which rake the settled magnesia to the centre of each tank from which it is withdrawn by pumps. The settled slurry produced in this way has a magnesium hydroxide content of approximately 300 gram per litre and is filtered to give a paste having a solids content of approximately 50%.

For use in the refractory industry the magnesia filter paste is calcined in rotary kilns, similar to cement kilns. The kilns are fired with pulverized coal, the maximum temperature obtained being about 1650° C. The kiln has an output of approximately 100 tons of 'Britmag' per day. This is the trade name of the magnesia produced by this process. In the hottest zone the rotary kiln is lined with magnesia-chrome refractories baked with 2 or 3 inches of fire-brick insulation.*

CHROMITE BRICKS

Chromite is a mineral in the chromium series of multiple oxides, the dominant compound being $FeCr_2O_4$. Chromite bricks are used mostly in steel furnaces, and in compartments connected with them, in which basic slags have to be dealt with. Chromite is a neutral refractory and consequently very valuable as a contact material for basic materials. It is also used in copper works, antimony and lead furnaces. Unfortunately it is costly and difficult to manufacture. The method of manufacture is similar to that for magnesite bricks but without the preliminary calcination. The same high temperatures are necessary in order to produce good chromite bricks. Analyses of chromite bricks give the following average results:

Chromic oxide	38% to 45%
Silica	4% to 5%

* See Dr W. C. Gilpin, B.SC., PH.D., 'Refractory Magnesia from Sea Water', *The Refractories Journal*, February 1953.

Alumina	16% to 20%
Iron oxides	25% to 27%
Magnesite	9% to 10%

Fusion commences between 1850° C. and 2000° C.

SILICON CARBIDE (CARBORUNDUM WARE)

Silicon carbide (SiC) is produced by the fusion of sand and coke in an electric furnace. Owing to its refractoriness and its high thermal conductivity it is used to a great extent in the manufacture of saggers, bats, props and other kiln furniture, for supporting the ware in tunnel ovens, for the muffles of muffle ovens, and so on. The thermal conductivity of carborundum is greater than that of the other refractory materials already described. Thermal conductivity is a measure of the rate of heat flow per unit area (say per sq. in. or per sq. cm.) through a given distance in inches or centimetres and per unit temperature difference (say per 1° C. or 1° F.). A material having a high thermal conductivity consequently conducts and dissipates the heat through the mass quicker than a material having a low thermal conductivity. Metals have a much higher thermal conductivity than ceramic products, which are not heat conductors, but heat insulators. The heat in metals is therefore much more quickly conducted and dissipated all over the whole article and thermal strains in metal articles are practically non-existent, provided the metal articles are free to expand and contract. This is the reason why metal saucepans containing a liquid as a rule do not crack when heated on an open gas flame, whereas saucepans made of conventional ceramic materials are more liable to break. Carborundum and graphite are materials which are intermediate between metals and ceramic materials as far as heat conductivity is concerned. (They are also intermediate electrically between conductors and insulators and are consequently used for the manufacture of electrical resistors.) In the manufacture of carborundum ware the carborundum is mixed with clay and shaped by the various shaping methods used in the ceramic industry, including the casting method. The firing has to be carried out in a neutral or reducing atmosphere. The firing temperature varies according to the carborundum content of the body and ranges between 1400° C. and 1600° C.

CARBON (OR GRAPHITE) REFRACTORIES

Carbon is not a ceramic material but, apart from its addition in the form of plumbago to crucible mixtures, it is important as a refractory lining under non-oxidizing conditions in, for example, the hearth of blast furnaces, smelting iron and electric furnaces for melting various alloys. The thermal conductivity of graphite is at least three times that of fire-bricks and its coefficient of thermal expansion is low and regular. High thermal conductivity and small heat expansion have a favourable influence on the thermal shock resistance of a material. Carbon refractories are consequently very resistant to sudden temperature changes. The refractoriness of the article depends on the quantity of carbon used. For mixtures very high in carbon, the refractoriness is above 1700° C. The carbon used is either mineral graphite (plumbago) or retort graphite (formed in gas retorts). Carbon refractories have the disadvantage of being burnt up rather rapidly when used in an oxidizing atmosphere. Graphite has been much used since the beginning of this century for the manufacture of crucibles which have to withstand sudden temperature changes. In the manufacture of graphite crucibles this country has been leading for many years. Graphite crucibles are also employed in metallurgical and other chemical operations on account of their reducing qualities. Between the two world wars, blast furnace hearths of carbon were used increasingly for smelting iron and were imported from the Continent. During the last war the manufacture of carbon blocks and linings was commenced on a large scale in this country.

The shaping of graphite refractories is done by the various shaping methods used in the manufacture of other refractory goods. The application of pressure during the shaping is very often of particular importance. The firing is done in a reducing atmosphere and the ware is embedded in pulverized carbon if necessary.

PURE OXIDE REFRACTORIES

The refractories described so far are for use below 1700° C. For temperatures above 1700° C. the selection of refractories is limited to pure oxide refractories. Melting points (MP) and limits of application of the most important metal oxides are listed below and are compared with silica, sillimanite and clay substance.

Refractory	Formula	M.P.	Limit of application
Alumina . . .	Al_2O_3	2050° C.	1950° C.
Magnesia . . .	MgO	2800° C.	2400° C.
Beryllia . . .	BeO	2570° C.	2400° C.
Zirconia . . .	ZrO_2	2700° C.	2500° C.
Thoria . . .	ThO_2	3050° C.	2700° C.
Lime . . .	CaO	2570° C.	2400° C.
Silica . . .	SiO_2	1710° C.	1680° C.
Zircon . .	$ZrO_2.SiO_2$	1900° C. [1]	1750° C.
Spinel . .	$Al_2O_3.MgO$	2130° C.	1900° C.
Mullite . .	$3Al_2O_3.2SiO_2$	1810° C.	1700° C.
Sillimanite .	$Al_2O_3.SiO_2$	1810° C.	1700° C.
Pure clay (theoretical)	$Al_2O_3 2.SiO_2$	1770° C.	—

Refractory oxides of themselves possess no plastic properties and consequently the manufacture of this ware presents considerable difficulty. Some bond or other has to be used in order to make the oxide bodies workable and plastic to a slight extent. Clays or bentonites are obviously suitable for making the bodies plastic but they reduce their refractoriness considerably. With this object in view, clays and bentonites have been added only in small quantities, but even then they decrease the melting point. Organic plasticizers such as the various types of dextrin and resins are also used, but they do not produce a really plastic paste, and make dense bodies

1. Decomposes above 1,900° C

slightly porous since they burn away during the firing, leaving small pores behind. Several oxides (particularly alumina) can be made plastic by treatment for several days with hot hydrochloric acid. Such treatment forms colloidal hydrates. These hydrates make the metal oxides plastic and assist sintering without decreasing the melting point.

Alumina. – Of the metal oxides listed above, alumina is the most widely used refractory. It has previously been mentioned that calcined bauxite is added to fireclay in order to increase the refractoriness of fireclay bricks. If the alumina content of an alumina clay mixture is higher than 90%, it is generally referred to as an alumina refractory. Alumina ware may be either porous or impermeable and may consist either of fused or recrystallized alumina. Alumina ware having an alumina content of 90% or higher, is suitable for service up to 1700° C. Alumina ware having 99% alumina content can be used up to 1900° C. Alumina refractories are much used, for instance, for lining high temperature furnaces, for high temperature muffles for the manufacture of crucibles, boats, tubes, etc., for very high temperature. Recrystallized alumina is a purer form of alumina than the fused grade. The widest use of recrystallized alumina is in the manufacture of sparking-plug insulators since – with the exception of very rare oxides – no other material has the same high dielectric strength at elevated temperatures and the same high resistance to sudden temperature changes. The best technical characteristics are achieved in alumina ware consisting of nearly 100% Al_2O_3. The raw material is hydrated alumina ($Al_2O_3 . H_2O–Al_2O_3 . 3H_2O$), which is wet ground, filter pressed, pressed into tablets and calcined at 1500° C. The calcined alumina is crushed and milled and a part of it is made plastic by treatment with hydrochloric acid. The acid-treated alumina is then mixed with alumina powder which has not been acid-treated. The plastic body can be jollied, extruded and may also be made liquid for casting purposes by the addition of water. This type of alumina ware is fired at between 1800° C. and 1820° C.

Lime. – Lime, limestone and dolomite are not stable against hydration even after firing above 2100° C. and hence they are rarely used as a refractory (with the exception of dolomite in steel furnaces). Much research work has, however, been carried out in order to stabilize these oxides by the addition of other metal oxides, without decreasing the melting point. Since lime is a very cheap material, the problem of its stabilization is of great practical interest.

Beryllia. – Beryllia is superior to alumina in refractoriness, thermal conductivity and dielectric characteristics, particularly at temperatures higher than 1900° C. The high material cost has, however, restricted the wider development and application of this oxide.

Zirconia and Zircon. – Zircon ($ZrSiO_4$) (zirconium silicate) is now being used to an increasing extent in the manufacture of refractory goods. Zircon refractories are used for electric furnaces, for high temperature insulating bricks, small high temperature saggers and laboratory ware. Zircon porcelains are used as spark-plug insulators and as other electrical insulators which have to withstand high temperatures and sudden temperature changes, and also for chemical apparatus. The development of zirconia (ZrO_2) refractories is a very recent one. The ordinary zirconia suffers from a pronounced volume inversion at 1000° C. usually disrupting the ware when this temperature range is passed quickly. This inversion, however, can be somewhat diminished by the addition of small amounts of magnesia without reduction of fusion temperature.

Magnesia. – Magnesite bricks (containing about 87 to 88% magnesia) have previously been discussed. Magnesium oxide has the disadvantages of large thermal expansion and poor load-bearing properties. The large thermal expansion makes the ordinary magnesia refractories very liable to crack at sudden temperature changes. Much research work has been carried out to find suitable additions which would not unduly increase the price of magnesite refractories. Small amounts of such expensive materials as beryllium oxide, titanium oxide, zirconium oxide, however, do not lower the thermal expansion sufficiently to warrant their use. Large additions of chromic oxide to magnesia, however, lower the thermal expansion and result in refractories possessing better resistance to thermal changes and almost the same refractoriness as pure magnesite.

Coefficient of Expansion. – The thermal expansion of refractories is of great importance to designers of ovens and all users of refractories. The following table is therefore of interest.[1]

Material	Coefficient of Thermal Expansion $0–1000°C$.
Silica brick	$90 \times 10{-7}$
Semi-silica brick . . . '.	$60 \times 10{-7}$
Fire-brick	$40 \times 10{-7}$
Bauxite brick . . .	$65 \times 10{-7}$
Magnesite	$100 \times 10{-7}$
Chromite	$90 \times 10{-7}$
Zirconia	$8.4 \times 10{-7}$
Sillimanite brick . . .	$60 \times 10{-7}$

Linear Expansion from $_0–t°C$.

Fused Quartz	Range	$0–30°$ C.	4.2×10^{-7} per °C.
		$0–100$	5.0 ,,
		$0–800$	5.46 ,,
		$0–1200$	5.85 ,,
Alumina (Al_2O_3)		$0–900$	$87.$,,
		$25–100$	65.8 ,,
Carborundum		$100–900$	47.4 ,,

1. Taken from *Technical Data on Fuel* and from *Handbook of Chemistry and Physics*.

$t°C$	Silica brick	Firebrick	Magnesite brick	Carborundum brick	Sillimanite brick
100	0.15%	0.06%	0.05%	0.11%	0.03%
200	0.65%	0.12%	0.1%	0.14%	0.06%
300	0.9%	0.18%	0.20%	0.17%	0.1%
400	1.05%	0.24%	0.35%	0.21%	0.15%
500	1.1%	0.30%	0.5%	0.25%	0.2%
600	1.15%	0.36%	0.65%	0.3%	0.25%
700	1.2%	0.42%	0.8%	0.35%	0.3%
800	1.23%	0.48%	0.95%	0.35%	0.4%
900	1.25%	0.54%	1.1%	0.4%	0.5%
1000	1.25%	0.60%	1.25%	0.4%	0.6%
1100	1.25%	0.66%	1.4%	0.5%	0.6%
1200	1.25%	0.72%	1.55%	0.5%	0.7%
1300	1.20%	0.78%	1.7%	0.6%	0.7%

Refractories Consumption and Refractories Consumers. – To get some idea of the extent to which the different types of refractory materials are used on the Continent in comparison with other refractories, the following statistics on German refractory consumption during 1944 may be useful. They were published by the American Military Government.[1]

	Per cent of total tonnage value
Fireclay ware	59.0
Silica refractories	11.9
Magnesite products	17.6
Other refractories	4.2
Crucible and graphite products . .	4.2
High-alumina refractories . .	3.1
	100.0

Refractories consumption and consumers in Germany in 1944 were as follows:

Consumer industry	Per cent of total deliveries in 1944
Iron and metals	43.2
Coke and by-products . . .	8.1

1. John M. Warde, *American Ceramic Society Bulletin*, 1946.

Consumer industry				*Per cent of total deliveries in* 1944
Power-generating plants	.	.	.	7.9
Chemicals	.	.	.	7.6
Bake ovens and stoves	.	.	.	6.7
Cement and lime	.	.	.	4.5
Ceramics	.	.	.	4.9
Glass and glazing	.	.	.	3.8
Locomotives and ships	.	.	.	0.9
Others	.	.	.	12.4
				100.0

Production figures in this country are as follows:[1]

Fireclay Bricks

1930 Tons	1935 Tons	1944 Tons	1945 Tons
837,000	943,000	980,000	871,000

Silica Bricks

1930 Tons	1935 Tons	1944 Tons	1945 Tons
171,000	205,000	235,000	207,000

Basic Bricks (Magnesite, chrome and chrome-magnesite)

13,400	16,500	42,900	46,800

The figures of production of dolomite are not included in the above statistics, but they also are very impressive.

A VISIT TO THE NEW NESTON WORKS OF
MORGAN CRUCIBLE COMPANY LTD

The reader will be interested to have a glimpse of the new works which Morgan Crucible Co. Ltd have built recently to replace the old Battersea establishment. There, many of the types of refractories described in this chapter are manufactured. In developing the new site, Morgan Crucible had three main objects in view:

1. *A Survey of the Refractories Industry.* Presidential address by R. A. Kirkby (General Refractories Ltd), *Refractories Journal*, February 1947.

(1) To rehouse the Battersea refractory department in more modern buildings, with the most up-to-date of equipment, and provide a layout that would facilitate not only regular economical flow, but the closest inspection and control at all stages of manufacture.

(2) To provide buildings and specialized plant for the bulk production of much improved and stabilized aluminous refractories from 43% alumina upwards, and also a complete range of low heat capacity or hot face insulating refractories.

(3) To make freely available new cements, castables and mouldables.

It had been decided that in the interests of efficiency the project must be a green field one. The new site covers 43 acres. The Midland Region main line with over half a mile of sidings forms its western boundary, the Liverpool Road its southern boundary. At present only the western third of the site (alongside the railway) is developed but there is room for considerable extensions, some of which are already on the drawing board.

As projected, the refractories now being manufactured can be divided into four broad groups:

(1) The MR Series. The introduction of MR1 Super Duty Fire Bricks fills a gap hitherto existing in the fire brick industry, namely the need for fire brick that can withstand conditions which call for particularly high volume stability at high temperatures and high hot strength with good resistance to physical and thermal spalling. This type of Super Duty Fire Brick has also a low after-contraction at temperatures up to 1600° C. with a high resistance to deformation under normal loads at temperatures in excess of 1600° C. The ware is fired to the highest commercially applicable temperature in order to obtain maximum Mullite development. Alumina contents are 43/44%; refractoriness is cone 35 (1,770° C.) which, by the way, is the refractoriness of pure china clay.

(2) The MI Series. This range of low heat-storage insulating refractories will embrace a number of different hot-face insulating bricks for service at a range of temperatures up to

1650° C. At the moment, the plant is working on bricks for use at face temperatures of 1570° C. MI Bricks are essentially kaolin bricks with a very open structure obtained by mixing combustible with clay and afterwards burning it out. They are exceedingly light in weight and considering their structure very strong, and in addition they have a very low thermal conductivity. Their heat capacity and storage is extremely low.

(3) The specialized refractories previously made at the Battersea Works, embracing furnace shapes, bricks, tubing, crucibles, muffles, scorifers and cupels, etc., in clay bodies, sillimanite bauxite, fused alumina, silicon carbide, magnesite, pure oxides, etc.

(4) The widest variety of refractory concretes, insulating concretes, mouldable refractories and refractory cements.

Production. It will be clear that with the wide variety of refractories manufactured at some point, usually during calcination, grinding or grading, very different materials intended for very different products require similar treatment. It would have been uneconomical in space and would have led to wasteful duplication of plant to separate the production lines for each group of products. Therefore, the various stages of processing are separated or combined to the best advantage.

Raw Materials. Specially selected raw materials from the United Kingdom and other parts of the world; clays, bauxite, sillimanite, etc. go into the works, for the most part by rail. Before binning, samples are sent to the process control laboratory for testing to determine that the materials meet the standard specification laid down. On acceptance, they are taken to the sidings, which are some 15 ft. above the works ground floor and are shot from the trucks directly into bins on the level of the works roadway. These bins are grouped adjacent to the milling and grinding plant feeding the main MR and Battersea production units. The internal railway system is planned to encircle the whole of the northern part of the works, making it possible to unload materials for the other products wherever they will be needed.

Calcination. A large proportion of the materials used have to be calcined before being made into refractories. This is done in a rotary kiln specially designed for calcination up to the highest temperatures. The calcined materials from the delivery end of the rotary kiln are mechanically elevated, sampled and tested by the Process Control Department, and if approved distributed and piled into brick-built bays. In this building a pulverizer and an air-separator and storage hoppers are being installed for the processing of bond clays.

Grinding, Milling, and Blending. This is a complicated plant, set up to produce first a range of all-in meshes, then to fractionate these, magnet and recombine to get the desired and closely controlled combination of mesh sizes, an essential in the production of high-grade refractories. The plant consists of crushers, pulverizers, screens, conveyors, elevators, and storage hoppers. It is designed for completely automatic operation, and any predetermined flow sequence can be set up on this automatic controller. In designing the plant, the prevention of contamination, particularly iron, has been a major consideration. Thus, all conveyors and bins are totally enclosed, and wherever possible any part of the plant coming into contact with the raw materials is either non-ferrous or stainless steel. As a further safeguard, all materials are passed over powerful electro-magnets, specially designed for dealing with this type of material. The material in process is subjected to examination by the Process Control Department at all stages.

Making. The making or shaping methods depend on the nature of the body and the particular pattern being manufactured; they fall under five headings: Hand-moulding, machine-moulding, machine pressing, extrusion, and slip-casting.

In one workshop, for example, there are lines of crucible-making machines, spinning various sizes of crucibles from plastic lumps in moulds, lines of presses which convert plastic lumps or weighed measures of damped mixture into cleanly-finished hollow-ware and shapes; extrusion presses in which the plastic body is squeezed into tubing which is then cut and finished. All components have then to be dried in a controlled atmosphere for final kilning. In contrast to the machine shop just described, in other sections of the works skilled craftsmen work at benches on intricate shapes which are assembled into special types of furnaces for subsequent firing. The bricks are manufactured by means of heavy presses of the semi-automatic or fully-automatic type or hand-moulded from plastic fire clay-mixings. The green bricks are loaded on to cars which pass through controlled driers and afterwards through tunnel kilns in a continuous process. The tunnel kilns at Neston are all oil-fired and equipped with the latest equipment for measuring and controlling the heat in the various sections of the kiln. Battersea Ware is fired up to 1600° C., MR Products above 1600° C., MI Products up to 1550° C.

REFERENCES

A Treatise on Ceramic Industries, E. Bourry, Scott and Greenwood.

The British Refractories Research Association, A. T. Green. *The Refractories Journal*, Oct., 1946.

Pure Oxide Refractories, D. Kirby.

Fused Magnesia, Burrows Moore.

Transactions of the British Ceramic Society, Feb., 1940.

Fuel Utilization and Economy in the Refractories and Heavy Clay Industries, E. Rowden (British Refractories Research Association) *The Refractories Journal*, Oct., 1946.

Grinding, Mixing and Preparing Clays, Alfred B. Searle, *Claycraft*, Dec., 1946.

CHAPTER XIV

Stoneware

STONEWARE is a type of clay ware which has a very hard, dense and almost impervious body. It is nearly vitreous and has a more or less glassy texture when broken. In physical structure it is similar to porcelain but it differs from porcelain in that it is usually made from plastic clays, whereas porcelain is made from kaolins (china clays).

Although some of the fine stoneware bodies – compounded from high-grade raw materials – are almost white after firing, stoneware is usually coloured, since most plastic clays are not white burning, but burn to a buff or grey colour. The predominating shades are yellowish to dark brown, greyish or bluish. The exact shade depends upon the amount of impurity in the clay and the conditions of firing. Stoneware also differs from porcelain in the degree of vitrification. Whereas porcelain is absolutely vitrified and practically non-porous, the vitrification of stoneware is not usually carried to the same extent. Coarser types of stoneware, such as those used for the manufacture of sewer pipes and other salt-glazed-ware pipes and similar articles, have a porosity of between 6% and 10%. According to British Standards Specification No. 65, pipes having a thickness of less than $\frac{3}{4}$ in. must have a porosity factor not more than 6%, whilst those having a thickness of $1\frac{1}{2}$ in. may have a maximum porosity of 10%. Similarly, for pipes with chemically resistant properties the figures are 2% and 8% respectively (British Standard Specification 1143).

The characteristic property of the finer grades of stoneware is an almost non-porous structure.

In large articles, however, there is a tendency for deformation to take place if they are fired at temperatures high enough to give complete densification. If a certain amount of porosity is allowed, with consequent lower firing temperature, the danger of deformation is much less.

As will be gathered from the foregoing remarks, the body structure of stoneware lies between those of porcelain and refractory ware. It differs fundamentally from refractory ware in that it contains more fluxes. It differs from porcelain in that the main raw materials are plastic clays and not kaolins. Because as a rule a higher degree of porosity is allowed with stoneware, and because plastic clays have a greater dry strength than kaolins, the manufacture of very large technical articles of stoneware is easier and cheaper than of porcelain.

In any study of ceramics, the reader will trace a progression of wares passing almost unobservably from one type to another, from fireclay to terra cotta, to stoneware, to porcelain. It is very difficult in many cases to draw a sharp line of demarcation between different types of ceramic ware. Although vitrified bricks and tiles, for instance, were quite naturally described in the chapter 'Bricks and Tiles', their ceramic structure and porosity are, however, very similar to those of stoneware sewer pipes described in this section. The main difference, in this particular case, is that the sewer pipes are, as a rule, salt glazed, whilst vitrified bricks and tiles are not. Salt glaze is, as a rule, only applied to stoneware.

Stoneware is used for the manufacture of paving tiles, salt-glazed pipes and fittings, preserve jars and similar goods, and to a very large extent for chemical apparatus. Fine stoneware is used for the manufacture of vases, statuettes and other decorative objects.

Raw Materials

The clays used in the manufacture of stoneware are, as mentioned above, plastic clays having good dry strength. The latter property is very important in the manufacture of large stoneware articles, as employed, for instance, by the chemical industry. Plastic stoneware clays, as a rule, contain enough fluxes to form at the final firing temperature (varying between 1200° C. and 1300° C.) a densified material. The fluxes are magnesia, lime, mica, feldspar, and iron oxide (in most cases in the form of ferric oxide (Fe_2O_3)). Mica and feldspar give the clay a greater firing range than lime. The lime content should consequently be low (less than 2%) and the alkali content relatively high. An ideal stoneware clay is a highly plastic clay containing, say, 1% iron oxide and 20% feldspar or mica in very finely-divided form (which is the form it usually takes in highly plastic clays). Such a clay gives good vitrification at temperatures ranging between 1250° C. and 1300° C. For large articles, grog (a pre-fired and granulated stoneware) is frequently added to reduce shrinkage and drying cracks. Very often several clays are mixed together for instance, refractory clays and vitrifiable or fusible clays, or clays of different plasticity in the requisite proportions, to give a body of the desired vitrification and plasticity.

Preparation of Stoneware Bodies

If various clays of different compositions are used, and these clays already contain the necessary fluxes, the mixture is made in a plastic state by using mixing machines and pug mills described earlier in this book. If, however, fluxes or grog (pre-fired granulated stoneware or fireclay) have to be added to the clay, it is preferable to use the wet mixing process in order to obtain a very thoroughly mixed body, particularly if an intimate mixture such as is needed for high quality stoneware is required. In this process the raw materials are weighed and charged into ball mills, water is added and the charge is ground for several hours. Grog is usually added to the mill when the grinding of the other materials is almost completed so that the grog particles may have a larger size than the other ingredients. (The grog can also be charged into the mixing arc, the requisite grain size being obtained by preparatory grinding.) The slip is then filter-pressed, passed through pug mills and allowed to age. The manufacturer may, of course, prefer to treat the clay in a de-airing pug mill.

Forming of Stoneware

'Stoneware' covers such a large variety of articles used for

G

widely varying purposes and possessing greatly differing char-cteristics, that practically all ceramic forming processes are used.

Stoneware Floor Tiles

Stoneware tiles can be made in at least two ways:

1. By moulding the body in a plastic state.
2. By pressing the body in the form of a semi-dry powder.

In the first case manufacturing methods as described in the chapter 'Bricks and Tiles' are used. The production of dense and vitrified stoneware floor tiles is, however, more difficult than that of porous or semi-porous roofing tiles, because vitrified tiles are more liable to warp during drying and firing in consequence of their greater shrinkage. Since, however, semi-dry pressed articles have a smaller drying shrinkage, the manufacture of vitrified tiles by pressing semi-dry powder is much easier than the manufacture of tiles by the plastic process.

For 'dry' pressing the body is prepared either by granulation of dried filter cakes or by mixing dry raw materials and afterwards adding the minimum amount of water. The ground body is moulded by hydraulic presses which may be hand, foot, or automatically operated. Single and multiple dies may be used.

British Standards Specification 1286 differentiates between floor quarries and floor tiles. 'Floor tiles have a finer finish and are manufactured to narrower dimensional tolerances than quarries. Floor tiles can be made from ceramic bodies as well as from ordinary clays, whereas quarries are usually made from the latter. Originally, there was a distinction in the method of manufacture, quarries always being made by a plastic process whilst floor tiles were semi-dry dust pressed.' In recent years, however, this hard-and-fast rule has ceased to apply. As a result, it was considered inadvisable to classify quarries and tiles according to their method of manufacture and so in the specification it was decided to classify on the basis of standards of finish and dimensional accuracy. It is laid down that all types shall be reasonably true to shape, flat and free from flaws, whilst in addition floor tiles shall have a fine smooth texture. The standard sizes of quarries are as follows:

9 in. × 9 in. × 1¼ in.   ¹6 in. × 6 in. × ⅝ in.
¹6 in. × 6 in. × ⅞ in.   6 in. × 3 in. × ⅝ in.
6 in. × 3 in. × ⅞ in.   ¹4 in. × 4 in. × ¾ in.

The standard sizes of floor tiles are to be:

²6 in. × 6 in. × ½ in.   6 in. × 3 in. × ½ in.
²4 in. × 4 in. × ½ in.   6 in. × 2 in. × ½ in.
²3 in. × 3 in. × ½ in.   6 in. × 1 in. × ½ in.

Stoneware Pipes

Stoneware pipes are used for carrying away sewage and other corrosive drainage in sanitation schemes, both domestic and industrial. These pipes are highly vitrified and salt glazed. They are usually circular in cross-section and are provided with a socket on one end large enough to take the unsocketed end of another pipe of the same size. Sewer pipes are usually made in sizes from 3 in. to 12 in. inside diameter, and occasionally in sizes up to 36 in. diameter.

RAW MATERIALS AND MANUFACTURE

In the production of stoneware pipes, the clays and shales used must be such that when they are fired and subjected to the salting process, well-glazed surfaces will result. As will be explained later on, the clay must be rich in silica because very aluminous or basic clays do not form a glaze when subjected to the salting process during the fire. The usual practice is to use a clay which will vitrify by itself, but if such clays are not readily available two or more clays are mixed to produce an easily vitrifiable body. Sometimes a fireclay is mixed with a very fusible clay or occasionally fluxes are added in small amounts to bring about the desired degree of vitrification. Stoneware pipes can be made on the potter's wheel, but they

1. Diagonal halves shall also be produced for these sizes.
2. Diagonal halves shall also be produced for these sizes.

are usually extruded, the socket being produced simultaneously in the same process. The clay cylinder which comes out of the die of a hydraulic or steam press strikes against a cup having the shape of the socket. The body, owing to its weight and its plasticity, bends round the cup. The cup is then released and the extrusion goes on until the desired length is reached, when the pipe is cut off to length by a wire.

British Standards Specifications Nos. 68, 539 and 540 provide for salt-glazed-ware pipes and fittings as follows:

Straight pipes, level invert taper pipes, radius bends, taper bends, and junctions.

They specify the thicknesses and lengths of these articles and the dimensions of the sockets and the groovings.

It is further laid down that the glazing shall be obtained by the action of the fumes of volatilized common salt on the material of the pipes and fittings during the process of burning. The interior and exterior surface of the pipes and fittings which will remain exposed after jointing must be glazed. To check that the pipes have the necessary mechanical strength, 5% of each batch may be selected for testing under the hydraulic test. The pipes, when subjected to this test, shall withstand an internal hydraulic pressure of 20 lb. to sq. in. without showing signs of injury or leakage.

Absorption tests may also be made on specimens from every hundred pipes or fittings ordered.

With regard to pipes for use under severe conditions of acidity, British Standards Specification 1143 has been prepared. The hydraulic test is, in this case, carried out at a pressure of 40 lb. to sq. in.

The absorption test is also more stringent than for ordinary salt-glazed pipes.

Chemical Stoneware

Stoneware is extensively used as a containing and structural material in the chemical industry. Its impermeability, resistance to the attacks of acids and other corrosive liquids, and its mechanical strength – particularly in compression – are all of great value. A wide variety of chemical stoneware articles is manufactured, including containers having capacities ranging from a fraction of a pint up to 3,000 gallons of liquid, pumps, valves, condenser retorts, cooling coils, tubes, adaptors, vats, and so on. (See Fig. 13.) The body has to possess very great uniformity since the finished products have to meet very stringent technical requirements. For this reason it is usually prepared by the wet mixing process. The body is compounded of various plastic clays, very often with small amounts of

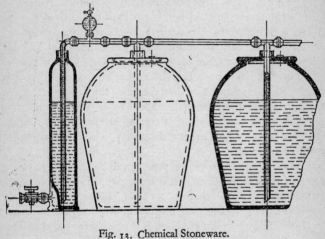

Fig. 13. Chemical Stoneware.
(By courtesy of Royal Doulton Potteries.)

kaolin and feldspar, and for larger articles, fireclay grog, stoneware grog, or porcelain grog is added according to the characteristics required. The forming of chemical stoneware of normal size is usually done by jiggering in plaster moulds. Large articles, however, are very often built up in wooden forms, by hand. Very large shapes, for instance, retorts or tall cylindrically-shaped containers may be jiggered in the following way:

The plaster mould is placed on to a revolving wheel on or just above floor level. A lump of soft plastic body is thrown into the mould and spread by a jiggering tool, to form the bottom of the container. The side walls are then formed by throwing more clay into the mould around the circumference of the bottom of the container being formed, and by jiggering it up to form a circular wall of clay surrounded and supported by the mould. The body must, of course, be of a very plastic consistency to make such operations possible without introducing cracks or fissures. The jigger blade is shaped to suit the inner contour of the container and is provided with grooves when internal shoulders have to be made. For shapes having a neck at the top (like large bottle-shaped containers, retorts and so on) the plaster mould is made in sections provided with tongues and grooves in order to give the sections a good fit. The parts are held together with iron bands. Rectangular shapes, such as vats, are made by first wedging a stiff plastic body in wooden forms. The slabs thus formed are dried to a leather hard condition and then they are joined together under pressure, after moistening the areas to be joined and after applying thereto a body slip of cream-like consistency. Before they are joined together, the slabs may, where necessary, be cut to size.

Complicated shapes such as pumps, valves, connections with many outlets, are made by first shaping parts of the whole piece, providing them with threads, recesses, and so on, as the case may be, and by then joining these prefabricated parts together in the usual way with a clay slip. It is often advantageous first to place the main part on to a horizontal wheel which can then be turned by hand to give easy access to those places on the main part where the other parts have to be stuck on.

Drying

Drying of stoneware is not an easy matter since stoneware clays are very plastic and consequently difficult to dry. Too quick or non-uniform drying of different parts of a large article would inevitably cause drying cracks. The ware is consequently dried very slowly on drying shelves, in stillages or on floors. In order to reduce the rate of drying, large complicated articles are often covered with damp cloth. Humidity dryers which make possible close control of humidity and temperature speed up the drying and reduce the danger of drying cracks and have found increasing use in recent years.

Firing and Salt Glazing of Stoneware

Stoneware is fired and glazed in a very interesting way which is peculiar to stoneware manufacture and which is not used in the other branches of the ceramic industry. Glazing of stoneware is usually achieved by throwing common salt (sodium chloride) or borax (sodium borate) into the kiln when the firing is approaching its final stage. Sodium chloride volatilizes at temperatures above 800° C. and forms a glaze when it comes into contact with clay at temperatures of about 1150° C. and higher. Sodium chloride dissociates; the chlorine, which combines with the water vapour escapes through the chimney in the form of fumes of hydrochloric acid, and the sodium combines with the silica (and also to a lesser extent with the alumina), of the clay substance of the stoneware articles and forms a sodium aluminium silicate which causes a thin glaze on the surface of the article. If borax is used instead of or in addition to salt, a sodium-silica-borate glaze is formed. The glaze formation is better and thicker if the clay is rich in silica. Highly aluminous clays or basic clay mixtures do not combine readily with sodium and do not form a suitable salt glaze in this way. The firing of salt-glazed stoneware is usually carried out in down-draught intermittent ovens. The salt is thrown through fire holes on to the glowing fuel at the back of each fire-box. The cold salt and the heat required for its volatilization lower the kiln temperature by about 250° C. The first charge of salt is introduced when the oven temperature is about 100° C. below finishing temperature. (The finishing temperature is between 1200° C. and 1300° C. according to the type and composition of the ware.) The salting is done in several operations at approximately half-hourly intervals and the temperature is raised between the salting operations by re-firing the kiln. During the salting operations the draught

of the kiln is reduced in order to give the salt vapours sufficient time to react with the clay and to prevent their being
carried away too quickly through the chimney. Two pounds
of salt are, as an average, required to cover one ton of salt-
glazed stoneware.

The firing cycle (i.e. firing and cooling) for chemical stoneware is about three weeks, and the firing time about one week.

Another method which takes less salt consists in introducing it through openings arranged at the top of the kiln. Particular care has then to be taken that the salt does not fall directly on to the ware, as this would cause uneven glaze thickness.
However, the evaporation of the salt is better and its distribution in the flames more uniform, when it is dropped into the
fire-boxes. For this reason this method is more widely used.

Firing and salt-glazing of stoneware up to 3 feet in height
are also successfully carried out in tunnel kilns. Basic refractory fire-bricks have to be used in the firing zone of the tunnel oven, otherwise salt glaze would form on their surfaces.
Salt is introduced from special outside furnaces.

The ware has to be placed in the ovens, or on to the kiln cars,
in open setting in order to give the salt vapour easy access to
all the surfaces which have to be glazed. Stoneware pipes are
placed upright, one above the other, up to a height of 8 ft. in
the case of intermittent ovens. Small pipes may be put inside
the larger pipes. In down-draught kilns the circulation of the
kiln gases is in the right direction to reach both the inside and
the outside of the pipes and to facilitate the glazing both on
the inside and outside surfaces.

In certain cases, surfaces which are inaccessible to the circulation of the kiln gases have to be slip glazed. In this case
they have to be treated with a suitable glaze (maturing at
1300° C.) by dipping into or brushing on a glaze slip, or by
applying the glaze by spraying with a gun.

Special Stoneware Bodies

In recent years the requirements of the chemical industry have
been, in special cases, of such a stringent nature that the

technical characteristics of conventional stoneware were no longer adequate and had therefore to be improved in various directions. In order to be able to withstand the sudden changes of temperature to which they may be subjected, the thermal shock resistance of stoneware bodies had to be improved. Theoretically there are two alternative ways of achieving this aim. One is to increase the thermal conductivity by adding to the stoneware body a material known to possess good heat conductivity. This is likely to improve the heat conductivity of the body. Silicon carbide is such a material. It has been found that a stoneware body in which silicon carbide is admixed has greatly improved resistance to temperature changes. Moreover, the addition of silicon carbide allows the manufacture of bodies which not only withstand sudden temperature changes but also have very good resistance to alkaline and acid solutions.

The second method of producing stoneware bodies possessing good resistance to sudden temperature changes is by decreasing their thermal expansion. This can be done in the following way:

The addition of magnesia or talc to clay facilitates the formation of cordierite crystals which impart to the body a very low thermal expansion. The thermal shock resistance of cordierite stoneware bodies is very good. It is, however, difficult to find suitable glazes which have a thermal expansion low enough to fit the low expansion body. Ingredients have to be added to the 'cordierite' bodies, in order to increase their thermal expansion and to find glazes which would not 'craze'.

To increase the resistance of stoneware to the attacks of basic chemicals, barium oxide is a useful ingredient.

Electrical Stoneware

For high-voltage insulators stoneware has to be made nonporous, by the addition of suitable fluxing materials, whereas for low voltage (indoor use) a very slight porosity of a ceramic insulating material has no detrimental effect. For high voltage 'Zero' porosity is, however, most vital. This does not mean that stoneware, generally speaking, is not suitable for the manufacture of high voltage insulators. The preparation of the body has, however, to be carried out in the same way as the preparation of porcelain insulator bodies and the shaping methods must also be the same. Stoneware insulators made in this way would, however, not be cheaper than porcelain insulators and are for this reason only occasionally manufactured for high voltage outdoor work. There are, however, numerous applications in the electrical industry for stoneware where the material is not under electric stress. For instance, electrical accumulator containers are often made of stoneware and give entirely satisfactory results.

Considering the foregoing, it is very difficult to draw a line of demarcation between stoneware and insulator porcelain. Paradoxically enough, one could even go so far as to include in the stoneware group, such bodies as are used in porcelain insulator manufacture, since they are non-translucent and often contain more plastic clays than kaolins. Considering, however, that insulator bodies are: (1) absolutely non-porous, (2) white, and (3) covered with a porcelain glaze, the common practice of calling them porcelain insulator bodies is justified.

Stoneware Vases and Statues

In very ancient times the Chinese used stoneware in the manufacture of vases and other ornamental objects. The reader may remember from Chapter I, 'History', that they made stoneware long before they developed the art of making porcelain. Some Egyptian pottery can also be included in the stoneware category. The same is true also for occasional specimens of glazed pottery manufactured in various parts of Europe in the Middle Ages. Stoneware was first made on a larger scale for household purposes in Germany (in the Rhineland) and in the Duchy of Limburg in the fifteenth century. Since that time it has flourished and faded out and flourished again, following the fickle fluctuations of prosperity and fashion.

As already mentioned, the brothers Ehlers brought the art of stoneware manufacture to England at the end of the seventeenth century, and the manufacture of white and red stoneware flourished here for a time in the eighteenth century.

The first ware – which he termed 'red porcelain' – made by Böttcher in Meissen, also belongs to the category of 'glazed stoneware'.

One advantage of stoneware, as compared with porcelain, is the much greater plasticity of the body, which allows it to be modelled by hand. It lends itself to the same processes as clay modelling and makes possible the creation of *objets d'art*, which, after being fired, possess the strength of stone. Porcelain bodies, on the other hand, are not sufficiently plastic to be modelled in this way. The modern studio potteries favour the use of stoneware bodies for the manufacture of vases and statues. In most cases they cover their stoneware products either with a soft earthenware glaze or a hard porcelain glaze. Salt glaze is nowadays, however, only very rarely used for covering art ware.[1]

A VISIT TO MESSRS DOULTON'S WORKS AT ERITH

Pottery and clay-working firms all over the world carry on business, as a rule, only in one branch of the ceramic industry. Brick-making firms may manufacture all types of bricks, but, generally speaking, they manufacture nothing but bricks.

Some large stoneware firms in various countries manufacture chemical stoneware, stoneware pipes and other stoneware products for industrial purposes, but they seldom manufacture anything other than stoneware. In a similar way, practically all earthenware firms manufacture earthenware only and porcelain firms porcelain only.

On the Continent there is one porcelain group which make all types of porcelain such as table ware, art ware and electrical porcelain (Rosenthal Porzellan). In this country two or three pottery firms manufacture both earthenware and bone china table ware, but there is only one firm in the world which

1. Full information of the characteristics of stoneware bodies can be found in Searle A.B. *An Encyclopaedia of the Ceramic Industries*. Ernest Benn Ltd, London, 1930.

manufactures stoneware, earthenware, vitreous china, fireclay, bone china, porcelain, laboratory ware, porous ceramic filters, porcelain insulators and art ware, namely, Messrs. Doulton & Co, Ltd.

The manufacture of stoneware was begun at Lambeth in 1815. With the development of the chemical industry and the ever-increasing demand for stoneware drain pipes, the Lambeth works were no longer able to meet the increasing requirements of industry and a new works was built at Erith to supplement the output. An additional works was also acquired in Tamworth for the same purpose.

The manufacture of earthenware and bone china table ware, figures and art ware is carried out in their works at Burslem which were acquired in 1877. In these works one of the first tunnel ovens in this country was built for earthenware and bone china glost firing. This is still in operation and is giving most satisfactory results. During the last few years new types of tunnel kilns, fired by gas and electricity have been introduced.

Sanitary fireclay, vitreous china, and earthenware are made in the Doulton works at Dudley and Hanley, Stoke-on-Trent, and stoneware drain pipes at Dudley, Erith, and Tamworth. Porcelain insulators are made at the Lambeth and Tamworth works.

It would be most interesting to give a short description of Messrs Doulton's various works, which cover practically the whole range of the ceramic industry, but the limited space available obliges the author to confine himself to a description of only one of Messrs Doulton's works, namely, that at Erith.

The first impression of a visitor to these works (which, except for the clay-preparation plant, are of single-story construction) is of their rational layout to ensure a through-flow of production from the clay plant to the kilns and adjoining railway sidings. The processing rooms are unusually spacious, well-lit and ventilated.

The production of chemical stoneware in England, while by no means a new industry, has very greatly expanded during the last twenty-five years, and this has brought about the introduction of various mechanized processes which, in many cases, have taken the place of the traditional potter's wheel.

Chemical stoneware is a specialized material for a definite job. This means that several different 'bodies' have to be produced to make various types of apparatus which may vary from a simple open vessel for storing acid or some other corrosive substance, to complicated plant working under pressure or vacuum at high, low or variable temperatures for the production of one of the modern synthetic drugs.

Obviously, different materials are required for such widely diverse duties, and one of the most important aspects of the manufacture of modern chemical stoneware is the constant laboratory investigation and control needed to evolve suitable bodies for specific duties. These include heat-resisting, acid and alkali-resisting, abrasion-resisting, low-porosity and other types of stoneware.

A visit to the Erith works reveals the almost unlimited variations of shape, size, colour and physical chemical and thermal properties of chemical stoneware plant; also the varied methods of manufacture and firing. Specially selected ball clays from the Company's own clay pits in Dorsetshire, together with other essential ingredients, are delivered into the works by railway trucks. The coal is unloaded from ships and barges at a special jetty whence it is moved by conveyor belt to storage bins. All freights of raw materials are tested before being accepted for use, and as blended clays are always used, each batch is 'balanced' to ensure uniformity of product.

For chemical stoneware manufacture, clay preparation is usually done by the " dry " process, that is to say the clays and other ingredients are ground through an edge-runner mill, the grog is added and the whole well mixed with the necessary quantity of water on a 'wet pan' edge-runner mill. The prepared clay is then passed through one or more pug mills and, after maturing for a period, is re-pugged and sent to the processing rooms.

As the size of chemical stoneware articles may vary from jars of a few ounces' capacity to large tanks and vessels of several hundred gallons, and as shapes also vary considerably, many methods of shaping are employed. The most usual are hand moulding or pressing, throwing, jollying, extruding and slip casting. In making certain complicated pieces of ware, two or three of these methods may have to be employed for different parts.

Hand moulding, or pressing, is the method usually adopted for the manufacture of such articles as rectangular tanks or other vessels which are not circular in section. This method is also used to produce particularly large pieces of ware of whatever shape.

Throwing is used for circular vessels when only small quantities are required, or the shape does not lend itself readily to jollying which is usually adopted for standard shapes or circular articles.

All pipes and similar articles are manufactured by means of an extrusion press, usually of the vertical type and similar to the machines used for production of ordinary sanitary drainpipes. For pipe lines in chemical works, paper and textile mills, especially where high pressures are involved, pipes are usually made with conical flanges which can be connected together by means of special couplings, thus facilitating replacement and inspection.

Slip casting is usually employed for the manufacture of small parts, the shapes of which lend themselves to this form of production. The clay in this instance is reduced to a liquid mass or 'slip' which is poured into plaster of Paris moulds as explained previously in this book.

It is an impressive sight to see the large drying-rooms at the Erith works, containing all manner of shapes in chemical stoneware, some of the pieces being up to 7 ft. or 8 ft. in height and of a somewhat similar diameter with perhaps a thickness of about 2 in.

It has been pointed out previously that the drying stage is one which must be most carefully controlled, otherwise strains resulting from unequal contraction would be set up and these would develop into cracks at a later stage.

When the articles are thoroughly dried they are either treated with an applied glaze, which is sprayed or painted on the surface of the dry clay, or they are placed in the kiln in an unglazed condition and salt-glazed during the burning operation.

If the articles have been finished with an applied glaze, which is usually brown, white or cream in colour, they must be protected during the firing process from the products of combustion of the coal which is still the normal fuel used for firing chemical stoneware kilns. It is only where large quantities of comparatively small standard shapes are being produced that gas and electric tunnel kilns are used by the stoneware industry.

After firing, all chemical stoneware is subjected to a rigorous inspection and frequently special tests are necessary to ensure that the article is suitable for the purpose for which it is intended. These may include pressure, vacuum, temperature, mechanical strain and other tests. When all the tests have been satisfactorily passed, many pieces have still to receive a final grinding operation to ensure first-class finish, or, in the case of moving parts, such as impellers for centrifugal pumps, perfect balance. An up-to-date engineering shop is therefore an essential feature of the works. After further testing and inspection the goods are passed as ready for shipment.

Perhaps the most lasting impression left on the visitor to Messrs Doulton's Erith Works is the fact that although many modern mechanical devices have been introduced to perform the more arduous and repetitive tasks, the complexity of shapes and the diversity of sizes means that there is still an astonishing element of hand workmanship and craftsmanship involved.

CHAPTER XV

Earthenware and Faience

THE reader may remember (Chapter I) that the French word
'faience' is taken from the name of an Italian town, Faenza. In France the description 'Faience' is applied to all porous
ware covered with a glaze. There is no such all-embracing
comparable word in English or German. The words 'earthenware' and 'Steingut' denote fine white faience, and the other
types of faience have their own more or less distinctive names
both in German and English. Examples in this country are
'glazed terra-cotta', 'majolica', 'delft' ware, flintware, and
so on. We in England understand by 'faience' ware having a
porous body, greyish brown or brown in colour, covered by
a white opaque glaze, and by 'earthenware' ware having a
porous body, white or cream in colour, covered with a translucent glaze.[1]

Faience, in the narrower sense of the word, is nowadays not
manufactured on such a large scale as earthenware. For this
reason we will deal first with earthenware, which is mainly
used for the manufacture of (1) Table ware and art ware; (2)
Wall tiles, and (3) Sanitary ware.

FINE EARTHENWARE

Fine earthenware is made from white burning clays, flint and
feldspar (or stone or pegmatite). The ware has to be fired
twice. First – before the glaze is applied – the body is 'bisque'
fired to a high temperature, sufficiently long to give it the
necessary mechanical strength. After this, a soft glaze – which
matures at a lower temperature – is applied, and the ware is

1. In Italy the ware made in Faenza – and indeed all ware which we call
faience – is called Majolica. We also understand under the term Majolica
a porous, greyish or brownish body covered with an opaque white glaze
– preferably, but not necessarily, Italian made.

subjected to a second firing, known as 'glost firing'. Without the glaze, bisque fired earthenware has a water absorption of 10 to 15%, and for this reason earthenware is always glazed. The glaze covers the article with a glassy impervious layer.

Earthenware Bodies. – These are made by mixing plastic clays (for instance ball clays), china clays, flint and feldspar. The latter material is very often introduced in the form of Cornish stone or pegmatite. The materials are mixed in proportions which will give a strong and hard but porous body when fired at temperatures ranging between 1150° C. and 1250° C.

Ball clay gives both plasticity for shaping and strength after drying (dry strength). China clay gives whiteness and helps to make the body workable. Flint opens the body and prevents deformation during drying and firing. Feldspar or stone acts as a fluxing agent and imparts to the body vitrification, strength and hardness after firing. The same raw materials are used for earthenware bodies as for other ceramic table ware. It is, however, not necessary to grind them as finely as for vitreous bodies, or porcelain bodies, because with earthenware the body is not fired to such temperatures where extensive solution of the particles takes place.

In the case of fine earthenware, an ivory colour is very popular. The clays used for ivory earthenware need not be as free from iron admixtures as the clays used for vitreous ware or porcelain or china. In these latter cases, the ball clay content is lower because a high ball clay content would give the ware a muddy colour, since the large amount of finely divided impurities present in all ball clays would be dissolved by the fluxes, and thus act as colouring agents.

The high ball clay content of earthenware makes the body very 'workable' and enables the shaping of the ware to be speeded up. Earthenware bodies lend themselves to mass production and automatic shaping processes. The feldspar or 'stone' content is lower than in vitreous bodies and in porcelain, since the degree of vitrification desired is much less. The proportions in which these materials are mixed depend, of course, on their composition, and on the temperature at which the ware is fired. Nevertheless, a few examples may be quoted since they give a general idea of the composition of earthenware bodies. The compositions of six typical English earthenware bodies are given in Bourry's *A Treatise on Ceramic Industries*, page 390, as follows:

Body Composition	A	B	C	D	E	F
% Blue ball clay	47	43	31	24	21	18
% China clay .	24	24	36	27	28	43
% Flint . .	22	23	21	36	38	24
% Pegmatite .	7	10	12	13	13	15

No indication is given as to the firing temperature but it is assumed to be between 1150° C. and 1200° C. (Seger Cone 3 to Seger Cone 7).

Three American examples published in the American paper *Ceramic Industry* (Raw Material Issue) may be of interest.

The temperatures are indicated by American (Orton) cones.

Orton Cone

7	corresponds to S.C. 6 (1200° C)
8	corresponds to S.C. 7 (1230° C)
9	corresponds to S.C. 8 (1250° C)

	Cone 7/7	Cone 8/8	Cone 9
American kaolins . .	19%	24%	40%
American ball clays .	25%	28%	14%
Feldspar . . .	21%	16%	11%
Flint	35%	32%	35%

German earthenware manufacturers use bodies of similar composition to the American above, but, as a rule, introduce 2/4% lime, and employ somewhat less feldspar. In this connexion, however, it must not be forgotten that, in this country also, lime is introduced into the earthenware body (perhaps unintentionally) owing to the fact that the flint is calcined by placing flint layers between slack layers, the slack always containing lime.

In Italy 'hard' earthenware and 'soft' earthenware are being manufactured. 'Soft' earthenware contains up to 15% lime and is bisque fired at 1000° C. and glost fired at 950° C.

The china clays or kaolins used for the manufacture of earthenware are, as a rule, brought washed and purified ready for use, as described earlier in the book.

Ball clay is not washed since it is found sufficiently pure in its natural state. The flint used in earthenware manufacture in this country is prepared by calcining flint pebbles to redness and by subsequently quenching and grinding. This preparation is usually carried out in special establishments by 'potters' millers' who supply the flint to the pottery works, in slip form (liquid state) in large containers. In the U.S.A. it is general practice to supply the quartz or sand to the potteries uncalcined and in powder form, ground to the specified fineness. On the Continent, quartz or, more often, sand, not calcined, is ground by the earthenware manufacturers themselves in Alsing cylinders which discharge directly into the mixers.

Tradition is the main explanation of why these various methods are used. The potters are conservative people and are disinclined to change traditional methods except when really necessary.

As in the case of the flint, the feldspar or stone is, in this country, also ground by millers and supplied in slip form to the potter. In the U.S.A. it is supplied ground to specified mesh size in powder form. On the Continent it is, together with the flint, ground and mixed in Alsing cylinders which discharge into the mixing arc where they are mixed with the blunged kaolin and clay.

The grain size of the ground materials is of great importance. In particular the degree of fineness to which feldspar (or stone) and flint are ground is decisive. If, for instance, the stone is overground, its fluxing power is increased. If fired at the usual temperature, the ware would then become too dense, would shrink too much, and would become soft and deformed during the bisque fire. If, on the other hand, the stone is underground, the ware would be too porous after firing and would have the appearance of being under-fired. In the case of flint, over-grinding would result in distorted ware and insufficient grinding would make the ware liable to cause glaze crazing. For this reason the grain size is regularly controlled, preferably by sieve analysis. For instance, a certain maximum residue is allowed when the slip is passed through the 200-mesh sieve (having 200 meshes per lineal inch) and which retains grains larger than 0.0029 in. and a certain amount is allowed to be retained by the 325-mesh sieve having 325 meshes per lineal inch and which retains all particles larger than 0.0017 in. Other controls such as elutriation and/or hydrometer analyses are also used.

The proportioning of the body can be done either by weighing the raw materials (with due consideration of their moisture content) or by measuring the volume of the slip in which the materials are suspended. In this country the latter method is in general use in earthenware manufacture. Each pint or gallon of slip must always contain the same amount of dry material. To make sure that this aim is achieved, a specified volume, for instance a pint or a gallon of each slip, is weighed. In the course of time it has been found by experience that the following weights per pint are particularly convenient for proportioning and subsequent mixing of the four slips used in earthenware manufacture.

> Ball clay slip weighs 24 oz. per pint (containing 6.6 oz. dry substance).
>
> China clay slip weighs 26 oz. per pint (containing 10 oz. dry substance).
>
> Flint slip weighs 32 oz. per pint (containing 18.33 oz. dry substance).
>
> Stone slip weighs 32 oz. per pint (containing 20 oz. dry substance).

After the four materials have been made into four separate slips of the density given above, definite volumes are measured out. This is done in the following way.

The clays are blunged in blungers. Slip house conditions permitting, a separate blunger is used for each clay. Water is then added to the blunger to give the required density. The supply of a measured amount of water can be controlled automatically. Flints or stones are either ground in cylinders and discharged into storage tanks, or as is usual in this country, they are supplied ready ground in slip form by the miller and are then discharged into storage tanks suitably located in the slip house. The correction of slip density can be carried out either in these storage tanks or better still in separate measuring tanks, by the addition of the necessary amount of water. For checking the density, a pint of each slip is weighed, but the weighing of much larger volumes of slip naturally gives more accurate results for subsequent adjusting of the density. The various slips, all of them corrected to the right density, are then discharged and mixed in a large tank – the mixing arc. The contents of the mixing arc are thoroughly mixed, sifted through fine sieves and passed through or over magnetos in order to remove particles of iron. The mixed slip is then pumped into a stock arc and from there pressed through filter presses (which were described previously). The plastic cakes are removed from the filter press and thrown into a pug mill where they are given the required homogeneity for subsequent moulding. In modern earthenware works de-airing pug mills, which increase the workability, plasticity and dry strength of the body, are used.

Shaping of Earthenware, Flat and Hollow-ware. – Earthenware body is very plastic and can be shaped by all the methods previously described.

Flat Ware and Hollow-ware of circular cross-section is generally made by jollying. The term 'flat ware' includes plates, saucers and dishes. Hollow-ware suitable for shaping by jollying includes cups, bowls, cylindrical vases, jugs, mugs, and so on. Articles which are usually made by the casting process include tea and coffee pots and all such hollow articles which are not round, or whose diameter is reduced towards the top, such as certain shapes of sugar bowls, creamers, vases and so on.

Oval dishes can either be jollied on special dish-making machines or they can be cast.

Flat ware is made in two stages. The first stage is the making of a 'bat' (a thin clay disc) and the second one is the jiggering of the bat on a plaster mould. For making the bat, a lump or ball of the body is placed on the wheel head and the machine started. A flat spreader descends, makes the bat, and then rises. The bat is removed from the wheel head by hand and is then thrown on a plaster mould (which has a shape corresponding to the interior of the plate) the mould being located on the

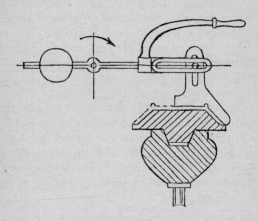

Fig. 14. *Jiggering* a plate.

jigger head. This plaster mould shapes the concave side of the plate (Fig. 14). The food side of the plate is shaped by a profile made of steel which is either lowered by hand or, in the case of certain modern jiggers, semi-automatically. Most semi-automatic plate-making machines are combined bat and jigger machines, both the bat spreader and the jigger profile being worked mechanically (pneumatically). In the case of hollow-ware, both machines are fitted with jolly heads for taking the plaster mould and this doubles the capacity. In semi-automatic plate-making, one man working without an assistant places and throws a bat of clay – which is automatically made by the pneumatic bat-making machine – on to the mould. After the plate has been jiggered by the automatic jigger, he removes the mould, with the plate on top of it, from the jigger-head and places it on a conveyor or on a shelf in a mangle dryer. One man without an assistant makes about 300 plates per hour, which is the capacity of a crew of two working on a hand jigger. Fully automatic plate-making machines make up to 1,200 plates per hour in a single line. Semi-automatic plate- and cup-making machines are now manufactured by quite a number of firms, both in this country and in U.S.A. The first experiments with fully-automatic and semi-automatic jiggers were made in Germany (Dorst) and France (Limoges).

The American Miller automatic jigger works on the following principles.

A clay cylinder is supplied by a de-airing pug mill which has a mouthpiece corresponding to the diameter of the plate or saucer to be made. The mouthpiece which is fitted with an elbow delivers the clay to the machine. A pneumatically-controlled cutter fitted with piano wires closes and cuts through the clay cylinder forming slices. Each of these slices falls on to the top of a plate mould located directly below, which is accommodated on an intermittently-moving belt. The mould is then moved to a plunger-head which raises and presses the clay slice against a heated metal die which roughly gives the shape of the plate. The mould is then transported by a belt and located beneath a spray of water and a rotating profile. It is raised against this profile and automatically jiggered and trimmed. One man supervises this automatic jigger machine. Recently Sulzer Brothers, Ltd., of Leeds, have developed fully automatic Plate and Cup-making machines working on a similar principle. The moving belt of the Miller machine is replaced by a chain, provided with rings, which carry the plaster moulds through the various shaping stages and through the dryers, on the exit end of which the dry plate is removed for subsequent mechanical trimming. In this machine neither the clay nor the plate is touched by the hand of an operator, until it leaves the dryer ready for trimming. The first Sulzer machine for earthenware is in operation at Wedgwood's in Barlaston, the first machine for Bone China at Booth and Colclough's China Works in Longton.

For jollying hollow-ware, for instance cups, a ball of clay is thrown into a plaster-mould placed on a jolly-head of a semi-automatic cupmaking machine, and the machine is then started. A suitably-shaped profile descends into the mould and spreads and presses the clay on to the inner surface of the mould. The tool shapes the inside of the cup and the mould shapes the outside of the article. The mould is then taken from the jolly-head and the clay article is removed, as soon as it has shrunk away sufficiently from the mould surface.

China and earthenware manufacturers are entirely satisfied with the quality of plates and cups made by automatic machinery. We in this country insist on a particularly high standard. It is now certain that automatic plate-making machinery will make the production of plates possible which meet the most stringent requirements. The teething troubles have been successfully overcome and both faultless cups and plates can be made by fully automatic methods. (See also 'American household china', p. 260.)

Handles are shaped separately either by casting or by pressing and are then stuck on to the cup, after a slip (made of the same body, and to which an adhesive may be admixed) is applied to that part of the handle which has to form the joint. Both cup and handle are at this stage in a leather-hard state. Automatic cup handling machines are now in successful operation both in earthenware and china factories.

Teapot spouts are all stuck on except when the whole teapot is cast in one piece.

Casting. – Casting slip is in most cases prepared from press cake or from 'scraps' (clay removed from bats or other plastic clay during jollying and jiggering). A fraction of 1% of sodium ash or sodium silicate is used as a 'deflocculent' in order to convert the plastic body into a liquid slip. Sometimes, however, the casting slip is made (in a blunger) direct from the raw materials by merely adding the deflocculent and the necessary small amount of water. The casting slip is either brought to the casters in tubs or buckets, the plaster moulds being filled with slip by jugs, or it is conveyed direct to the moulds in pipe-lines using gravity feed, if possible. (The principle of casting has been described earlier.) The casting of earthenware, gener-ally speaking, offers no particular difficulties. The casting time is, however, longer than in many other ceramic branches, for example in porcelain manufacture, owing to the large amount of plastic clays present in the body. The amount of moulds necessary for producing a given number of articles is conse-quently considerable. The gravity of the slip has to be checked regularly by weighing the weight per pint of slip, which in the case of earthenware is between 33 and 35 oz. per pint. Vacuum treatment improves the homogeneity of the slip and removes air bubbles. When the article in the mould has ac-quired the necessary thickness, the surplus slip is poured back into the jug, or into drains which collect all excess slip.

Sponging, Fettling, Towing. – All surfaces which have come into contact with the plaster mould are slightly rough and are smoothed by sponging, in the production of high quality ware. The edges of the plates show marks and are either sponged in the leather-hard state, or they are cleaned after drying by means of a sharp tool and by coarse flax or hemp (towing). Towing is a quicker process than sponging, since the strength of the white-hard article allows the application of greater pressure.

Drying. – Before the articles are placed in saggers for bisque firing they have to be dried very thoroughly. Drying increases the strength of the clay ware, and the articles can be handled with less danger of breakage, if they are absolutely dry. Plates are piled into the sagger in bungs up to ten plates high. The load which the lower plates have to support is therefore con-siderable. If they are not absolutely dry they will break.

Various types of dryers are used. The more modern dryers are often at the same time conveyors which convey the ware from the jollyer, through the drying stoves, to the fettlers. For providing the required drying temperature of about 140° F. (60° C.), steam raised in boilers is often employed, but the most economical heat source is waste heat drawn out of the kilns, particularly if tunnel ovens are used. Since drying has to be done the whole year round, it is logical to use the oven waste heat which is also available the whole year round for this purpose. Dobbins (such as are made by Boultons of Burslem) are very popular because of their low heat consumption.

Another form of heating – infra-red heating – is also employed for drying earthenware, particularly in the United States, in cases where drying has to be speeded up. With rapidly working plate-making machines, it is necessary, in order to reduce the number of moulds required for a given article, to return them as quickly as possible to the machine.

Sagger Placing. – For all bisque firing in intermittent ovens, and very often in the case of tunnel ovens, earthenware is placed in saggers. They are piled one on top of the other. In the case of round, intermittent ovens, the piles of saggers are arranged concentrically and in such a way as to provide a flue for the flames towards the dome. In up-draught kilns it is usual to separate the piles at the required distance by pieces of fireclay. No matter which type of kiln is used it is essential to place as many articles as possible in one sagger so that the best possible use is made of the available space. The heat near the walls is greater than in the middle of the oven. For this reason articles which are less liable to be deformed by high temperatures, cups for example, are placed in the outer rings. Articles, however, which are most liable to become deformed, such as large dishes and large plates, are placed in the middle of the oven. In the case of tunnel ovens the hottest parts are the top saggers and the saggers near the outer wall. The lowest temperature prevails in the middle bottom saggers. However, the temperature variation in tunnel ovens is, as described previously, only between one and two cones, as compared with five cones in the case of up-draught intermittent kilns.

Bisque Firing. – Bisque firing of earthenware is carried out at temperatures between 1150 and 1250° C., in either intermittent ovens or in tunnel ovens. The most common type of intermittent oven in this country is the up-draught oven (Fig. 15). The design of this oven has not changed very much dur-

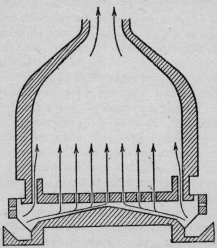

Fig. 15. Updraught kiln.

ing the last century and the firing methods also have, generally speaking, not changed. Great attention is being paid to this fact, and the Pottery Research Association has carried out much work in this respect. The results of this have been published in an article by A. Dinsdale and Marcus Francis in the *Transactions of the British Ceramic Society*, January, 1945. The firing of an intermittent up-draught oven burned in the conventional way was investigated and described. The article describes how in normal firing practice for intermittent ovens a heavy baiting is put on every three or four hours, and how

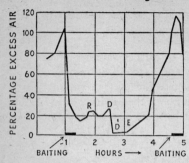

Fig. 16. Variation in excess air between baitings for intermittent oven.

the air supply is adjusted in stages to suit the condition of the fire-bed. The nature of the controls is so crude that it is impossible to maintain constant conditions with any degree of accuracy. The changing conditions of combustion during a complete cycle from baiting to baiting are well illustrated in Fig. 16, which shows the percentage of excess air in the flue gases at different times between the baitings when the firing was already well advanced. On baiting, the excess air drops rapidly from over 100 to below 20%. As some of the volatiles are burned off, the excess air rises steadily to 25%, and at this point (Point R) the quarter dampers are dropped. This reduces the excess air temporarily to 20%, but after ten minutes it again begins to rise, at which stage the firedoors and regulator holes are closed (Point D). This reduces the excess air to below 10% so that the amount of air supplied is barely sufficient to ensure complete combustion. In point of fact about 0.5% of carbon monoxide is detected in the flue gases at this stage (D to E) and the oxygen content is only 0.6%, indicating that the air supply is inadequate. In parts of the oven the atmosphere may have been actively reducing. From this point onwards, as the fires burn down, the excess air increases slowly at first and then more rapidly, until it reaches nearly 120% immediately prior to the next baiting (Point F).

This example serves to illustrate the point that with heavy intermittent baiting the controls are completely inadequate for maintaining the necessary supply of excess air. From the thermal standpoint too much excess air involves loss of heat carried away (as sensible heat) in the flue gases; too little air involves loss of heat due to failure to utilize the full calorific value of the fuel; and heavy baiting also results in the loss of heat in the form of smoke and unburnt volatiles. A further important factor is the lowering of the theoretical flame temperature when large quantities of excess air are present. It is clear that if the combustion temperature is reduced to that of the setting, no useful heat work can be done by the gases passing through the oven. Indeed, if the temperature is reduced below that of the setting, not only will some of the fuel burnt be wasted, but the temperature of the ware will temporarily fall. It is a common thing to find this happening in intermittent oven practice using the normal method of baiting. Fig. 16a shows this for a position in the first ring of a biscuit oven during the later stages of the firing. The curve clearly illustrates the rapid rise of temperature which follows a baiting and the fall in temperature as the fires burn down.

Investigations have proved that smaller and quicker baiting, or continuous feeding by mechanical feeders, improve the conditions and decrease the fuel consumption. The introduction of mechanical feeders and automatic stokers in existing factories is, however, difficult, since the necessary space is not available in most cases.

Moreover, although the fire mouths of the ovens are at the right height for manual baiting, they are too high to allow the best arrangement of hoppers, for feeding the mechanical stokers. Nevertheless, considerable improvement can be made in the design of the fire mouth and of the grates, and it is proved that it is possible, without much capital investment, to modify ovens and fire mouths to facilitate the staggering of the heavy baiting and the maintenance of steady

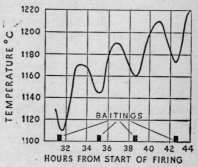

Fig. 16a. Temperature schedule in intermittent china biscuit ovens.

conditions and controlled air supply. Savings up to 30%
compared with the traditional methods have been observed
by improving the design of the firemouth, grates and baiting
methods. A very thorough study of these investigations is
strongly recommended to everybody in the pottery industry
interested in the question of fuel saving.

Oil is also used as fuel for firing intermittent pottery ovens
in places where coal is expensive or scarce. In Denmark, for
instance, oil fuel is used for firing earthenware and porcelain in intermittent ovens. Although the cost per thermal unit
is, generally speaking, greater for oil than for coal, the continuous supply of oil fuel by gravity or pressure feeding
saves much manual work and gives desirable firing conditions. The net result is that, on the whole, the use of fuel
oil is only slightly more expensive than that of coal. The
coal position may make this method of firing intermittent
ovens more generally acceptable.

Tunnel Ovens. – For the firing of earthenware bisque, several
types of tunnel ovens are in operation and/or under construction at the time of writing. The most common type in this
country is the gas-fired, open-flame, multi-burner type. The
construction of oil-fired tunnel ovens and oil-firing installations as a standby to other fuels is also provided in several
cases. Electric tunnel ovens and producer gas ovens for earthenware bisque firing are also used in this country. In the U.S.A.
a great number of gas-fired and oil-fired tunnel ovens are employed for firing earthenware bisque, whereas in Germany
producer-gas-fired and electric tunnel ovens, and in Sweden
and Switzerland electric tunnel ovens, are preponderant.

The up-draught intermittent oven and its method of firing
have been developed during the last century by trial and error.
Both the design of the oven and the method of its firing are
peculiar to, and almost exclusively used in, earthenware manufacture, and to some extent in bone china manufacture. The
tunnel oven, however, has been designed and perfected on
more scientific lines and no special type has been developed

for earthenware manufacture only. For this reason the reader can be referred to the general description of tunnel ovens earlier in this book. Placing of the ware in tunnel ovens is done either in saggers or in open setting. In the case of electric tunnel ovens open setting is the rule because electric energy is too expensive to allow the employment of heat-wasting saggers, and the atmosphere is so clean that protecting the ware by placing it in saggers is superfluous. The conditions in tunnel ovens fired by town gas are also favourable for open setting of earthenware bisque. Approximately double or three times the amount of fuel is needed for firing ware when it is placed in saggers, compared with open spacing.

Glost Firing of Earthenware. – The ware from the bisque oven is first thoroughly cleaned. This can be done by means of a brushing machine consisting of two circular brushes, placed face to face, and driven in opposite directions, or by air blast, or by a combination of brushing and air blasting. After cleaning, the ware is glazed. Two methods of applying the glaze on earthenware biscuit are in general use, (1) Dipping, and (2) Spraying.

1. The article is dipped in a trough containing the glaze slip. It is porous and so absorbs some of the water from the slip. A thin layer of the solid glaze materials is therefore deposited on the surface of the ware. The thickness of this coating will depend on the porosity of the ware, the time of immersion and the density of the slip. The porosity of all types of ware not being uniform, the density of the glaze has to be adjusted by the dippers according to the porosity of the ware. Very porous ware must be moved in and out of the glaze slip more quickly than less porous ware. Mechanization of the dipping process is therefore for this reason almost impossible, as far as earthenware glazing is concerned. The spraying process, however, lends itself more readily to mechanization. This consists in applying a glaze slip in the form of a fine spray by means of an aerograph or sprayer in which two tubes are arranged at right angles, one of which is connected with a

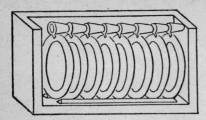

Fig. 17. Use of Saddles and Thimbles.

reservoir of glaze slip and the other to a supply of compressed air. A great number of automatic spraying machines have been developed for earthenware glazing, particularly in U.S.A., both straight machines and circular machines, all using sets of jets spraying at various angles – 400 to 500 dozen pieces of earthenware can be glazed per hour on such a machine by only one man and four girl assistants.

Glost Placing. – Placing of the glazed ware is more difficult than the placing of bisque ware and takes up much more room, since each article has to be separated from the other by small fireclay supports in order to prevent them from fusing together during the firing, should they touch each other. The small fireclay supports are designed in such a way that they support the ware on a sharp point which leaves only a very small pointlike mark on the glaze, after firing and removal of the support. Plates are supported by 'pins' or 'saddles and thimbles' as shown in Fig. 17 and 18, and cups and pots are often supported on three points of a 3-armed 'stilt'. The most modern way of placing plates and saucers is the use of 'pin cranks'. These are refractory tripods the uprights of which are provided with small pins. The plates are placed on the points of these pins: the use of pin cranks

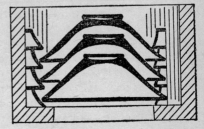

Fig. 18. Cross section of three dishes – to show use of bowl pins.

does away with saggers and saves much space in the oven.

Glost Firing. – Glost firing of earthenware is carried out in up-draught intermittent ovens similar to, but smaller than, those used for bisque firing. The saggers are piled one on top of the other in the same way as in bisque oven practice, but the edges of the saggers are covered by a layer of plastic clay (wad-clay) to produce an airtight seal between individual saggers. This is necessary in coal-fired ovens, because carbon particles, sulphur, and reducing vapours must not come in contact with earthenware glazes. In gas-fired tunnel ovens airtight sealing of the sagger is not necessary. Glost firing of earthenware can also be done in tunnel ovens either of the open-flame or of the muffle type. If open-flame ovens are used the ware has to be placed in saggers. If muffle ovens are used the ware is placed on refractory 'bats' supported by 'props'. The firing temperature for earthenware glost is 1040° C. to 1150° C. If, however, earthenware is made in a single-fire process, that means if the glaze is applied to the ware before firing, a higher temperature is usually employed because in this case the body has to obtain the necessary strength at the maturing temperature of the glaze. Apart from the case of sanitary ware (which will be described later on), the single-fire process is used to a large extent for the manufacture of earthenware hollow-ware such as cups, pots, vases, and so on.

Earthenware Glazes. – Earthenware glazes are fired at temperatures ranging from 1040° C. to 1150° C. (Seger cones 03 to 3). It is not possible to produce glazes, which melt at these temperatures, from water-insoluble substances, and so it is first of all necessary to convert water-soluble substances into non-water-soluble substances.

Earthenware glazes are obtained by using a frit (glass) made by mixing and melting such water-soluble substances as borax, boric acid, or soda ash, with feldspar, Cornish stone, flint, whiting, or china clay, by grinding the frit and mixing the

H

powdered frit with other non-water-soluble materials such as china clay, flint, stone, lead-bi-silicate, and so on. The non-water-soluble materials which are mixed and ground, together with the frit, in a mill, are called mill materials. The frit has, as a rule, a lower melting point than the glaze. The composition of the frit is chosen so that at a relatively low temperature it will melt into a liquid which will flow easily out of the frit kiln into a vessel containing water. Frit kilns, as a rule, are fired continuously. The raw materials are charged at one end. They melt on an inclined plane and collect at the lower part of the hearth from which they can be run off, as soon as a sufficient quantity of molten material is collected.

Lead imparts to the glaze brilliance, lustre, and smoothness. Glazes which contain lead develop most colours better than leadless glazes and are more 'fool-proof' in the plant. Small errors in compounding lead glazes have a lesser influence on the property of the finished ware. Since lead is a poison, glazes are classified by the Ministry of Health as:

(*a*) Lead glazes.
(*b*) Low solubility glazes.
(*c*) Leadless glazes.

The Ministry gives the necessary guidance as to those exceptional applications for which lead glazes may be used, and what precautions have to be observed in the interest of the operatives.

The terminology chosen needs explanation since the word 'lead' refers in this classification only to the acid-soluble part of the lead content. In order to determine to which class a glaze belongs it is treated with diluted hydrochloric acid of specified concentration. If after a treatment of specified duration more than 5% is dissolved in the acid, the glaze is termed a 'lead' glaze. If between 5 and 1% is dissolved, the glaze is called a 'low solubility' glaze, and if less than 1% is dissolved the glaze is called a 'leadless' glaze. It is interesting to note that if lead is introduced into the glaze in the form of lead bi-silicate, or if the lead is incorporated in the frit, the test just described will classify the glaze as a low solubility glaze or even as a leadless glaze. The glazes which fall under class (*a*) lead glazes, are those which contain unfritted lead oxide as a mill material, or those which have a frit containing boric acid plus lead oxide.

Owing to the shortage of lead during the recent war, leadless glazes were developed in various countries. These gave very satisfactory results where borax or boric acid was available. Barium carbonate and strontium carbonate are very useful ingredients in leadless boric acid glazes. In Germany during the war neither lead nor boric acid was available. Satisfactory glazes were, however, developed in which complex fluorides such as sodium-silico fluoride (Na_2SiF_6) were used.

The following are two examples of low solubility earthenware glazes:

			Glaze 1	*Glaze* 2
Frit.	Feldspar	. .	225 lb.	105 lb.
	Flint	. .	30 lb.	80 lb.
	Borax	. .	195 lb.	240 lb.
	Whiting	. .	20 lb.	44 lb.

The glaze contains :

Frit	. .	250 lb.	130 lb.
Lead bi-silicate	.	113 lb.	66 lb.
China clay	. .	30 lb.	20 lb.
Feldspar	. .		53 lb.

Two examples of leadless glaze are:

Glaze 1

Frit.	Borax	. . . .	35.7%
	Calc. flint	. . .	28.6%
	Whiting	. . .	14.3%
	Cornish china clay	. .	14.3%
	Soda ash	. . .	7.1%

Glaze containing:

Frit	. . . .	90.9%
Cornish china clay	. .	9.1%

Glaze 2

Frit.
Borax	.	.	.	.	25.1%
Soda ash	.	.	.	.	3.6%
Feldspar	.	.	.	.	4.8%
Cornish stone	.	.	.	22.2%
Silica rock	.	.	.	.	16.8%
Whiting	.	.	.	.	16.8%
Cornish china clay	.	.	.	10.8%

Glaze containing:

Frit	.	.	.	.	92.0%
Cornish china clay	.	.	.	5.7%
Silica rock	.	.	.	.	1.1%
Cornish stone	.	.	.	.	1.1%

(These recipes are published by Furnival, *Leadless Decorative Tiles, Faience and Mosaic*, and quoted by Felix Singer. *Ceramic Glazes*, published by Borax Consolidated Ltd)

Decoration of Earthenware. — Earthenware lends itself admirably to the various methods of decoration described earlier in this book. Both under-glaze and on-glaze decorations are widely used. When the ware is decorated underneath the glaze, the relatively low temperature of 1050° C.–1100° C. employed for glost firing allows the use of a great range of brilliant colours When earthenware articles are decorated by means of on-glaze colours, they, too, acquire a very brilliant appearance during their sojourn in the enamelling kiln. Most earthenware glazes become soft at the temperatures prevailing in the decorating kiln (750 to 800° C.). They combine with the fluxes in which the colour pigments are embedded. The result is that the decoration is not only brilliant, but also offers good resistance to wear and tear.

Coloured Earthenware Bodies and Glazes. — To enhance the attractiveness of earthenware, both the bodies and the glazes are themselves often coloured. This is done by adding colouring oxides to the glaze and to the body. Both effects appear, at first glance, quite simple, but actually it is not too easy to obtain uniform colour, particularly in the case of glazes. A thick layer of coloured glaze naturally appears to be darker than a thin layer of the same glaze. As a rule, therefore, the edges of plates, cups, saucers, and so on, glazed with a coloured glaze, are lighter than the centres. Glazes which do not get very soft during the glost fire and consequently do not run, give greater uniformity of colour.

In the case of earthenware tea and dinner sets, coloured bodies with transparent glazes are preferable, since individual pieces of the same dinner set should have the same colour. Here again it is not always easy to obtain the same shade throughout the oven since articles of coloured bodies become darker, the higher the bisque temperature. Since the temperature distribution is more uniform in tunnel ovens than in intermittent ovens, it is easier to obtain uniformity of colour if the former are used. Plain coloured earthenware is very attractive and will appear on to the market in increasing quantities as more tunnel ovens come into operation.

GLAZED WALL TILES

White and coloured glazed wall tiles are usually made from earthenware bodies. The glaze is either a transparent or a coloured one and its appearance is more important than the strength of the body. The porosity of the body is slightly higher than of earthenware table ware, and the bisque firing temperature is slightly lower. Glazed wall tiles are made by the two-fire process, the bisque fire temperature being between 1150° C. and 1200° C. and the glost fire temperature about 1050–1100° C. Wall tiles are standardized in this country to B.S.S. 1281 (1945). This specification aims only at providing a standardized range of sizes and does not lay down standards of durability. As regards quality and finish, it states only that the tiles shall be reasonably true to shape, flat and free from flaws. The standard sizes are as follows:

6 in. × 6 in. × $\frac{3}{8}$ in.   4 in. × 4 in. × $\frac{3}{8}$ in.   6 in. × 6 in. × $\frac{1}{4}$ in.
6 in. × 3 in. × $\frac{3}{8}$ in.   4 in. × 2 in. × $\frac{3}{8}$ in.   6 in. × 3 in. × $\frac{1}{4}$ in.

6 in. × 2 in. × ⅜ in.   4 in. × 1 in. × ⅜ in.   4 in. × 4 in. × ¼ in.
6 in. × 1 in. × ⅜ in.

Since a tile is glazed only on the side which will be exposed, the porous body can absorb water. This absorption of water may cause the body to expand enough to put the glaze under tension and cause crazing. Crazing impairs the appearance of the glaze surface. The expansion is caused by absorption and re-hydration of aluminium silicates in the body. Very often 'crazing' does not show up in service until after several months. By subjecting the finished tiles to an autoclave treatment, however, the moisture expansion may be speeded up and may cause crazing immediately. This test is carried out regularly to make sure that no crazing is to be expected. In the autoclave a pressure of 100 to 200 lb. sq. in. is applied to the test specimen, the test being repeated several times.

Wall tiles are usually made by the dry pressing process. The body is generally prepared in a similar way to other earthenware bodies. The slip is de-watered in a filter press, and the filter cake dried to the proper moisture content by using waste heat from the tunnel oven. The body can, however, be mixed and prepared completely dry and the moisture content adjusted to the correct figure after mixing. The body, whether it is prepared by dry or by wet mixing, is passed through a disintegrator in order to reduce it to granules of the required grain size. The latter are delivered by bucket or screw conveyor to the storage bins and thence by gravity chutes into boxes for delivery to the maker.

Much research work has been done on wall-tile bodies in recent years, particularly in the United States, striving to reduce the tendency to moisture expansion, by replacing feldspar by talc. The talc content must either be considerably smaller, or considerably larger than the clay content, since the firing range of bodies containing approximately equal amounts of talc and clay is very small. If the feldspar is to be completely replaced by talc, considerable amounts have to be used in order to obtain sufficient densification and a large thermal expansion (which is important in order to avoid glaze 'crazing').

Professor McNamara (Pennsylvania State College) describes the following composition of a talc wall tile body as very successful.

Talc .	.	.	.	38%
Ball Clay	.	.	.	22%
Kaolin	.	.	.	6%
Flint	.	.	.	34%

Talc has also a favourable influence on the pressing qualities of the body and makes possible the use of very dry powders for pressing.

Pressing is done in metal dies by (1) hand pressing, (2) semi-automatic pressing, and (3) automatic pressing. To prevent sticking, the metal dies are either oiled after a certain number of pressings or heated by gas or electricity. The powder can also be mixed with an oil emulsion, to facilitate mould release. The tiles, as they come from the press, are placed on or into setters or direct into saggers, and the saggers are then put into dryers. The most economical method of drying is to place the saggers on the tunnel oven car, which is first pushed into a dryer heated by waste heat from the tunnel oven, and then directly into the bisque tunnel oven. The length of a tunnel oven for wall tiles is, as a rule, greater than one for earthenware table ware. A length of 400 ft. is quite usual for wall tiles in bisque firing, since it is desirable to heat the ware very slowly. A peak temperature of about 1150 to 1200° C. is reached in about 90–100 hours. The manufacture of wall tiles lends itself very well to mechanization. For this reason hand presses and intermittent ovens are only employed nowadays under special circumstances. Glazing has also been mechanized, mechanical dipping or spraying machines being used. The glost firing is nowadays, in most cases, also done in tunnel ovens. For this, the tiles must be supported on setters or on projections in the saggers in order to prevent the glaze from sticking. The general manufacturing process is otherwise quite similar to the manufacture of earthenware table ware, previously described.

CHAPTER XVI

Porcelain and China

PORCELAIN ware has a white translucent body. It is dense, vitrified and impermeable to water.

The translucency distinguishes it from white stoneware; the density and impermeability distinguish it from terra-cotta, faience and earthenware.

The name porcelain can be traced back even before the sixteenth century. It was originally used to denote objects manufactured of mother-of-pearl from the shell called porcelain (in Portugese *Porcellana*). Later, in the eighteenth century, porcelain came to mean the brilliant white translucent ceramic table ware which we, in this country and in the United States, know as china or china ware.

TYPES OF PORCELAIN

In the course of time, all sorts of porcelain or china have been developed in various countries. The differences are, of course, mainly due to two factors:

(1) Raw materials employed and proportions used.

(2) Manufacturing methods.

Depending upon (1) and (2) various degrees of whiteness and translucency are obtained.

Apart from variations in the body of the porcelain itself, different types of glazes, having varying degrees of hardness according to the temperature at which they are formed, are used for different types of porcelain.

Porcelain can be classified as follows:

(1) Hard porcelain table ware. ⎫
(2) Electrical insulator porcelain. ⎬ Hard glaze feld-
(3) Laboratory porcelain. ⎭ spatic porcelain.
(4) American hotel china. ⎫ Soft glaze feldspa-
(5) American household china. ⎬ tic china.
(6) Bone china. ⎭
(7) Soft porcelain.

The types differ in body composition and manufacturing methods; these, in turn, affect the mechanical strength and translucency of the ware.

All porcelain and china bodies are vitrified, that is to say, they are fired to a point where, to all intents and purposes, all the pores in the body are filled with a glassy bond. Under these circumstances, the fired body has practically no absorption. The following are typical figures:

Hard porcelain, insulator porcelain, labor-
atory porcelain . . . . Zero
American household and hotel china . Less than 0.3%
Bone china . . . . . 0.3% to 2.0%

Such slight porosities do not impair the translucency of the bodies; even at the upper limit of 2% absorption, bone china may still be very translucent. Moreover, porosities of such a nature are not objectionable in the case of domestic and hotel ware.

(For comparative purposes, it may be recalled that semi-vitreous china has an absorption of from 4% to 10% and fine earthenware 10% to 15%.)

The physical characteristics of vitrified bodies are superior to those of semi-vitrified bodies. Ware made from vitrified bodies is usually considered as being of a higher grade than semi-vitreous or porous ware, because it is more difficult and expensive to manufacture and also because of the pleasing appearance of a vitrified translucent body. The final value, however, of a ceramic piece very often depends upon its decoration and finish. Highly-decorated pieces of earthenware may be more expensive than a plain porcelain article.

Dinner ware which constitutes a large portion of all porcelain products is made from a wide variety of bodies. Much confusion exists in the mind of many people, especially consumers, over the terms used in connexion with dinner ware. This can be explained by the fact that the correct terms have been abbreviated by laymen. For instance, in America, semi-vitreous china is very often called 'porcelain'. This ware is correctly called 'semi-porcelain' but the term is often short-ened to 'porcelain' by retailers and by the public. It would be correct to call by the description 'porcelain dinner ware' only that ware which is made of hard feldspatic porcelain and to call bone china, American hotel china and household china, not 'porcelain' but 'china', because the manufacturing methods are different from what was originally called 'porce-lain'.

Raw Materials

Porcelain and china are made from white-burning raw materials. The principal ones are:

(1) Kaolin (china clay).
(2) White-burning ball clays.
(3) Flint or quartz.
(4) Feldspar, or minerals containing feldspar, Cornish stone and pegmatite.

Bone ash is used as additional flux in bone china. Frits are used as fluxes in soft porcelain (frit-porcelain).

All raw materials must be as free as possible from iron oxides or other impurities which impair the whiteness of the body.

Ball Clays. – Ball clays – whose function is to increase the plasticity of the body so that it can be more easily shaped – usually contain many impurities and for this reason they are kept to a minimum compatible with the necessary working properties of the body. This is very important in the case of vitrified porcelain bodies, but not so important in the case of semi-vitrified porous bodies to which a higher percentage of ball clays can be added without giving the body a muddy appear-ance. The explanation is as follows:

During the firing process the vitrified bodies form a pro-portion of fused fluxes which have the power of dissolving any impurities in the ball clay. If these impurities occur in sufficient quantities the resultant vitrified body has a muddy appearance. In the case of technical porcelain for insulator bodies a white colour is not very important, and ball clays can be used in greater proportions.

The fact that only very small amounts of ball clay can be used in the manufacture of household porcelain or china bodies, makes shaping much more difficult than in earthenware manufacture.

Kaolin (or China Clay). – This is the principal constituent of porcelain and china bodies and usually forms 50% of the contents. In order to minimize the influence of possible variations in composition several types of kaolin are mixed together.

The china clays or kaolins used in porcelain and china are much less plastic than ball clays and this makes the bodies more difficult to manipulate.

It is not possible, commercially, to obtain raw materials absolutely free from impurities and they all contain a small amount of iron oxide which gives the ware a yellowish tinge when it is fired under oxidizing conditions; this yellow colour may be eliminated either by using a reducing fire in the kiln (as in the case of Continental hard feldspatic porcelain) or by adding a very small percentage of cobalt oxide to the body. Cobalt gives a blue tinge which compensates for the cream tint produced by the iron in an oxidizing atmosphere. The resultant colour is white or bluish-white according to the amounts added.

Feldspar (Cornish Stone). – Next in order of importance comes feldspar with its fluxing powers. It begins to melt before the other materials as the firing progresses, and above 1200° C. it becomes a viscous liquid. It acts as a solvent and dissolves the kaolin, clay and flint in varying degrees, according to the temperature used in firing, forming a translucent vitrified material. Instead of pure feldspar, Cornish stone or pegmatite can be used. Both of these materials contain:

> Feldspar
> Silica
> Clay.

Feldspar is non-plastic and decreases the plasticity of the body.

The difference between the softening and melting temperatures of feldspar is very large and so feldspatic porcelain has a fairly large firing range. This means that the difference between the deformation point and the vitrification point is large.

Frits and Bone Ash. – If the feldspar is replaced by frits (as in the case of soft porcelain) or by bone ash (as in the case of bone china) the bodies are more likely to be deformed if the oven temperature slightly exceeds the vitrification point. Feldspar is non-plastic. Bone ash is slightly plastic.

Flint. – Flint, or sand, is the source of silica in the porcelain body. Silica, like feldspar, is non-plastic and decreases the plasticity of the body. For vitrified bodies such as porcelain, silica is ground into much finer particles than it is for porous bodies like earthenware. The smaller the grain size the more extensive is its solution in the glassy feldspatic matrix formed during firing.

This glassy bond or matrix, rich in silica, has a small coefficient of thermal expansion which decreases as its silica content increases. In porous bodies like earthenware, silica is present in crystal form instead of in the form of glass, just mentioned. Silica in crystal form has a high thermal expansion and this explains why earthenware has a larger expansion than porcelain.

HARD PORCELAIN

Hard porcelain is used for the manufacture of:
(1) Domestic and hotel table ware.
(2) Electrical insulators.
(3) Chemical laboratory ware.

The manufacturing methods and compositions of the various types of feldspatic hard porcelain are different and will be discussed separately.

'Hard' porcelain is an apt description because, generally

speaking, its intense hardness distinguishes it from other types. This hardness is obtained by firing at temperatures as high as 1300° C. to 1400° C. (hard fire). The glaze melts at the same temperature at which the porcelain body becomes vitrified.

[Other types of porcelain, like bone china and American household and hotel ware, are manufactured in a different way; at this stage it suffices to say that in the case of bone china and American china the sequence of operations is as follows:

(1) Unglazed body first-fired until it is vitrified at a temperature of 1200° C./1250° C. (bisque-fire).

(2) Fired and vitrified articles are then covered with a glaze.

(3) The ware is then fired in a second fire (glost-fire) at a considerably lower temperature – 1100° C./1150° C.

The glazes used for this purpose have, consequently, a lower melting point than hard porcelain glazes. They are softer because they contain less silica, which material gives the glaze mechanical hardness.]

In the case of hard porcelain, the sequence is as follows:

(1) Unglazed body first fired at 900° to 1000° C. (bisque or pre-fire).[1]

(2) Pre-fired articles glazed.

(3) The ware is then fired at 1400° C. when body vitrifies and glaze fuses.

Hard porcelain does not always need two separate fires; thick-walled articles, like electrical insulators, are glazed in the clay state, after careful drying in a properly heated atmosphere; in this case only one firing at 1300–1400° C. is needed; thin-walled articles like table ware are very weak in clay state and have therefore to be hardened usually at a temperature of between 900–1000° C. before they are dipped into the glaze.

This process is carried out in a chamber in the upper floor of intermittent ovens, heated by the waste heat of the main

1. The translation of the French term *dégourdir* or the German term *verglühen* into English is difficult, and the term 'bisque-fire', mostly used, is somewhat misleading. Pre-hardening fire would give a clearer idea. There is no English term equivalent to the German and French terms, since hard porcelain table ware is not made in Britain.

chamber in the lower floor or, in the case of continuous kilns, in the second tunnel heated by the waste heat of the main tunnel.

The purpose of this hardening process is only to eliminate the water from the body, leaving the ware strong enough to be handled for glazing. In this state the body is very porous and absorbs eagerly the necessary amount of glaze when the ware is dipped. The ware is then air-dried for a certain time and it is then placed in the kiln and fired at between 1300–1400° C. Since, at this temperature the body is vitrified, i.e. fired to a point where eventually all the pores of the body are filled with a glassy bond, and the glaze is molten, considerable inter-action takes place between the glaze and the body. This factor contributes considerably to the greater mechanical strength of hard porcelain compared with other types of porcelain.

Hard Porcelain for Table Ware. – For household and hotel ware the porcelain body is made up, theoretically, as follows:

Clay substance – kaolin or china clay   .   50%
Feldspar 25–30%
Silica (flint) or Quartz 20–25%

This is a composition which gives, at 1400° C., a vitrified translucent porcelain. If the firing temperature is lower, say, 1300° C., the feldspar content has to be increased to approximately 35% and the other ingredients correspondingly reduced.

The above are theoretical compositions based upon numerous analyses of hard Continental porcelains and also of the old Chinese porcelain.

The constituents, kaolin and feldspar, are seldom absolutely pure:

(1) The kaolin may contain feldspar and silica.
(2) The feldspar may contain clay and silica.

In the compounding of the body it is therefore necessary to adjust the amounts of kaolin, flint and feldspar according to their actual composition. Take the case of a porcelain body of the following theoretical composition:

Clay substance	.	.	.	.	52.5
Feldspar	.	.	.	.	22.5
Silica (quartz)	.	.	.	.	25

100.0

Now, suppose that the kaolin used contains:

70% clay substance
20% silica (quartz)
10% feldspar

and that the feldspar contains:

60% feldspar
40% silica (quartz)

the kaolin content would have to be increased to 75%. The feldspar would have to be 25% and pure silica or quartz would not be required.

$$75\% \text{ of } \left\{ \begin{array}{l} 70\% \text{ clay substance} \\ 20\% \text{ silica} \\ 10\% \text{ feldspar} \end{array} \right\} = \begin{array}{l} 52.5\% \\ 15\% \\ 7.5\% \end{array}$$

$$25\% \text{ of } \left\{ \begin{array}{l} 60\% \text{ feldspar} \\ 40\% \text{ silica} \end{array} \right\} = \begin{array}{l} 15\% \\ 10\% \end{array}$$

Preparation of Porcelain Bodies. – In the preparation of both household and technical porcelain bodies, the most elaborate processes known in the ceramic industries are involved. All the materials have to be of most constant quality; in most cases feldspar and silica have to be treated in the plant before they are used, since their grain size, as marketed, is too coarse.

The most commonly used method of hard porcelain body preparation is as follows:

The flint, feldspar and kaolin are carefully weighed, with due regard to its moisture content. The flint and feldspar are then fed into separate grinding cylinders, together with a small pre-determined amount of kaolin and water; the latter ingredients are added in order to prevent the flint and feldspar from 'settling' and forming a hard deposit in the grinding cylinder. The kaolin is dissolved in water in a blunging machine until it acquires the nature of a very thin paste or 'slip'. After they have been wet-ground to the desired fineness, the flint and feldspar are mixed with the kaolin slip in a very thin state in a mixing arc. The watery mixture or slip is then passed through sieves and then over magnetic separators in order to remove any coarse particles and iron-bearing materials. As the slip is purified it is collected in an 'agitator' (or storage) tank; as might be gathered from the title, the slip is kept in circulation in order to prevent its settling. From the agitator the slip is pumped into a filter press; the purpose of which is to remove all but 25% to 30% of the water from the mixture, leaving behind a series of 'cakes' which can be handled. The cakes are removed, stored in a cellar and allowed to 'age' for a certain length of time in order to increase the workability of the body. In large factories where very considerable quantities of body are required every day, the necessary storage facilities for ageing purposes are very often not available and, in many plants, the body goes without ageing from the filter press direct to the de-aiting pug mill.

The clay cylinders which are extruded from the pug mill are then transported to the various shaping departments for jiggering, jollying, casting, etc.

Shaping. – In the case of casting, the clay body has to revert to a liquid state; to achieve this, a de-flocculant, such as sodium carbonate or sodium silicate, is added to the plastic body, together with a small amount of water as described previously.

Porcelain for dinner ware and hotel ware is formed by jiggering or by casting. Simple hollow-ware like cups and oval dishes is usually jiggered but it is also possible to cast them. So-called 'flat-ware' like saucers, plates and shallow dishes, is usually jiggered, but more complicated hollow-ware like teapots and coffee-pots is cast. The method of shaping finally adopted depends very much on the plastic nature of the body and the quantity of each article to be produced.

The most popular method of making porcelain plates is by moulding on a 'jolly'; it is done in two separate operations similar to plate-making in earthenware manufacture. First a 'bat' is made; this is a flat disc of clay formed on a rotating plaster disc by means of a suitable tool. In earthenware manufacture the bat can be taken off the plaster disc by hand and transferred to the plaster-of-Paris mould which forms one side of the plate. Porcelain bats have to be treated differently. Since porcelain bodies are delicate the bat must be transferred with great care to the mould. To enable the transfer to be carried out successfully, the bat is produced on a linen base stretched in a frame fitting over the head of the batting machine. The frame and the bat are then lifted over to the mould and the bat is transferred very gently in order to avoid deformation. The bat, lying on the plaster-of-Paris mould, is then pressed down on to the mould with the aid of a sponge and the ball of the thumb, beginning at the centre. The mould shapes the upper side of the plate, i.e. the plate is upside down. The bottom of the plate, which has been pre-shaped by the sponge and the thumb, is then formed by a steel profiling tool which is pressed down on to the plate, rotating on the mould (as in earthenware manufacture).

Fully automatic plate-making and cup-making machines described in the sections 'Earthenware' and 'American China', also lend themselves to the manufacture of hard porcelain. In Continental porcelain factories, however, they have been used so far only to a small extent, with the exception of the Rosenthal factory (Selb, Bavaria). Semi-automatic machines are, however, used extensively in German and French porcelain works.

Porcelain table ware is usually dried in mangle dryers. The ware is transported on a conveyor (mangle) through chambers heated by waste heat from the ovens. Drying of porcelain table ware is not such a difficult problem as in earthenware manufacture, because the porcelain body is lean and gives off its water readily.

Pre-firing. – As previously mentioned, hard porcelain table ware is hardened, as a rule, in the upper chamber of intermittent ovens, and this upper chamber is heated by the waste heat from the lower chamber. During the hardening process, the articles are placed in saggers. Large saggers are used and the articles can touch each other, since at the temperatures used no vitrification takes place and no sticking or fusing together can possibly occur.

Glazing. – In the manufacture of porcelain table ware, two methods of applying glazes are used:
(1) Immersion (dipping).
(2) Spraying.

The latter is used when the ware has not been pre-fired but only dried (this is occasionally done in the case of low-priced cup manufacture), because the ware in 'clay state' is too fragile to be dipped.

Two types of glazes are used for covering hard porcelain:
(1) Feldspatic glaze.
(2) Calcareous glaze.

(1) *Feldspatic Glaze.* This is a mixture of the same ingredients as are used in the porcelain body together with:
(*a*) A large amount of feldspar.
(*b*) Other fluxes, such as dolomite, magnesite or lime.

The purpose of these admixtures is to bring the melting or fusing point of the glaze mixture down to the vitrification point of the body. It is difficult to do this by adding feldspar only, hence the further addition of other fluxes.

(2) *Calcareous Glazes.* In these glazes, lime and dolomite are the main fluxing agents.

The following are examples of hard porcelain glazes for S. Cone 14–15 (1410–1435° C.). Glazes 1–3 are feldspatic, glaze 4 calcareous.

	1	2	3	4
Quartz	34.5	32.0	27.0	44.0
China clay	9.5	7.0	8.0	30.0
Feldspar	32.5	37.0	32.0	—
Calcium carbonate	12.0	11.0	16.5	—
Calcium sulphate	—	—	—	13.5
Grog (biscuit porcelain)	11.5	13.0	16.5	12.5

Final Firing of Glazed Ware. – The glazed ware is now placed in the saggers for the final firing which is carried out at about 1300–1400° C. This firing combines the effect of the two

separate firings, which in the manufacture of earthenware, bone china and American china are called 'bisque-fire' and 'glost-fire' respectively. The saggers are used in order to protect the ware from direct contact with the flame. The placing of the ware in the saggers

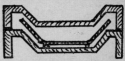

Fig. 19. Placing of a tureen
(hard porcelain)
in individual sagger.

is important as the various pieces must not touch each other or the sides of the saggers. The glaze becomes soft at the maximum temperature and the articles, if allowed to touch, would stick together. (See Fig. 19.)

Plates are placed in individual saggers, after the glaze has been removed from the annular ring at the foot, in order to prevent sticking to the sagger. Hollow-ware, such as a cup, can be placed in two ways:

(1) On its foot, the right way up.
(2) Upside down – resting on its lip.

In each case the glaze is first removed and in the case of (2) the lip is ground and polished after the firing is completed. In the case of thin-walled cups and other hollow-ware, rings or other supporting means are used in order to prevent deformation (Fig. 20).

 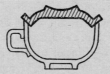

Fig. 20. Various methods of placing cups (hard porcelain)
using rings or setters.

Kilns

Intermittent Type. – Hard porcelain is normally fired in intermittent kilns of the down-draught type. The kilns used are smaller than those employed in earthenware manufacture and have a cubic content of 2100 to 2900 cubic feet (60 to 70 cubic metres).

Decoration of Hard Porcelain. – Decoration of hard porcelain can be:

> (1) 'On-glaze' decoration.
> (2) 'Under-glaze' decoration.

Since glazed ware is fired at 1300–1400° C. many colours which would withstand the softer glost-fire of earthenware, bone china and American china, are completely or partially dissolved by the glaze at this temperature. The range of under-glaze colours for hard porcelain is consequently rather limited. All under-glaze hard porcelain colours are tender and subdued (with the exception of cobalt blue), and the bright effects obtainable with other types of porcelain cannot be achieved. If the artist-designer, however, takes the nature of under-glaze colours fully into consideration, very attractive effects can be obtained, as exemplified by the art porcelain of Copenhagen Pottery Works and other Continental porcelain manufacturers. Under-glaze colours are prepared by combining colouring oxides with refractory mixtures of kaolin, alumina, silica or powdered porcelain body at very high temperatures and by grinding the product thus obtained.

Because of the limitations of the palette, and the special technical difficulties of under-glaze decoration in hard porcelain manufacture, most of the decoration is done 'on-glaze'. The same ceramic colours are used for 'on-glaze' decoration as for other types of porcelain, china or earthenware.

The 'on-glaze' colours consist, as described previously, of a mixture of colouring metal oxides and a 'flux' which is a glass having a very low melting temperature (600–700° C.) and consisting mainly of borax and lead compounds. With soft glazes the interaction between on-glaze colours and glaze is more intimate than with hard glazes. The hard porcelain glaze being still completely hard at the temperature of the enamel kiln, the on-glaze decoration applied to it presents a slightly matt appearance, whereas on 'soft glaze' types of porcelain, china and earthenware, the colours are more glossy.

Some distinguishing characteristics of porcelain, china and earthenware

It has already been explained that one can distinguish porcelain and china on the one hand from earthenware on the other, because the former are translucent and the latter opaque. One can also distinguish hard porcelain from other types of porcelain by trying to scratch the glaze with a hard knife. If the glaze is scratched, the ware is not hard porcelain. If one does not want to run the risk of damaging the glaze one can inspect the foot of the article. If the foot is matt and not covered by glaze it is hard porcelain. (It will be recalled that the glaze has to be removed from the parts of the hard porcelain articles which come in contact with the supporting sagger during the firing.) Another distinguishing characteristic is the appearance of the colours; under-glaze colours on hard porcelain are subdued; bright under-glaze colours can only be produced on other types of porcelain. The on-glaze decoration on hard porcelain has a matt surface; on soft-glaze porcelain on-glaze decoration has a glossy surface.

BONE CHINA

The manufacture of bone china is confined almost exclusively to England. With the exception of one pottery firm in Sweden (Gustavsberg), there are no other European or American firms manufacturing it. Bone china is a development originating from fine stoneware. It is called by this name because bone ash is introduced as an additional flux to Cornish stone or feldspar. The combination, bone ash plus stone or feldspar, is a very powerful flux and produces an extremely translucent body. Bone ash possesses a certain amount of plasticity and this property makes it possible to compound bodies which are plastic enough to be jollied and cast without the addition of ball clay.

The only clay used in bone china is china clay of highest quality.

Bone Ash. – The ash used in the manufacture of bone china is produced by calcining the bones of oxen. Bone ash is a material consisting essentially of tri-calcium-phosphate. Although this substance is now produced chemically this inorganic material has so far not been used in the manufacture of bone china, primarily because the synthetic ash is completely non-plastic.

Bone ash in ceramic mixtures has the following remarkable properties:

1. It imparts to the body translucency even if the body is not quite dense, and not fired to vitrification point, but still porous.

2. It is a strong flux when small amounts are added to clay, but it is a refractory when large amounts are added. For instance, the lowest melting point of all bone ash – clay mixtures, was found to be that of a mixture consisting of 30% bone ash and 70% china clay, which melts at bisque fire temperature.

3. It improves the plasticity of the body.

Manufacture of Bone China Bodies

Bone china bodies have the following composition:

China clay . . . . . 20% to 30%
Bone ash . . . . . 27% to 46%
Cornish stone . . . . 20% to 32%

(Ref. Searle, *An Encyclopædia of the Ceramic Industry*, Vol. I, p. 111.)

Bodies which have a higher bone ash content have as a rule a proportionately smaller Cornish stone content.

The preparation of the bone china body is carried out in a similar way to that described for hard porcelain. The Cornish stone and bone ash are, as a rule, purchased by the china manufacturers in the form of finely-ground dry powder. The materials are weighed, with due regard to their moisture content, and mixed, together with china clay and water, in a blunger. (In Sweden, feldspar and bone ash, together with a small amount of china clay, are ground together in a grinding cylinder and are then mixed together with the balance of the china clay, by blunging in a blunger.)

The mixture then passes through sieves and over magnets and excess water is removed in filter presses. The bone china bodies are less plastic than other bodies used for the manufacture of table ware because they contain as a rule, only 20% to 30% china clay, and no ball clay, whereas hard porcelain bodies contain about 50% china clay and very often a small amount of ball clay. On the other hand, it must not be forgotten that bone also contributes to the plasticity of the body.

Shaping and Drying Bone China. – Because it is less plastic the bone china body has to be handled more carefully than hard porcelain bodies, and this applies to both the jollying and casting processes. Otherwise the shaping processes for bone china are the same as for hard porcelain.

After the shaping processes the ware is transferred to the drying stoves where, owing to the lean nature of the body, the water is given off readily. The dried articles have very poor mechanical strength and great care has to be exercised when handling them during the cleaning, sponging and placing into the saggers for biscuit firing. Considerable progress has been made, however, by the industry in this respect during the last few years.

Bisque Firing. – The firing of bone china is quite different from that used in hard porcelain manufacture and resembles more the firing of earthenware. The sequence of operations is as follows:

(1) Unglazed ware is fired at about 1300° C. at which temperature it becomes vitrified and translucent (bisque-fire).

(2) Ware is then glazed.

(3) Ware is glost fired at about 1100° C. and at this temperature (which is about 200° C. lower than the 'bisque' temperature) the glaze materials fuse and the ware is covered with a brilliant glaze.

The firing of bone china, particularly the first (bisque) fire, is a very difficult operation, because:

(1) Bone china has a very high shrinkage which may cause deformation and cracking.

(2) Bone ash, in combination with stone and clay, produces, when it melts, a very fluid liquid. This flux gives the body a very short firing range.

A very even heat distribution in the bisque oven is of vital importance for two reasons: If the ware is slightly under-fired it is highly porous and tends to cause crazing; and if the ware is slightly over-fired it deforms rapidly.

Bone china is generally bisque-fired in intermittent kilns of slightly smaller size than those used for firing hard feldspatic porcelain and of much smaller size than those used for firing earthenware. The reason for this is that it is easier to obtain uniform heat distribution in smaller ovens. At the present moment several of the leading bone china manufacturers are using tunnel biscuit kilns (the glost firing of bone china is carried out generally in tunnel ovens).

Bone china becomes soft at vitrification temperature and so, in order to prevent deformation, plates, saucers and other flat ware are embedded in alumina. Alumina has completely replaced silica as a bedding material in the bone china industry.

Bone china hollow-ware and cups are not embedded in alumina, but are placed in those parts of the oven in which relatively low temperatures are maintained. If necessary, cups and hollow-ware are prevented from deforming by supports, rings, etc. made of the same body.

Glazing of Bone China. – After completion of the bisque fire, the adhering alumina particles are cleaned off the ware by brushing or by air-jets and the ware is then dipped into the glaze slip. Since bone china is practically non-porous it does not absorb the glaze, in contrast to porous earthenware. In the case of bone china the glaze has therefore to adhere to the surface and must consequently be more sticky and heavier than earthenware glaze (to demonstrate this point it may be stated that comparing one pint of bone china glaze slip with one pint of earthenware glaze slip, the weights are 32 oz. and

28 oz. respectively). In the case of bone china glaze slip the water in which the glaze is suspended is not absorbed by the body but remains in the layer of glaze until it is dried off.

The drying of glazed bone china is therefore a longer and more important operation than the drying of glazed earthenware. It is best done by utilizing the waste heat from the ovens in mangle or other continuous dryers.

Glost Firing. – Except in the case of muffle type or electric tunnel kilns where 'open-setting' is possible, the glazed ware is, as previously mentioned, placed in saggers and fired in the glost oven at a temperature of about 1100° C. This is a low (soft) temperature compared with the temperature of 1400° C. required in the firing of hard porcelain glaze. Bone china glaze is, consequently, called a 'soft' glaze. 'Soft' is, of course, a relative term, as anyone whose fingers have come into close contact with fragments of glazed bone china will confirm.

Bone china glaze may have the following composition:

Frit			*Glaze*		
Borax	.	21	Frit	.	100
Cornish Stone	.	26	China clay	.	2
Flint	.	21	Cornish stone	.	4
Whiting	.	13	Flint	.	2
Nitre	.	1	White lead	.	65
Soda ash	.	3			——
China clay	.	15			173
		——			
		100			

This recipe is taken from McNamara, *Ceramics*, Vol. III page 488 (Pennsylvania State College, 1944).

Owing to the white lead content in the glaze materials this glaze is a 'full lead' glaze, and is not permitted in Great Britain. By introducing the lead in the form of lead bi-silicate a low-solubility glaze would be obtained which, while having the same properties as the glaze referred to above, would be less dangerous to the operatives.

Glost Firing of Bone China. – The glazed articles could be placed in individual saggers (in the same way as hard porcelain is placed for the final firing), each plate or saucer being put in a separate sagger; but this would be costly and would take up much sagger space and sagger material. The placing is therefore done as in earthenware manufacture. Several plates or saucers are placed in the same sagger, each piece of ware being separated from the others by small fire-clay supports called:

(1) Pins.
(2) Thimbles.
(3) Spurs.
(4) Saddles, etc. etc.

These supports are shaped in such a way that ONLY the point of the support (thimble, spur), or a sharp edge (saddle) *comes in contact with the ware.*

After firing the saggers are emptied and the supports have to be removed from the ware. It is obvious that the sharper the point or edges of the supports, the smaller will be the marks left on the ware after their removal.[1] To prevent this sticking of the supports to the glazed articles, as far as possible, the former are covered with a layer of refractory material, such as flint, bone ash or alumina.

Bone china glost firing is carried out in up-draught intermittent ovens or in tunnel ovens at 1100° C. The atmosphere must be clean (no smoke) and slightly oxidizing (slight surplus of air) so that a clean and brilliant glaze may be developed.

Bone China Decoration. – Bone china may be decorated under-glaze or on-glaze. It lends itself to a wide variety of decoration. Owing to the relatively low temperature (1100° C.) to which the under-glaze colours are subjected, the palette is very rich. On the other hand, as the glaze becomes soft at the temperature of 750–800° C. prevailing in the decorating kiln, the on-glaze colours sink into, and combine with, the glaze. On-glaze colours of bone china are, consequently, very brilliant, so much so that it is often difficult to say whether the

1. The smoothing and polishing of these marks is called "ginetting."

colour is applied on-glaze or under-glaze. The colours contrast very strongly with the extremely brilliant whiteness of the bone china and the resulting colour effects are more lively and charming than can be obtained with any other ceramic material.

A VISIT TO THE ALL-ELECTRIC FACTORY OF JOSIAH WEDGWOOD & SON LTD, BARLASTON

In 1938 the directors of Wedgwoods decided to abandon the historic site at Etruria which they had occupied since 1769. They realized that in order to maintain a leading position in a highly competitive modern world a company must have the advantage of the most up-to-date plant and layout. For some years now coal mines and ironworks have dominated the scene at Etruria bringing in their train ground subsidence and dirt, detrimental to factory buildings, pottery and workers alike. These conditions, combined with the need for a more modern layout, influenced the decision to establish a new home on firmer ground and in purer air in the attractive countryside near Barlaston.

The foundation stone of the new works was laid in 1938. The fine earthenware section of the new factory was completed in the early autumn of 1940, one year after the outbreak of war. Further construction had to be postponed because war supplies had priority. In 1945 building was restarted.

At the time of the author's first visit to Wedgwoods' new factory in spring 1947, not only was the manufacture of earthenware carried out from the slip house to the finished ware house, but in addition bone china, made in Etruria, was glazed, glost fired, and decorated. That part of the factory in which the making and bisque firing of bone china will eventually be carried out was still under construction and the foundations of the world's first electric bisque oven for bone china were just laid down. Needless to say, the new factory incorporates all the latest refinements for the manufacture of pottery. Outstanding features of the factory are the cleanliness and brightness of the workshops and the layout which gives a streamlined flow of production and eliminates unnecessary transport. Each process adjoins the next one, so there is established a continuous flow from the moment the raw materials are received from the factory's own railway siding at one end of the works on to the slip house, through the making shops, bisque tunnel ovens, bisque ware house, dipping house, glost tunnel ovens, glost ware house, decorating department into the finished ware house, from which the goods are delivered to the waiting lorries at the other end of the works. Since the principles of earthenware and bone china manufacture have already been described, only some of the special refinements employed at Barlaston will be mentioned here.

Starting with the slip house, in which the earthenware bodies are made, it is particularly interesting to observe the ingenious method employed to ensure a constantly uniform body composition. The principle of compounding earthenware bodies, by measuring the volumes of the four different slips of which the final body is composed, has been discussed previously. The method so described suffers from the fact that the gravity of the various slips is controlled by weighing only a pint of each slip, previous to the mixing. This pint is taken from a blunger which frequently contains several hundred gallons and it is assumed that the weight of this special pint of slip is the same as the pint weight of the remainder. This assumption is the source of great inaccuracies. In the slip house at Barlaston this inaccuracy is obviated by the use of a 186-gallon measure, instead of a pint measure. This measure takes the form of a tank into which the slip is discharged. The number of gallons and the weight of the slip can be ascertained and adjusted according to requirements, prior to mixing.

This device and the whole layout of the slip house constitute a great improvement compared with conventional body preparation. The result is greater uniformity of the body and consequently smaller manufacturing losses.

The slip is, after mixing, de-watered in five filter presses, each of which has a capacity of about 4 tons per day. The filter cakes taken out of the press are homogenized in six vertical pug mills, about 20 tons of earthenware body passing through the pug mills daily.

Practically all the shaping methods described earlier in this book are used in Barlaston, particularly jollying, casting, throwing and turning. Several of the photographs in this book illustrate the shaping methods used at Barlaston.

A method not previously mentioned is the application by hand of pre-shaped ornaments (previously pressed in 'pitcher' moulds) on to the surface of clay ware, in a leather-hard state. This method of ornamenting provides rich embossments which may have a colour different from that of the body, for instance a blue embossment may be applied to an ivory body. 'Pitcher moulds' are moulds made of earthenware biscuit.

Various types of vases are made by throwing and subsequent turning. Others are made by casting. In the production of teapots, coffee-pots, sugar-bowls and other hollow-ware this process is used to a large extent, the slip being delivered to the casters through pipes and rubber hoses arranged over the casting tables.

Plates, saucers, dishes and cups are, of course, jollied. Conventional plate- and cup-making machines are used. The great variety of different shapes manufactured at Barlaston, makes the use of automatic or semi-automatic machines less attractive than in factories where only a few shapes are being made, and those in very great quantities. Nevertheless, interesting experiments with automatic machines have been successfully concluded and Sulzer automatic cup and platemaking machines will soon further streamline the production.

On the occasion of his visit to Barlaston the author noted one very useful and unusual automatic machine which fixed handles on to the jollied cups, in a leather-hard state, with greater speed and accuracy than could be done by hand.

Drying of the unglazed, unfired clay ware is done in Boultons Dobbins, and the drying of glazed ware in horizontal dryers. The ware, after having been dipped into the glaze slip, is placed on moving belts which run through tunnel dryers, heated by waste heat from the ovens.

Of particular interest, of course, are the electric tunnel ovens. Josiah Wedgwood & Sons were the first firm in this country to use electric tunnel ovens for firing earthenware bisque and glost firing. On the Continent, particularly in Sweden and Switzerland where enormous hydro-electric power stations supply electricity at very cheap rates, considerable experience has been gained in designing the best electric tunnel ovens for firing pottery. The Swiss firm, Brown Boveri & Co., designed the electric kilns now operating so successfully in the new works at Barlaston. These are the first electric tunnel ovens to operate using electricity produced by coal fuel. The advantage of electricity compared with gas for firing pottery tunnel ovens is, as mentioned previously, the cleanliness of the oven atmosphere. It is no longer necessary, therefore, to protect the ware from the flames by a muffle (as in the case of muffle kilns), or by placing it into saggers (as in the case of open-flame ovens). The ware is placed on refractory shelves (called 'bats'). The distance between the individual bats regulated by the height of refractory supports (called 'props'). This method of 'open setting' allows the placing of about three times the amount of ware possible in oval or round saggers. This means that three times the number of 'oven dozens' can be fired in the same oven with the same consumption of kilowatts were the ware placed into saggers.

The bisque and glost firing of earthenware and the glost firing of bone china are carried out in two twin electric tunnel ovens. The trucks in the glost oven travel in the opposite direction to the cars in the bisque oven. The purpose of this arrangement is to use the heat of the cooling ware in the bisque tunnel for pre-heating the ware in the glost tunnel. Air circulation exchanges the heat from the cooling end of the bisque tunnel through the walls into the adjacent pre-firing zone of the glost tunnel. The length of both tunnels is about 275 ft. The width of the cars in glost oven No. 1 is smaller than that of the bisque oven cars, but the setting height is the same in both cases. In the new twin tunnel oven, No. 2, the glost oven and biscuit oven cars have the same widths. The

speed at which the cars travel through the glost kiln is quicker
than through the bisque kiln, in order to allow what is called
an adequate 'soaking' in the bisque oven. This means that the
ware has to be heated more slowly in the bisque oven, and
has to be exposed for a longer time to the maturing temperature than is necessary for fusing the glazes in the glost oven.
The temperature in the bisque oven is about 1200° C. and in
the glost oven 1100° C. Firing cycle in the bisque oven is
60 hours, in the glost, 30 hours. Thermo-couples indicate the
temperature which is also checked by various Bullers' rings
placed on each truck. The temperature difference between
the top and bottom of each tunnel car is not more than about
15° C. The firing control is completely automatic. Electricity
consumption in Kiln No. 1 is 450 kW., in Kiln No. 2 550 kW.

Saggers, are of course, quite unknown in the factory since
all ware is placed in open setting. The bats on which the ware
is placed are made of a mixture of sillimanite and very refractory clay. The props which support the bats are made of an
aluminous refractory. The oven furniture (bats and props) has
a very long life. Its structure is so fine and its surface so smooth
that during the firing no small particles are released which
may spoil the ware. In the case of sagger placing these are such
an annoying cause of spoilt ware and 'seconds'. Bungs of
about ten plates are placed in the bisque oven on setters made
by Wedgwoods. Embossed plates are embedded in sand just
as china plates are embedded in alumina. In the glost oven all
the plates, saucers, and other flat ware are placed horizontally
in cranks made of refractory material and held in position by
pins made by Wedgwoods. The cranks have a similar shape
to those generally used in decorating kilns, but are made of
a very refractory material. Each china plate is supported individually on a bat on which three refractory saddles are
placed. During the glost fire china becomes softer than
earthenware, and for this reason it has to be supported more
carefully.

It can be seen from the foregoing that on that side of the
twin oven where the bisque ware leaves the kiln the glazed

ware enters the glost oven. This arrangement facilitates streamlining of production.

The bisque ware house which is very well assorted, is arranged near the exit end of the bisque ovens and the dipping house is adjacent to the bisque ware house and the entrance of the glost tunnel ovens. Since the atmosphere in the electric oven is, as mentioned above, extremely clean, discoloration due to reducing atmosphere is quite unknown in electric glost ovens, and another cause of rejects and seconds thus eliminated.

Decoration. – A great variety of decoration methods is employed by Wedgwoods. As a matter of fact there is hardly any known method of decoration and ornamentation which is not used for one purpose or another in their decorating department and all the methods described earlier can be studied here. In potteries producing decorated ware of the highest artistic standard it is more important to use methods which give the desired artistic effect than to try to mechanize the decoration department. For this reason a firm like Wedgwoods, although mechanizing more and more the production of the white ware and using the most modern tunnel ovens, still employs the greatest variety of time-honoured decoration methods.

Since the author's first visit to Wedgwood's new factory in 1947, the firm has moved the whole of their bone china manufacture from the old factory at Etruria to Barlaston. Apart from more up-to-date making machinery in the well-lighted new premises, the main improvement is in the biscuit firing. The first electric tunnel kiln in the world for firing bone china biscuit is some 200 feet long, designed by Brown-Boveri in conjunction with Wedgwood. The kiln uses Globar elements in the hottest zone and Kanthal in the pre-heating, and employs the counterflow principle.

The original plan envisaged in 1938 has now been completed. Whereas in 1938 and 1945 the factory employed some 800 people, the numbers now employed total 1,800. The better layout, coupled with a sensible degree of mechanization, has resulted in an increased productivity per person of some 30 per cent.

AMERICAN HOTEL CHINA

This is a unique type of ware made, until recently, only in the U.S.A. The body is similar to the Continental type of hard porcelain, but the glaze is very similar to bone china glaze. The body is prepared and shaped like that of Continental hard porcelain but is fired, unglazed, like bone china in a bisque fire at about 1250–1285° C. (Orton Cone 9–11).[1]

The ware is then glazed like bone china and fired like bone china in a glost oven, but at a slightly higher temperature than that used for the glost firing of bone china, in the region of 1150° C. The glaze is, consequently, much softer than that of hard porcelain which is fired at 1300–1400° C. American hotel china (and also American household china) may consequently be described as a 'soft glaze feldspatic china'. It combines, to some extent, the good properties of hard porcelain and bone china, the body possessing the large firing range of feldspatic porcelain and greater plasticity than bone china bodies. It is, consequently, easier to shape and fire than bone china. Since, furthermore, the glaze is fired at the same temperature as the glaze of bone china, the range of under-glaze colours is extremely large; moreover the on-glaze colours combine intimately with the glaze at the temperature of the decorating kiln (750–850° C.) and have a more brilliant appearance than the on-glaze decoration of hard porcelain. On the other hand the body does not possess the same degree of translucency and whiteness as bone china and the glaze is not as resistant as hard porcelain glaze.

Body Composition. – The body must be made from high-grade white-burning materials.

China clay and ball clay were formerly imported to the

---

1. In America Orton Cones are commonly used for firing control; in this country Seger cones, or Buller's rings.

I

United States from Great Britain, but now American kaolins are used to a great extent. In America, very plastic white-burning secondary kaolins are found, for instance, in Florida; this makes it possible to produce rather plastic china bodies without the use of ball clay, the omission of which has a favourable influence on the whiteness of the body. The ingredients of the body, for American hotel china, are the same as those used for hard porcelain. The feldspar content is, however, increased since hard porcelain is fired at 1350–1400° C., whereas American hotel china is fired at 1250–1285° C. In addition to feldspar, a small percentage of lime or dolomite is introduced as a flux in the batch. The following two compositions (taken from the American monthly *Ceramic Industry*, January 1943 issue, are typical of a hotel china body fired at 1270° C.:

Flint	.	.	.	.	35	37
China clay	.	.	.	20	22.5
Florida kaolin	.	.	.	13	12.5
Ball clay	.	.	.	.	9.5	10.0
Potash feldspar	.	.	.	21	13
Soda feldspar	.	.	.	.	–	3
Lime	.	.	.	.	1.5	0.83
Magnesite	.	.	.		0.83
					100	99.99

These bodies will not become absolutely dense at 1270° C.; a water absorption of 0.3% is admissible according to the Standards Committee of the White-Wares Division of the American Ceramic Society.

The more vitrified the article becomes at the finishing state of the bisque fire, the greater will be the danger of deformation and rejects. The aim is, consequently, to compose American hotel ware batch in such a way that it contains:

(1) Enough fluxes to make it almost non-porous.

(2) Enough silica to prevent deformation.

The practical compromise is a body which is practically

dense (having a water absorption of 0.3%) and which is only slightly translucent.

Shaping. – The shaping methods are the same as those used in the manufacture of hard porcelain table ware. However, since in the U.S.A. very great quantities are usually required, and the dimensions of the articles are standardized to a very great extent, automatic *pottery* machines are now being used in the large manufacturing firms. To give an example, one of the largest jollying machines now in use and made by the Miller Pottery Engineering Co, produces 240 jollied porcelain articles per minute (345,600 pieces in 24 hours). Twelve pieces of hollow- or flat-ware (cups, bowls, saucers, fruit dishes, plates and the like) are produced at each revolution of the main shaft, which rotates at the rate of 20 revolutions per minute. The machine does the work of 180 operatives in one shift or 720 operatives in a 4-shift day.

Firing. Bisque-firing of American hotel ware is nowadays carried out exclusively in tunnel-ovens. Open flame gas-fired tunnel ovens are commonly used and the setting is done either in saggers or in open-setting on refractory bats separated by refractory supports. Plates are, however, mostly fired in setters because they are embedded in sand or alumina in a similar way to bone china bisque. The ware does not, however, become quite as soft as bone china, and embedding is not as important as in bone china manufacture. The most recent development in placing American china is the use of individual setters of a smooth refractory material. The setter is designed in such a way that its bottom surface has the same contour as the plate and deformation of the latter is thus prevented.

Glazing and Glost Fire. – The glaze is slightly harder than bone china glaze but, as previously mentioned, much softer than hard porcelain glaze. A typical example of soft glaze for feldspatic porcelain is as follows:

Feldspar	.	.	.	.	30.9
Whiting	.	.	.	.	5.5
Flint .	.	.	.	.	6.7
Lead-bi-silicate	.	.	.	47.6
Clay .	.	.	.	.	7.1
Zinc oxide	.	.	.	2.2

$$100.0$$

Glazing, drying of the glazed ware, placing in the glost oven and glost-firing are all done in the same way as described for bone china manufacture. Supporting of the ware during the glost-firing is, however, not quite such a serious problem as in bone china glost-firing, from the standpoint of warpage, since feldspatic porcelain is more rigid at 1150° C. than bone china at 1100° C.

The decoration methods are the same as in bone china manufacture, but automatic machines are used and replace many hand operations.

Standardization. – Hotel porcelain is, of course, constantly subjected to the most severe handling and is made in U.S.A. in three types, depending upon the severity of the service. These three types are:

(1) Double-thick ware ($\frac{5}{16} - \frac{3}{8}$ in. wall thickness – for the most severe service – lunch counter service).

(2) Single-thick rolled-edge ware ($\frac{6}{32} - \frac{1}{4}$ in. – Hotel and restaurant service).

(3) Single thick, without rolled edge, ware.

AMERICAN HOUSEHOLD CHINA

Like American hotel china, American household china is a type of ware developed in the U.S.A. The body composition of household china is very similar to hotel china. In this ware, however, translucency is considered important, to compete with Continental porcelain and bone china. In order to obtain greater translucency in household china, at the firing temperature of hotel china, the percentage of fluxes in

the batch has to be increased. This not only increases the
translucency of the fired body but also decreases its water absorption (0.1%). A typical American household china has the
following composition:

China clay	40%
Ball clay (or Florida kaolin) .	10%
Feldspar	30%
Flint	18%
Dolomite	2%

Such a body, fired at Orton Cone 10 (1270° C.) results in a
very translucent porcelain of white or cream colour. All
materials have to be of highest quality.

Manufacture. – The manufacturing methods are the same as
described for American hotel-china; this refers to shaping,
bisque-firing, glazing, glost-firing, and decorating. In many
cases American household and hotel ware are manufactured in
the same factories and are bisque and glost fired in the same
kilns. The making of both hotel and household china is one of
the most highly-developed sections of the ceramic industry in
the U.S.A., and the manufacturers of these types of ware have
entered the field of high-quality table china and compete with
Continental porcelains and English bone chinas. Before the
war, most of the high quality china and porcelain marketed in
the U.S.A. was imported from this country and from Central
Europe, but during the war the American ceramic industry
added high quality ware to its manufacturing programme.
The results are being felt not only on the American market but
also in other markets where, before the war, American hotel
and household china were practically unknown. The enormous assured home market makes it possible for the American
ceramists to use mass production methods which cannot be
contemplated in countries without such a home market.
Many potters believe that high quality ware can only be made
with conventional manual equipment. This is nothing but
wishful thinking. The outlook for automatic pottery machines

is very bright and now that 'teething' troubles have been over-come further development work is rapidly improving their efficiency. The skill of the individual potter, working with manual equipment, remains, however, the same as it was centuries ago and has reached the highest state of perfection; no further improvement in this skill therefore can reasonably be expected, and besides the price of kilowatt hours will go down, and the price of man hours go up, as time goes by. (See page 47).

VITREOUS CHINA TABLE WARE

Very recently the manufacture of soft glaze-hard paste china has been started in Holland and Italy and called Vitreous China table ware. The body, glaze, and the manufacturing methods are identical with those described under the heading American Hotel China and American Household China.

To summarize, this material combines the advantages of earthenware manufacture with certain advantages of hard porcelain (hardness and translucency).

The soft glaze used on this ware imparts great brilliance and wear resistance to on-glaze decoration. For these reasons, it can be assumed that the manufacture of this type of porcelain will be taken up in other countries as well.

CHAPTER XVII

Sanitary Ware

'SANITARY ware is the term used for fixtures such as sinks, bath tubs, lavatories, closet bowls and similar products. Sanitary ware is made of:

1. Fireclay, often with an 'engobe' to conceal the texture and colour of the body.
2. Earthenware.
3. Vitreous china.

EARTHENWARE

In this country most sanitary ware is made of earthenware of a texture and composition similar to that used in general earthenware manufacture and covered with an earthenware glaze. Some, however, in this country is also made of fireclay and vitreous china. In the U.S.A. and on the Continent, on the other hand, most sanitary ware is made of vitreous china covered with a hard glaze.

Bath tubs and sinks are also, of course, made of enamelled cast-iron. Since, however, the latter type of ware is not generally considered here as ceramic ware, it does not come within the scope of this book. (In the U.S.A. the American Ceramic Society and the ceramic periodicals deal extensively with all the problems connected with 'porcelain' enamels for cast-iron and sheet-iron.)

Sanitary ware was first made by the Romans. After the fall of the Roman Empire this branch of pottery fell into complete oblivion from which it only emerged, in this country, in the middle of the nineteenth century. For some time sanitary ware was manufactured exclusively in England but since the beginning of this century works in France, Germany and America have also been producing sanitary ware of a high technical standard.

FIRECLAY

Bodies used for sanitary fireclay ware are similar to those bodies discussed in the chapter dealing with fireclay and stoneware. The dark colour of the body is hidden by a glaze of the same composition as that used in earthenware manufacture but it is made opaque by the use of tin or another opacifier. Better still, to conceal the colour of the body, an 'engobe' may be placed between the glaze and the body.

An engobe is a mixture applied in slip form to cover the body before the glaze is put on. The engobe can be applied by pouring or spraying it over the bisque ware (or the body in a green state, as the case may be) or the ware can be dipped into the engobe. The engobe is frequently applied to the body in a green state before firing, but in order to prevent distortion of the clay in the case of thin-walled articles, it is often applied after bisque firing. If a single fire process is used in the manufacture of fireclay sanitary ware, feldspatic porcelain glazes often containing zinc oxide or tin oxide are employed and the firing is done between 1200 and 1300° C.

VITREOUS CHINA

The bodies and glazes used in the manufacture of vitreous sanitary ware are similar to those used for porcelain insulator bodies. The great advantage of vitreous sanitary ware is the fact that it is completely dense and non-porous. There is no need to explain why the property of not absorbing moisture is most desirable for every ware used in sanitation and hygiene. The requirements as to non-porosity are, however, not quite so stringent as for electrical insulators. A porosity of 0.3 % is admissible (compared with zero for insulators and 10 to 15 % for earthenware).

Some recipes for vitreous sanitary bodies are published in the American monthly *Ceramic Industry* and are as follows:

Ceramic Industry, Ceramic Materials Issue
Solid Cast – Orton Cone 9
(All-American Body)

Feldspar	33.5%
Flint	17.0%
Kamec clay (kaolin) . .	23.0%
Edgar Florida clay (plastic kaolin) .	9.0%
Old Mine No. 4 ball clay .	8.0%
Kentucky Ivory ball clay . .	8.0%
Talc	1.5%

Orton Cone 10
(All-American Body)

Georgia kaolin . . .	26.3%
Maine feldspar . . .	32.6%
Flint	17.7%
Kentucky ball clay No. 4 .	7.0%
Tennessee No. 5 ball clay .	7.0%
Florida kaolin . . .	4.7%
North Carolina kaolin . .	4.7%

Orton Cone 11

English china clay . . .	16%
Florida kaolin . . .	4%
Tennessee ball clay No. 5 .	12%
Old Mine No. 4 ball clay .	5%
Flint	27%
Feldspar	36%

SHAPING AND FIRING OF SANITARY WARE

Originally most sanitary ware was made by hand-pressing plastic bodies into plaster moulds. This process is, however, slow, and requires much skilled labour. It does not lend itself to mass production methods which must nowadays be employed in order to meet the ever-increasing demand for sanitary products. For this reason, shaping is done almost exclusively by slip casting in plaster moulds.

In the production of sanitary ware the slip-casting process has reached a very advanced stage. The individual pieces of ware are large, are intricately shaped, and have thick walls. The conventional method is to pour the slip into open plaster moulds until the article has acquired the required wall thickness. This takes one to two hours according to the composition of the slip. The excess slip is then poured out and the article is allowed to remain in the moulds until it has dried sufficiently, to obtain the necessary strength so that it can be removed from the mould. The conventional method of joining separately-cast parts with a slip, under slight pressure, is extensively employed. Many special casting techniques have been developed. In one of these special methods certain parts of the article are first cast in moulds and allowed to become mechanically strong. They are then removed and are placed in another large mould. The slip is then poured around the preformed parts, thus joining them into a single unit. This process facilititates the formation of interior parts such as the traps in closet bowls. By this method it is possible to form very complicated shapes which, after firing, are a one-piece product.

'Drain' casting is another technique used in the production of sanitary ware. In 'solid' casting the slip is poured between four plaster surfaces and allowed to form a solid body. In drain casting, on the other hand, the slip is poured between the plaster surfaces and allowed to remain there until a coating of sufficient thickness has formed on the plaster surfaces. The slip which has remained liquid between the hardened surfaces is then allowed to run out from the centre of the casting by opening a hole, leaving a hollow space between the clay surfaces. Drain casting makes it possible to manufacture large and complicated parts having hollow walls instead of solid ones. This reduces the weight of the finished articles, and also makes the drying and firing easier.

In large sanitary works the casting process is highly mechanized. Belt conveyors, which carry the moulds from one member of a team to the next one, are used. For complicated articles made in large quantities, teams of up to nine casters are employed.

Drying of sanitary ware has to be carried out with special care. The problems are similar to those with which the porcelain insulator manufacturers are confronted. Both sanitary ware and insulator bodies are very plastic, containing a high proportion of ball clay. Large and intricate shapes are common in both these industries. In the manufacture of sanitary ware, carefully-controlled humidity dryers are used. Hot, humid air is used to begin with and the moisture content is then gradually reduced. These dryers have simplified the problem tremendously. Large bath-tubs can safely be dried in humidity dryers within twenty hours, whereas they take weeks to dry in conventional dryers.

Infra-red drying is also successfully employed in reducing the drying time of large articles.

Most sanitary ware is fired in tunnel kilns. These are particularly advantageous in this branch of the ceramic industry, since bulky and heavy articles are much easier to place on kiln cars than into periodic kilns. Moreover, the ware can be placed in open setting on refractory slabs supported by refractory posts, whereas in intermittent ovens the ware is surrounded by large and heavy saggers.

Sanitary ware made of fireclay or earthenware bodies is, as a rule, fired twice (bisque and glost fire). Ware made of vitreous china is produced either by the single-fire process, in which the glaze is applied to the dried ware and is then fired to a temperature at which the body vitrifies and the glaze fuses, or by a two-fire process. In the latter case the glaze is applied to the dense body vitrified in the first firing and the article is fired a second time. In the single-fire process a hard glaze similar to a porcelain glaze is used. In the two-fire process a softer glaze – which matures at a temperature about 200° C. lower – is employed. This is similar to the soft glaze referred to in the section dealing with the manufacture of American hotel porcelain.

CHAPTER XVIII

Insulator Porcelain

WHEN industry in general and the electrical industry in particular demanded insulating materials impervious to moisture, unattackable by atmospheric conditions, having smooth and and easily cleanable surfaces, it was only natural that, in those countries which were already producing hard porcelain for household purposes, the same factories also started to make insulator porcelain and other technical articles, in addition to their domestic and art ware. On the other hand, in the U.S.A. and England, where hard porcelain was not manufactured, special factories were set up to deal exclusively with the manufacture of.electro-technical porcelain. This difference in origin and development, i.e. existing factories on the one hand and the new factories on the other, explains the difference in the manufacturing methods of hard insulator porcelain in the U.S.A. and Great Britain on the one side, and the Central European countries, Japan, and Russia on the other.

In the latter countries porcelain insulators are fired at temperatures of approximately 1400° C. and upwards in a reducing atmosphere. The manufacturers there had concentrated principally on porcelain table ware and were accustomed to producing white ware with a very hard glaze unattackable by acids and by scratching with steel knives and forks.

These characteristics were, of course, only of secondary importance to the manufacturers who intended to concentrate on electrical porcelain insulators exclusively, and who had not previously made hard porcelain. As a result, American and English porcelain insulator manufacturers fired at a somewhat lower temperature – approximately 1300° C., in a neutral or oxidizing atmosphere and used more ball clay.

The materials produced by the two manufacturing methods differ in colour; the Continental, Russian and Japanese have a white, and the English and American an ivory, colour. The mechanical and electrical characteristics of the materials are, however, very similar.

The composition of electrical insulator bodies is, as already mentioned, similar to that of hard porcelain bodies for domestic porcelain and china, but the latter have two characteristics which are of very little significance in the case of electrical insulators, viz, whiteness and translucency. Since a white colour is of small importance in the case of electrical insulators, quite a considerable part of the kaolin can be replaced by the more plastic ball clay, or similar clays. Since translucency, which is considered of great value in the case of table ware, is not necessary at all in the case of electrical insulators, the feldspar content can be reduced, and the silica content increased. These alterations improve the mechanical strength, reduce the brittleness associated with translucent porcelain, and increase the toughness and the resistance to temperature changes.

More important even than good mechanical properties, are the electrical properties of an insulating material. Special attention is therefore paid by the insulator manufacturers to obtaining electrical characteristics as good as possible without sacrificing mechanical characteristics. The electrical properties (in common with the mechanical properties) depend upon body composition, method of shaping, method of firing, and glaze characteristics. In no branch of the ceramic industry have slight alterations in body and glaze composition such great influence on the usefulness of the finished article, as in the manufacture of electrical insulator porcelain. The most accurate methods of preparing, controlling and checking the composition and proportions of the raw materials, the shaping processes, the kiln conditions, etc, have been introduced and are continually being improved.

The dimensions of the finished insulators must, in many cases, be extremely accurate within very close tolerances.

For certain applications in the electrical industry, new insulating materials, such as plastics, have been developed in recent years. To meet the competition from these materials, manufacturers of ceramic insulating materials have adopted the most modern methods of manufacturing and testing.

It is not surprising, therefore, that the electrical branch of the ceramic industry has always been a kind of pacemaker in the development of new body compositions and in the adoption of new manufacturing methods.

In principle, the body preparation is very similar to that used in porcelain table-ware manufacture. Apart from the fact that the accurate maintenance of the correct proportions of raw materials employed is more important, one other difference between the manufacture of electrical porcelain and other types of porcelain is that most insulator works need, in addition to plastic bodies and casting slips, bodies in powdered form for the production of articles made by the pressing method. The manufacturers make this powder from the plastic body – either as it comes from the filter-press, or by using scraps from the jollying or turning department – dry and mix it with lubricants and pass it through a disintegrator. Grains of different sizes are formed and sorted according to their dimensions by means of rotating sieve cylinders.

Shaping of insulators is done by:

(1) Jollying.
(2) Casting.
(3) Turning.
(4) Extruding.
(5) Pressing.

Methods (1) and (2), jollying and casting, have already been mentioned as the main shaping methods for table ware. These methods are employed also in insulator manufacture where they have been mechanized to a very great extent.

Additional shaping methods have, however, to be used, owing to the great variety of shapes demanded by the electrical designer. When long articles of symmetrical cross-section are required, method (4), extruding, is used. Vertical and horizontal presses are used as well as normal and de-airing pug mills. The cross-section of cylinders or tubes of special shape is formed by the extrusion die; long cylinders, or tubes of complicated cross-section, can be made by this method; grooves or ribs, perpendicular to the axis, are cut into the extruded cylinders or tubes by method (3), turning, just as metal parts are turned on the lathe.

Method (5), pressing in steel dies, is used when large quantities are required or when other methods cannot be used. Very complicated articles can be made in this way. This method is also generally used for making small low-tension insulators which do not require great dielectric strength. It is also used for insulators whose shape does not readily lend itself to other shaping methods.

Drying of the shaped articles is more difficult in the case of porcelain insulators than in the case of porcelain table ware:

(1) Because porcelain insulator bodies are more plastic as they contain more ball clay and other plastic clays.

(2) Because porcelain insulators are very often of large dimensions and of very irregular wall thickness.

Fast drying in hot, dry air, would result in cracking, as drying of clay ware is accompanied by contraction and thin portions dry more quickly than thick portions. Drying of ceramic articles starts on the outside surfaces which are in contact with the dry, warm atmosphere. Because of this, articles whose surface area is large compared with their thickness, dry more quickly and contract to a greater extent. Where contraction takes place at different rates in various parts of one article, internal stresses are set up and there is a tendency for cracks to occur. This tendency is common to all branches of the ceramic industries, but it is particularly prominent in the manufacture of such articles as large and complicated insulators. Very slow drying, in a dry atmosphere, is the obvious way out, but if quicker drying of large and complicated articles is desired, it may be carried out in a hot humid atmosphere. Humidity dryers of the chamber and tunnel types produce the desired conditions.

Firing of Porcelain Insulators

The firing of porcelain insulators is nowadays done almost exclusively by the one-fire process. Hardening by firing prior to glazing is not necessary since dry electrical porcelain articles in their clay state are mechanically strong enough to withstand handling and covering with glaze, either by spraying or by immersion in the glaze solution. Firing is carried out, almost everywhere, in tunnel ovens.

Technical Characteristics of Porcelain

Electrical Porcelain. – Porcelain insulators have an enormous field of indoor and outdoor applications, ranging from the humble domestic, or industrial switch-base at 200 volts to the enormous bushings and overhead line insulators for 380,000 volts and over, to say nothing of two million volt-testing transformers, etc. Porcelain is equally suitable for direct and alternating current work, the latter being principally at 50 or 60 cycles per second. For high-frequency work, other ceramic insulating materials, such as steatite (talc), are used. They are described in the chapter 'High-Frequency Ceramics'. The most important electrical characteristics of insulating materials are:

1. (*a*) Volume resistivity.
   (*b*) Surface resistivity.
2. Breakdown strength (dielectric strength).
3. Power factor.
4. Dielectric constant (permittivity).

Of these (3) and (4) are of particular importance in condenser design, and in high-frequency work generally. For this reason they are dealt with in the section dealing with high-frequency ceramics.

1. *Resistivity.* – An insulating material is a material which

offers great resistance to the passage of electric current. The resistivity is that property of an insulating material which determines its suitability for use as an insulator. The measurement of the resistivity of a given material, therefore, indicates whether it is an insulating material or not. If the volume resistivity of a material measures less than 1 megohm–cm^3, it is, in accordance with the A.S.T.M. standards on Electrical Insulating Materials, not normally considered as an insulating material.

Current can pass either through an insulating material or across the surface layer, or both ways. The resistance of an insulating material consists, consequently, of volume resistivity and surface resistivity.

(*a*) *Volume Resistivity.* – Volume resistivity is conveniently expressed as the resistance of a centimetre cube of a material when it is tested between two electrodes covering opposite faces of this cube, if no current flows through the surface layer. It is expressed in ohms or megohms per cubic centimetre.

It is of interest to note how the resistivity of porcelain compares with a few other typical insulating materials.

				Megohm per cm^3
Ivory	.	.	.	2×10^2
Celluloid	.	.	.	2×10^4
Marble	.	.	.	1×10^5
Plate glass	.	.	.	2×10^7
Amber	.	.	.	5×10^{10}
Fused quartz	.	.	.	5×10^{12}
Ceresin	.	.	.	$> 55 \times 10^{12}$
Porcelain	.	.	.	1×10^{14}

Volume resistivity is dependent on the nature and the temperature of the material. It decreases with increasing temperature. If values of volume resistivity are quoted without reference to the temperature it can only be assumed that they were measured at room temperature. The volume resistivity of porcelain at various temperatures is as follows:

Volume resistivity at		*ohms-cm*^{3}
	$-20°$ C.	10^{16}
	$+20°$ C.	$> 10^{14}$
	$+200°$ C.	10^{10}
	$+400°$ C.	10^{7}
	$+600°$ C.	2×10^{5}
	$+800°$ C.	3×10^{4}

(b) *Surface Resistivity*. – Here again, purely for purposes of definition, a test cube of side 1 cm. is taken. Surface resistivity is the resistance between two electrodes covering opposite faces of a cube when all the current flows through the surface layer. The surface resistivity of a material, therefore, is mainly determined by the film of water, oil or other substance deposited on the surface of the insulating material. It is thus dependent on the nature and thickness of the film and also on the quality of the surface of the insulating materials, since smooth surfaces hold less moisture or other deposits than rough surfaces.

A material having high volume resistivity does not necessarily have high surface resistivity. By glazing or by polishing the surface of a ceramic article it may be made smoother and its surface resistivity thus increased. A recent development of great interest is the use of silicones (a new silicon plastic) as a surface covering for ceramic materials. It is water-resistant and water-repellent, and considerably increases the surface resistivity. It may, in certain instances, make the use of a ceramic glaze superfluous.

In a dry atmosphere glazed porcelain has approximately the same surface resistivity as unglazed porcelain ($2-4 \times 10^{13}$) ohms/cm. square. In an atmosphere of 98% humidity, however, unglazed porcelain of a rough texture has a surface resistivity of only 1×10^{9} ohms/cm.^{2} whereas that of glazed porcelain is one hundred times greater, 1×10^{11} to be precise.

2. *Breakdown Strength*. – The principal property of an insulating material for high voltage work is its breakdown strength. This value is expressed in volts per mil (thousandth of an inch) or in k.V. per mm. and is calculated by dividing the

breakdown voltage (the voltage at which the material breaks down under the electric stress) by the thickness of the test specimen. The breakdown strength varies to a great extent depending upon the test conditions, particularly the thickness of the test specimen, and the rate of test voltage increase. In Fig. 21 the breakdown strength is shown in k.V. per mm. for test specimens of various thicknesses, the three curves A B and C indicating different rates of voltage increase. One can see that the same porcelain test specimen has a puncture strength of 24 k.V. per mm., if the test specimen is 2 mm. thick and the voltage rapidly increased, and only 16 k.V. per

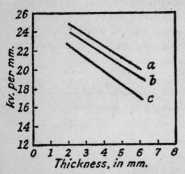

Fig. 21. Puncture strengths of Porcelain.

mm., if the test piece is 6 mm. thick and the voltage slowly increased. In many publications covering breakdown strength of insulating materials the thickness of the test specimen is not given. Such information is, of course, valueless. It is also important to specify whether the test current is direct current or alternating current, and in the latter case, the frequency in cycles per second. When direct current is applied, the breakdown strength is 30% higher than with alternating current of power frequency. As the frequency increases the temperature within the test specimen rises and the dielectric strength drops. For normal porcelain, the dielectric strength is greater at low frequencies than at high frequencies, owing to the electric losses referred to later on. Ceramic products formed by plastic processes (such as jiggering and extrusion) normally possess higher dielectric strength than products of the same body formed by dry pressing. This is because the homogeneity of a body shaped in plastic state is better than that of articles produced by powder pressing.

Mechanical Characteristics of Porcelain

Because broken cups and saucers are not unknown (the impact strength of porcelain is one of its weakest features), the layman is generally under the impression that porcelain is in every respect a fragile material and inferior to so-called 'unbreakable' materials. This is, however, not the case. The mechanical properties of porcelain are, on the contrary, very favourable, particularly if the load is continuous or steadily increased. The compressive strength, for instance, is fifty tons per square inch for test specimens made by the plastic process, and thus approaches the compressive strength of cast-iron. This compressive strength is about three times as great as bakelized paper and similar plastic materials. Bending and tensile strengths of porcelain are, however, considerably smaller than the corresponding properties of cast-iron.

Tensile Strength of Porcelain Compared with Cast-iron and some Organic Insulating Materials

	lb. to sq. in.
Porcelain (Plastic) . . .	7,000
Porcelain (Pressed) . . .	1,500
Phenolic resin, wood-flour filled	4–11,000
Phenolic resin, fibre filled . .	6,500–8,000
Cast-iron	18,000–60,000

Compressive Strength

	lb. to sq. in.
Porcelain (Plastic) . . .	80,000–100,000
Porcelain (Pressed) . . .	20,000
Bakelized paper . . .	16,000–20,000
Polystyrene . . .	14,000
Analine formaldehyde resin .	18,000
Cast-iron	100,000–120,000

Impact Strengths. – When we speak of the impact strength of a body we refer to its ability to resist fracture due to blows.

The impact strength test measures the energy expended in breaking a test specimen in one single blow. Compared with its tensile and compressive strengths, the resistance of porcelain to blows is small but it still compares favourably with many of the so-called unbreakable plastic materials and is better than that of normal glass. Standard pendulum machines are used for carrying out impact tests and a standard test specimen has to be broken by the pendulum in one blow. The greater the impact strength of the test specimen, the less the energy that will remain in the pendulum after breaking the test specimen, and the smaller will be the angle through which the pendulum swings. To allow comparison of porcelain with other materials, the following figures for impact strengths are given:

Cellulose	0.3–1.0
Phenolic resin, wood filled .	0.3–0.5
Laminated phenolic, paper filled .	0.3–3.8
Porcelain, extruded . . .	0.9

All the figures are in ft. lb. to sq. in.

High-Voltage Transmission Line Insulators

Insulator manufacturers have, during the last century, developed – in co-operation with the electrical industry – innumerable designs for indoor and outdoor applications. It is impossible in a small book of this type to do full justice to the subject. Strings of nine cap and pin insulators are used for the insulation of the 132 kV transmission lines of the British Electricity Authority. These lines transmit electrical energy over large distances from the generating stations to the main centres of energy consumption. Everybody notices these transmission lines when travelling by train or car, but few realize how much experience and elaborate detailed work is embodied in each of the insulator units composing the insulator strings. The various technical characteristics are mentioned in order to acquaint the reader with the requirements of the users.

The surfaces of suspension insulators are, as a rule, covered with a brown glaze which should be under compression in order to improve the mechanical qualities of the porcelain body. Before and after assembly, each unit is subjected to a number of electrical and mechanical tests. The tests which have to be carried out on overhead line insulators are described in B.S.S. No. 137 (1941) 'Porcelain and toughened glass insulators for overhead power lines (3.3 k.V. and upwards).' When the layman reads this specification he will be surprised to learn how many tests have to be made on high voltage insulators, and he will wonder whether they are all necessary and whether they increase the costs of the insulators unduly. It has, however, to be borne in mind that the safety of a transmission-line depends on the soundness of each insulator. The direct and indirect costs caused by insulation breakdown are enormous compared with the cost of an insulator, since a short circuit caused by the failure of one insulator may interrupt the current transmitted in the power line.

Some of the tests specified are as follows:

Not less than three of the purchased insulators have to be subjected to:

(1) Fifty per cent dry impulse flash-over test. Twenty applications of the impulse shall be made, the polarity reversed and the negative flash-over voltage measured for both polarities.

(2) Dry flash-over and dry one-minute test. The first test is obviously intended to measure the dry flash-over voltage. The voltage has to be increased gradually until flash-over occurs. The insulator has to be flashed-over at least four more times and the flash-over voltage recorded.

(3) One-minute rain test and rain flash-over test. The insulator has to be sprayed throughout the test with artificial rain in the form of a finely-divided uniform spray falling on the insulator at an angle of 45° C. to the vertical. The voltage has to be gradually raised until flash-over occurs and the insulator flashed-over at least four more times and the flash-over recorded.

Sample Tests. – One per cent of the batch offered for inspection has to be tested by the following tests:

Temperature – cycle test.   Mechanical test.

Electro-mechanical test.   Puncture test.   Porosity test.

Of these tests, the porosity and the temperature cycle test are of special interest to the ceramist.

In the temperature cycle test the insulator has to pass through the following cycle three times in succession. It shall remain for T minutes in a water-bath at a temperature not less than 70° C. higher than that of the main water-bath. It shall then be taken out and immersed as quickly as possible in the main water-bath left in this for T minutes.

$$T = (15 + W/3),$$

W being the weight of the insulator in lb. The insulator shall withstand the three temperature cycles without damage to porcelain or glaze, and shall, after the third cycle, be subjected to the electrical routine test in order to make sure that no damage has occurred.

The porosity test is carried out in the following way:

Pieces freely broken from an insulator are immersed for 24 hours in an 0.5% alcoholic solution of fuchsin under a pressure of 2,000 lb. to sq. in. (140 kg. per sq. cm.). No signs of penetration must be shown after this treatment.

Routine Tests. – Each insulator is subjected to the following electrical test:

The test voltage is applied to the insulator in a way described in detail in B.S.S. 137. The voltage is then increased until flash-over occurs. The voltage has to be maintained at this value for at least five minutes. If a failure occurs the test has to be repeated again for five further minutes after the last punctured insulator has been removed from the batch.

Mechanical Routine Test. – Each insulator is subjected to a tensile load 20% in excess of the maximum specified working load. The load has to be maintained for one minute without injury to the insulator.

CHAPTER XIX

Low Loss Ceramics

The Importance of Low Dielectric Losses in High-frequency Work. –
Each non-conductive material coming within the influence of
an alternating field, consumes a certain amount of electrical
energy and transfers it into heat. The energy so consumed increases with increasing frequency and is also dependent on
the power factor of the insulating material. In most cases the
heat thus developed is lost energy, and in order to keep this
loss in high-frequency work as small as possible, insulating
materials having a low power factor have to be employed.
The power factor is consequently an important dielectric
characteristic of an insulating material. (We read nowadays
much about high-frequency heating. In the case of high-frequency heating, use is made of the heat developed in the
material treated in a high-frequency field. The power factor
of such a material has to be large because otherwise not much
heat could be generated within it.) Whereas for low-frequencies
porcelain is a highly-satisfactory material, for high-frequencies other materials have had to be developed, since the power
factor of porcelain is too high, and it would get hot.

With the advent of radio, radar, television, and other
branches of electronic engineering, high-frequency alternating
currents have been used to an increasing extent.

To those readers who are not electrical engineers, the following remarks may be helpful.

There are two main types of electric current, namely direct
current and alternating current. We are concerned at the
moment with alternating current only. The ordinary alternating current, which we use from the mains for lighting, heating, driving electric motors, etc., changes its polarity or direction 25, 50 or 60 times every second. Most of the electrical
energy consumed to-day is generated by alternators (electro-

magnetic machines). Stationary armature (rotating field) alternators are the type commonly used for lighting and power services. They are driven by steam or internal-combustion engines, water turbines, windmills, and so on.

Currents which alternate at such high frequencies that they fail to actuate any sound-reproducing apparatus, such as a telephone diaphragm, are termed 'high frequency currents'. The limiting frequency is generally assumed to be about 10,000 cycles (10 kC) per second, and frequencies higher than this are called 'high frequencies'. As a rule, high-frequency currents are not generated by rotating alternators but by electronic valves (oscillators) which are used in all branches of electronic engineering. Before high-frequencies were introduced, insulation problems were relatively straightforward, but after its introduction, materials which were used satisfactorily in power-frequency applications were found mostly unsuitable for high-frequency work. Whenever the power factor was too high the insulating materials became hot as a result of the dielectric losses occurring.

Steatite – Clinoenstatite Bodies

Steatite was first used in Germany for low-frequency and low-voltage work where fine dimensional tolerances and great mechanical strength were required. It possesses better dielectric properties than porcelain. When the inauguration of the radio industry called for high-frequency insulating materials, steatite was the starting point in the development work which produced the low loss ceramic materials so essential in the design of all radio, radar, television, and similar instruments.

Steatite is a mineral composed almost entirely of cryptocrystalline talc ($3MgO.4SiO_2.H_2O$). Talc occurs in many parts of the United States, in the north-eastern part of Bavaria, in France, Morocco, Egypt and Indo-China. Originally it was pulverized and mixed with a small amount of clay, in order to make it more plastic, and with small amounts of feldspar, in order to make it dense at a firing temperature of about 1400° C. During firing the talc is decomposed and clinoenstatite ($MgO. SiO_2$) and free silica are formed. The crystalline structure of the fired steatite article is responsible for the low-power factor. The feldspar, which is admixed as a flux, combines with the free silica and with the clay and its decomposition products and forms a glassy bond. This glassy bond has, however, an unfavourable influence on the power factor and for this reason feldspar has been replaced by alkaline-earth carbonates. This replacement considerably improves the homogeneity of the crystal structure of the fired product and as a result of this the dielectric properties are also improved.

The composition of some steatite bodies are given in the following table, published in *Ceramic Whitewares*, by Rexford Newcomb, Jr. (Pitman Publishing Corporation).

Composition of Clinoenstatite Bodies

Component	Body A	Body B	Body C	Body D
Steatite talc	87%	90%	60.0%	88%
Potash feldspar	6%	5%	–	–
Plastic kaolin	7%	5%	15.0%	5%
Magnesium carbonate	–	–	7.5%	–
Barium carbonate	–	–	17.5%	6%
Calcium carbonate	–	–	–	1%
Firing Temperature Orton Cone	14	13	12–13	13

The term 'steatite' is very often applied to cover all ceramic bodies which contain talc. Strictly speaking, some of these talc-containing bodies should be called clinoenstatite bodies. Where a body contains sufficient talc so that, after firing, a crystalline clinoenstatite network is formed, it is nowadays generally called a 'clinoenstatite' body. Such bodies are widely used nowadays in the radio industry, for instance, for wave bend switches, tube sockets and supports, trimmer bases, condenser plates, coil forms, variometers, crystal holders, co-axial cable spacers, let-in and stand-off insulators, and for many other similar applications. Not only have clinoenstatite bodies favourable dielectric properties, but they also have very favourable mechanical properties, e.g. greater tensile and compressive strengths, and greater impact strength than porcelain. The volume resistivity at elevated temperatures is also higher than porcelain. Generally speaking it can be said that the replacement of feldspar by barium and magnesium carbonates improves not only the dielectric properties, such as power factor and volume resistance at high temperature, but also the mechanical characteristics.

Properties of Two Typical Clinoenstatite Bodies

		Body A	Body B
Power factor	60 cycles . . .	0.30%	0.14%
	1000 k.C. . . .	0.20%	0.8 %
	10 M.C. . . .	0.18%	0.06%
(Certain clinoenstatite bodies have a power factor at 10 M.C. of only 0.01%.)			
Permittivity		6	6
Breakdown strength kV. per mm. .		15	30
Volume resistivity at 700° C. in ohms .		2.3×10^4	4.8×10^8
Tensile strength lb./sq. in. . .		8,500	10,000
Compressive strength lb./sq. in. .		75,000	85,000
		lbs./sq. in.	lbs./sq. in.
Resistance to impact ft. lb./sq. in. .		1.8	2.1

Manufacturing Methods. – Clinoenstatite articles can be made by the following methods:

1. (*a*) *Dry Pressing.* Powdered talc is a self-lubricant and can consequently be pressed in metal dies without the addition of water. The dry powder can be prepared either by dry mixing the raw materials or by wet mixing the raw materials in slip form, removing the water in a filter press, drying

the filter cakes and disintegrating the filter cakes into fine granules. The size of the granules is of great importance. To increase the mechanical strength of the pressed article before firing, suitable binders are admixed to the powder.

(b) *Semi-dry Pressing.*

2. *Extruding tubes and rods in plastic state.*

3. *Throwing and turning.*

4. *Jollying.*

5. *Casting.*

Clinoenstatite bodies, to which a considerable percentage of magnesium carbonate or magnesium oxide is added, approach, in their composition, the mineral forsterite, which has the formula $2MgO . SiO_2$. Such bodies have particularly favourable dielectric properties. For instance, the power factor is 0.04% measured wet after immersion in water. The volume resistivity at 700° C. is 1×10^8 ohms per cm. cube. However, the thermal expansion of clinoenstatite bodies with large MgO additions is larger than those of the conventional clinoenstatite bodies. The thermal expansion of the latter bodies [1] is about 7.7×10^{-6}, whereas the forsterite type of clinoenstatite body has a thermal expansion of 9×10^{-6}.

Cordierite Bodies

Clay admixed to talc acts as a flux. Of all clay-talc-mixtures, the mixture with the lowest softening point is the following:

30% clay
70% talc

This is an interesting mixture because after being fired to 1280° C., its thermal expansion is only $\frac{4}{7}$ of talc and $\frac{1}{4}$ of porcelain. The extremely low thermal expansion is caused by the formation of the mineral cordierite ($2MgO . 2Al_2O_3 . 5SiO_2$). Fig. 22 illustrates the softening and firing temperatures of various talc clay mixtures. It shows that the firing range (this means the difference between firing temperature and softening

1. Published by Thurnauer (American Lava Corporation).

temperature) of mixtures consisting mainly of talc, with only small additions of clay, and also mixtures consisting mainly of clay, with small additions of talc, is large. This makes the use of such bodies an easy proposition for industrial purposes. Mixtures of 50 to 25 parts clay and 50 to 70 parts talc have, however, a very small firing range. The mixture of 30% clay with 70% talc has practically no firing range at all! It softens

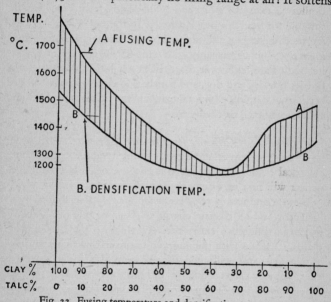

Fig. 22. Fusing temperature and densification temperature of talc-clay mixtures. Shaded area indicates firing range.

and fuses at the same temperature. Bodies which so closely approach the theoretical composition of cordierite are therefore difficult to handle and are more or less of theoretical interest only.

In order to widen the firing range other materials such as zircon are added to the batch. The thermal expansion of the body, however, rapidly increases when the theoretical composition of cordierite is altered by any addition.

The thermal expansion of 'cordierite' bodies manufactured on an industrial scale, and fired in commercial tunnel kilns, is therefore larger than the expansion of pure cordierite. Such bodies are used for many articles which have to withstand terrific thermal shocks, for instance, in the manufacture of electrical heater plates and cores for electrical resistors.

The dielectric properties of cordierite bodies are somewhat similar to those of porcelain bodies and are not particularly suitable for very high frequencies. In the radio industry cordierite is, however, useful for those articles whose dimensions must not alter appreciably with temperature changes. Cordierite bodies are, however, used in much larger quantities for burner nozzles and tips, and for thermo-couple insulation and other applications which take advantage of the high heat and shock resistance of cordierite.

High Permittivity Ceramics for Electrical Condensers. – In order to make this chapter more easily understandable for the non-electrical reader, the nature and purpose of an electrical condenser will first be briefly explained.

If two conductors, say two metal plates, are separated by an insulator and an electric charge is given to one plate, then a potential difference exists between the two plates. The two plates, together with the intervening insulating material, have capacitance and will theoretically keep this capacitance for ever. Because they 'condense' or hold the capacitance they are called condensers or capacitors. The capacitance of a condenser, which means the amount of electricity in farads it can hold, depends on the shape and size of the electrodes and the nature of the intervening insulating material. This insulating material has a sort of 'binding power' which may be very great or on the other hand may be as small as that of air. (The dielectric constant of air is 1.) This binding power is called the dielectric constant or permittivity. A material like porcelain, which is able to bind five times as much electricity as air, has therefore a permittivity of 5.

Ceramics can be used much more advantageously than other

materials in the manufacture of condensers, because of the following reasons:

1. The fact that metal electrodes can be formed on the ceramic. This is done by using a ceramic paint, prepared by mixing precious metal compounds and a ceramic flux, which, after being fired, adheres firmly to the ceramic surface.

2. The power factor of certain ceramic materials is very low.

3. The permittivity of certain ceramics is higher than that of other materials.

4. Ceramics are not attacked by humid and hot atmospheres.

5. The permittivity of certain ceramics decreases or increases with the temperature. This temperature dependence of the permittivity can be regulated at will, which is not possible with other materials.

Rutile Bodies

Rutile bodies consist mainly of the crystal rutile – a titanium dioxide (TiO_2). Rutile crystals have an extremely high dielectric constant (89 perpendicular to the crystal axis and 173 parallel). Finely pulverized and prefired rutile crystals are mixed with a small portion of plastic clay or bentonite which has the sole purpose of making the mixture workable. The addition of a large proportion of clay would decrease the dielectric constant considerably and would also adversely affect the favourable power factor. Only very small additions of clay or bentonite can therefore be used. The resulting material is, consequently, not very plastic and can only be formed into simple shapes such as tubes, caps or discs. Fortunately in most cases only very simple shapes are required in the manufacture of condensers. The dielectric constant of rutile bodies has a strongly negative temperature coefficient, in other words, with increasing temperature the dielectric constant decreases. Very much use is made of this property nowadays, in the manufacture of compensating capacitors (capacitors which compensate the positive temperature drift of an oscillatory circuit.)

The power factor of rutile bodies is very satisfactory at high frequencies, but increases considerably at lower frequencies. This disadvantage has been largely overcome by the use of rutile-zirconium dioxide mixtures. The permittivity of such modified rutile bodies is still rather high and permittivities up to 80 may be obtained. There is a demand on the part of radio and radar manufacturers for condensers with very well-defined differing temperature coefficients of capacity. This demand has been met and it is possible to provide for very accurate temperature compensation. The leading manufacturers of high-frequency ceramics make ranges of rutile bodies, in which the permittivity and temperature coefficient of permittivity vary. For instance, the American Lava Corporation manufactures two dielectric materials with positive temperature coefficient between $-30°$ C. and $+100°$ C., the permittivity of which is independent of the temperature, and 15 different materials with different negative temperature coefficients ranging from -10 to -750 parts per million per degree Centigrade. The power factors of these materials are all very favourable, namely between 0.05 and 0.03%.

Magnesium Orthotitanate Bodies

Those bodies mentioned in the previous chapter which have temperature coefficients of permittivity zero, or near zero, are characterized by a particularly low power factor. Several of these bodies are magnesium orthotitanates prepared by mixing approximately equal quantities of magnesia and calcined rutile according to the molecular formula $2MgO.TiO_2$ (the molecular weight of magnesia being 40 and of titania 80). After firing to a temperature of approximately $1400°$ C., the mineral magnesium orthotitanate is formed and imparts its favourable dielectric characteristics to the material. The dielectric constant is about three times as great as that of mica, which the reader will know is extensively used in condensers. The power factor is as good as that of mica and the temperature variation of permittivity is zero for certain types. This material is, consequently, an ideal dielectric for condensers, where temperature independence of capacity, a low power factor and small dimensions are desirable. It has been found that although the crystalline structure of magnesium orthotitanate bodies is very uniform, the size of the individual crystals is rendered more uniform by the addition of zirconium dioxide. This, in turn, makes the dielectric characteristics more uniform and independent of the frequency applied, and improves particularly the dielectric characteristics at low frequencies.

Ultra-high Permittivity Ceramics

The latest achievement in the field of condenser dielectrics is the development of ceramics possessing a permittivity of 1,000 and more. Barium and strontium titanates are the predominating constituents. The Erie Resistor Co of America are producing ceramic condensers, the ceramic material (an alkaline

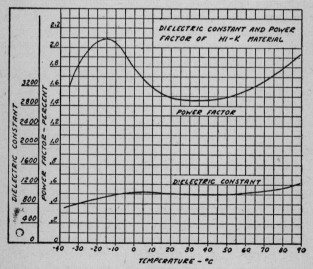

Fig. 23. Ultra-high permittivity ceramic at various temperatures
(By courtesy of Erie Resistor Corporation.)

K

earth titanate) has a permittivity of 1,200. The permittivity has a strong positive temperature coefficient between −40° C. and +40° C., the power factor is rather high and varies with varying temperatures. U.h. permittivity ceramics are now made also in Great Britain. Fig. 23 illustrates the power factor and permittivity of this material and their variation with temperature. This type of condenser material is of particular interest in the following circumstances:

1. Where small dimensions and high capacity values are essential.

2. Where the power factor and temperature stability of the capacitance are not of particular importance.

The use of ceramic condensers with their inherent advantages is thus made possible in cases where previously paper condensers and electrolytic condensers have been used. Ceramics with such a high permittivity will find increasing applications, provided the power factor can be improved and the temperature dependence can be made more regular. Much research work has been carried out in order to achieve this aim and many patents have been published lately which give interesting information. Considerable improvements are claimed by the use of the following compositions:

1. Barium or strontium titanate plus barium or strontium zirconate.

2. Barium and strontium titanates plus barium and strontium stannates (tin compounds).

3. Alkali earth titanates plus magnesium or calcium zirconates.

4. Calcium titanates plus barium and strontium stannates and zirconates.

Several of the bodies described in these patent specifications have permittivities of 9,000 and more! The power factor of materials with extremely high permittivities is in most cases still much too high. There are, however, materials described as having a permittivity of 2,500 and a power factor of 0.35% which is a very great improvement compared with the first barium titanates developed. Such bodies must become tremendously important for use in high capacity condensers. Condensers made from such a material have a capacity five hundred times greater than that of those of the same size made of porcelain, glass, mica, steatite or paper. Some other properties of these new insulating materials may find interesting application, namely: (1) the dependence of their permittivity on (*a*) temperature, (*b*) voltage applied; and (2) the dependence of the volume resistivity on (*a*) temperature, (*b*) voltage.

Zircon Porcelains

The use of zirconium as a refractory material has been mentioned in the chapter 'Refractories'. A new development, zircon porcelain, has received much use and attention in the United States, as a high-frequency ceramic material. The main advantage of zirconium porcelains compared with clinoenstatite and other high-frequency ceramics is their larger firing range. This property is very welcome under mass production conditions since it decreases the manufacturing losses. Within a firing range of about 120° C. they are claimed to be absolutely dense and non-porous. The Titanium Alloy Manufacturing Co. published the composition and characteristics of zirconium porcelains developed in their Research department. Of particular interest is the following composition:

Zirconium silicate . . .	59.2%
Calcium zirconium silicate .	29.6%
Ball clay	11.2%
Dielectric constant . . .	8.6
Power factor at 1 M.c. . .	0.03%

The Westinghouse Co. of America and others manufacture zirconium porcelains on a commercial scale.

Visit to Messrs Buller's Works at Milton

The demand of the electrical industry in the United States for ceramic insulators is so large that it is, generally speaking, sub-divided into various branches, each specializing in certain types of insulators. There are factories which concentrate on the manufacture of such high-voltage porcelain insulators as can be produced by plastic methods (jollying, extruding). Others are concerned only with the manufacture of such low loss materials as can be produced by die pressing, others only make high-voltage overhead line insulators and so on. In Great Britain the distances covered by power transmission lines are smaller, and the electrical industry itself is smaller and consequently also the quantity of insulators required. On the other hand, the number of different types of insulators manufactured in this country is greater, first of all because a considerable proportion of the production of the British insulator industry is for export and various countries require different insulator types. Because of these conditions the insulator industry is not split up to such an extent as in the U.S.A. and there are two or three large insulator factories in this country manufacturing the whole range of ceramic insulating materials required by the electrical industry.

This makes the electrical porcelain industry in this country very flexible and versatile. The peak demand for insulators of the power-generating and power-transmission side of the electrical industry does not, as a rule, coincide with the peak demand for porcelain of that part of the industry which caters for house installation and radio. Fluctuations in the insulator industry as to the employment of both labour and productive capacity are thus reduced to a minimum.

A visitor to the works of Messrs Bullers in Milton (North Staffordshire) soon obtains an impressive idea of the enormous variety of insulators of all shapes, both large and small, required by the electrical industry. He will also be amazed at the number of manufacturing processes necessary to make all the various types.

In order to follow the flow of production let us first have a look at the large sliphouse where the clay mixtures or bodies required by all the shaping departments are produced.

In the sliphouse the mixing and compounding is done by the wet method described earlier in this book. At the Milton factory, however, the mixing is even more thorough, owing to the fact that all the body ingredients not only are all mixed in an ark, but they are also ground and mixed together in Alsing cylinders for several hours. The body slip is then de-watered in a battery of large filter presses. The filter cakes have three destinations: (1) For preparing a plastic body in de-airing pug mills. (2) For preparing the casting slip in blungers. (3) For preparing a pressing powder by first drying, then dis-integrating and – in the case of wet pressing – mixing the granules with a water-oil emulsion. To give some idea of the clay consumption of the Bullers factory it is interesting to note that there are ten large de-airing pug mills used for preparing the plastic body.

As already mentioned, the plastic body can be shaped by: (1) Jollying. (2) Extruding. (3) Turning. All these shaping methods are employed at Milton.

In the jollying department we observe how a great variety of high-voltage transmission line insulators are manufactured. Insulators with deep grooves and thin, projecting ribs are jollied by hand. A great number of standardized suspension and pin type insulators are made semi-automatically on the hot press. The outer part of the insulator surface obtains its shape from a plaster mould. The inside is shaped by a metal plunger, heated by a gas flame, which presses into the plastic body and squeezes the surplus clay away.

Very large porcelain jackets for high-voltage bushings are made in the jollying department either in a single piece or in sections which are carefully joined together in plastic state. The building up of bushings – larger than a man – from small sections, is a fascinating and highly-specialized art. A series of large bushings, about 80 in. in height and 34 in. in diameter, were being made by this method when the author visited the works a few years ago. But now bushing parts 10 ft in height and 4 ft in diameter are made, to cope with the higher volt-ages which have come into operation in recent years.

In the extrusion department, slices cut from plastic cylinders (prepared by the de-airing pug mill) were placed in hydraulic presses. A battery of twelve such hydraulic presses was in operation, extruding rods or tubes from various bodies. For instance, a refractory material is used for extruding bars for electric fires, porcelain for the production of resistor tubes and special low-loss bodies for coil formers. Most of these extruded tubes and rods then go to the turning department, after drying, where grooves or threads are cut on semi-automatic lathes.

A great variety of insulators is produced in the turning department. The blanks, as they come from the de-airing pug mill, are first dried and then turned to the desired shape on semi-automatic lathes.

Many different types of high- and low-voltage line switch-gear and transformer insulators which formerly were shaped in a plastic state by jollying, are now turned on semi-automatic lathes, a greater speed of production and greater accuracy being simultaneously obtained.

In the pressing department all the various methods described earlier in this book are employed; wet pressing, semi-dry pressing, and dry pressing. Large and complicated articles are pressed by hand and smaller articles (both wet and semi-dry) are produced in automatic presses which deliver the ware on to conveyor belts. For dry pressing, large American automatic presses are used, capable of pressing one article in three seconds.

The articles are glazed either by dipping (whenever possible using semi-automatic methods) or, in the case of pressed ware, on automatic spraying machines, similar to those described in the chapter dealing with table ware.

The greater part of the output is fired in three gas-fired open-flame tunnel ovens, but coal-fired bottle ovens and gas-fired intermittent ovens are also used, particularly for firing articles which are too large to pass through the tunnel ovens.

The three tunnel ovens have the following lengths:

300 ft
220 ft
180 ft

Particular care is taken to use the available setting space to the best advantage. Originally, saggers of the conventional shape similar to those employed in intermittent ovens were used. After many experiments, rectangular saggers were introduced which, at the same time, allow a greater setting density per sq. ft., and also allow a more uniform flow for the flames and hot air. A further improvement is the open setting method which would be used exclusively if refractory oven furniture were more readily available. Using refractory oven furniture exclusively it is possible for Messrs Bullers to accommodate per unit truck space over three times as much ware as they could in the original circular saggers that were used when the ovens were first built.

The various tests which the insulators have to undergo were described earlier. Large well-laid-out testing stations are available at Milton for carrying out these tests. For design tests, sample tests and research, a high-voltage laboratory is available which makes it possible to test insulators at voltages up to 500,000 volts. A 250 kVA generator set produces 50 cycle alternating current of accurate sine-wave-form. The generator set includes a pilot exciter, main exciter, generator and driving motor.

The voltage is regulated by controlling the voltage of the pilot exciter (a small machine easy to regulate) which provides the magnetizing current for the main exciter. This in turn provides the magnetizing current for the generator, the voltage of which can be varied between zero and 2,000 volts. The transformer has a ratio of 1/250 so that a voltage of 500,000 volts can be produced.

In the mechanical laboratory insulators up to 10 ft. long can be subjected to 25 tons tensile load, post insulators can be subjected to a bending load up to 2 tons, and torsion tests up to 100,000 lb. per inch can be made.

Insulator aggregates up to 10 ft high can be subjected to the rigorous combined tensile and vibrating cantilever tests required on this type of apparatus. There are also facilities for gas and hydraulic testing up to 4000 lb. per square inch on porcelain tubes and weather sheds such as are used for the terminations of gas-filled cables, air-blast switch gear, and so on.

In the physical laboratory, power factor, permittivity, temperature coefficient of permittivity, volume resistivity at various temperatures, surface resistivity under various humidity conditions and the thermal expansion of the various materials, can be measured.

CHAPTER XX

Super Refractories and Ceramic-Metal Combinations in Aircraft Power Plant Construction

As a result of their high refractoriness, ceramic materials have received much attention during the last years for possible use in the construction of aircraft power plant components. Heat resistance is of very great importance in view of the high temperatures involved. The best available metal alloys are used in these machines to the permissible limit of their mechanical properties.

Further increases in operating temperatures can therefore only be considered if it is possible to improve the metal alloys by the use of rare and more expensive metals. Availability is often, particularly from the military standpoint, of great importance. Improved materials must at the same time be easily obtainable. Fortunately, most of the promising ceramic materials are in good supply, but their properties have to be improved to meet extraordinary requirements. In the United States the Armed Forces have put very great amounts at the disposal of the various ceramic research institutions and universities, and striking progress has been made in the development of entirely new materials. While these new materials are not yet used for gas turbines, there is a possibility that further improvements will be made, and that the new materials, particularly ceramic metal combinations called 'Cermets' will contribute to further improvements in the efficiency of these machines. The development programme of the American Armed Forces includes three applications:

Firstly: use of refractory bodies for highly stressed components in gas turbines.

Secondly: application of ceramics in rocket-thrust cylinder liners.

Thirdly: protective ceramic coating for metal components
to minimize corrosive action of combustion
gases.

This programme does not include the well-known application of ceramics for the manufacture of sparking plugs and
electrical components used in radio and radar equipment,
which were dealt with earlier in this book in the chapter on
Pure Oxide Refractories and Low Loss Ceramics.

The ceramic components envisaged in gas turbine con-
structions, such as nozzle vanes, and cans, are not only subjected to very high temperatures, but also to very rapid
changes in temperature, and in addition the mechanical
stresses change very rapidly. Brittle materials are therefore out
of the question, and materials had to be developed which combine the properties of highly refractory materials and non-
corroding metals. These new materials, 'Cermets', are mixtures of metals and ceramics. Cermet components are generally
formed by powder metallurgic methods which consist of
grinding and pressing the powder mixture and then sintering
at very high temperatures.

The metal powders and ceramic powders are ground and
mixed for extended periods of time in steel mills. Various
alcohols are used as fluid vehicles and materials like Tungsten
carbides are used as grinding agents. The extended grinding
operation picks up, of course, impurities from the mill and
grinding agents, but it has been found that little difference in
the properties of the standard materials was caused by these
impurities.

Innumerable metals and ceramics were used, and in the
Journal of the American Society 1950 and 1951, very interesting papers can be found describing the various cermets
which were prepared from all types of materials, such as
Boron Carbides, Zirconium Carbides, Titanium Carbides, and
Carbides of many other refractory metals. One of the most
interesting and promising cermets is described in an article
by A. R. Blackburn and T. S. Shevlin in the November 1951
issue of the Journal of the American Society. This cermet con-

sists of 30 parts chromium and 70 parts alumina ($Al_2 O_3$).
This mixture, after thorough grinding and mixing, was fired
at a temperature of 3100° F. (1700° C.).

Some of its more interesting mechanical properties are as
follows:

Compression strength	75° F.	320,000	lb. per sq. inch
Tensile strength	75° F.	35,000	,, ,, ,, ,,
	1600° F.	21,560	,, ,, ,, ,,
	2000° F.	18,490	,, ,, ,, ,,
	2400° F.	14,120	,, ,, ,, ,,

For the sake of comparison it is of interest to note that the
tensile strength of
Duralumin   is   56,000 lb. per sq. inch
Wrought Iron is 40,000 ,, ,, ,, ,,   (at room
Cast Iron is 28,000 ,, ,, ,, ,,   temperature)
whereas the tensile strength of Clinoenstatite bodies (which
are mechanically among the best ceramic materials) is only
10,000 lb. per sq. in.

In this connexion it is necessary to add a few words about
fatigue failure*. The figures referred to above indicate how
sample pieces behave when they are stressed once only, whereas in service materials often have to undergo thousands,
sometimes many millions, of reversals of stress. The turbine
shaft of a gas turbine engine may be revolving at 15,000 r.p.m.
The turbine plates also vibrate in a complex manner. The
tensile strength figures mentioned above are therefore not
necessarily a measure of the capacity of a metal to stand up to
such repetitions of alternating stresses, and the number of
reversals of stresses which material can stand without breakage is the endurance limit of this material. The endurance
characteristics of most of the metals have been carefully
investigated in the past, but for ceramics and for the crossing
of ceramics with metals (the so-called 'Cermets') much
investigation into their endurance properties have still to be

* W. Alexander and A. Street, *Metals in the Service of Man* (Pelican
Books, 1944).

carried out. It can, however, be stated that the new cermets developed in recent years possess improved properties in this respect, as compared with pure ceramics. Whether or not they will be good enough for use as components in gas turbine manufacture, remains to be seen. There can be no doubt, however, that, as time goes on, many applications will be found for new materials combining to a certain extent the heat-resisting and non-corroding properties of ceramics with the greater heat conductivity, elasticity, and mechanical strength of metals.

Another power plant application of ceramics and one more in keeping with the conventional use of ceramics is in rocket engine thrust cylinders. A refractory ceramic liner is used in both combustion chamber and exhaust nozzle. In addition to being exposed to extremely high temperatures, the combustion chamber and nozzle materials are subjected to severe thermal shocks on ignition and also to corrosive effects of hot gases under very high pressure. Under these conditions, ceramic refractories can be made to last much longer than metals. Ceramics which have proved most satisfactory for these applications are limited to the super refractories which at the same time have excellent erosion and thermal shock resistance. Some of these super refractory materials have melting points approaching or higher than 3,000 centigrades, such as Tungsten Carbide, Zirconium Carbide, Titanium Carbide, and Molybdenum. Very large amounts of money have been spent in America for research work in ceramics, cermets, and super refractories, and great progress has been made in the development of these new materials. One can safely assume that ever higher temperatures will be used in the future by industry generally and by the aircraft industry in particular, and that the ceramist of the future will be in the position to meet the requirements of the engineer.

APPENDIX

EXPORTS OF THE BRITISH POTTERY INDUSTRY IN THE YEARS 1938, 1951, AND 1952, ACCORDING TO THE ACCOUNTS RELATING TO TRADE AND NAVIGATION OF THE UNITED KINGDOM, DECEMBER 1952. PUBLISHED BY H.M. STATIONERY OFFICE.

CLASS III Articles Wholly or Mainly Manufactured	Value		
	Year	Year ended 31st December	
	1938	1951	1952
Tiles –	£	£	£
Glazed wall and hearth tiles:			
To Union of South Africa .	13,585	232,113	258,720
„ Australia	80,250	574,501	362,370
„ Canada	10,315	354,356	317,715
„ Other British Countries	78,633		
„ „ „ „ and the Irish Republic . }		424,509	589,924
„ Foreign Countries . .	18,123	1,224,719	777,279
Total	200,906	2,810,198	2,306,008
Other tiles	37,210	258,014	271,660
Sanitary ware –			
To Eire	55,538	426,889	254,128
„ Union of South Africa .	76,367	354,582	322,843
„ India, Pakistan, &c. . .	43,182	250,310	183,921
„ Other British Countries .	209,101	1,620,337	1,896,528
„ Denmark	48,023	131,632	76,694
„ Egypt	15,482	128,964	70,696
„ Argentine Republic . .	52,308		
„ Uruguay		94,946	143,065
„ Other Foreign Countries .	143,887	704,905	687,488
Total { Of earthenware, white, coloured, or cane and white (including vitreous ware) . . .	449,034	2,836,197	2,596,664
Of fireclay, glazed or enamelled	122,509	513,004	583,591
Other sorts, including all drain pipes, angles, bends, elbows, and traps	72,345	517,317	455,108
Total	643,888	3,866,518	3,635,363

	Value		
China, including translucent pottery and all pottery known as china or porcelain, other than electrical ware –	Year	Year ended 31st December	
	1938	1951	1952
	£	£	£
To Eire	7,717	234,319	189,812
„ Union of South Africa .	17,059		
„ Australia	67,412	525,242	393,408
„ New Zealand . . .	39,134	204,143	248,456
„ Canada	177,888	2,284,142	2,090,103
„ Other British Countries .	23,004	344,937	415,196
„ United States of America	63,257	1,584,996	1,642,751
„ Other Foreign Countries	28,885	228,615	317,511
Total	424,356	5,406,394	5,297,237
Electrical ware (including insulators)	151,249	1,145,892	1,248,165
Earthenware of all other descriptions –			
To Eire	44,103	304,527	201,743
„ British West Africa . .	3,992		
„ Union of South Africa .	147,584	1,069,698	858,302
„ India, Pakistan, &c. . .	42,039		
„ Pakistan		265,101	138,802
„ Ceylon		149,648	96,866
„ Australia	348,257	2,277,093	1,572,982
„ New Zealand	148,244	665,929	879,849
„ Canada	527,271	2,603,066	2,183,851
„ Other British Countries .	100,561	909,123	934,104
„ Norway	29,998		
„ Denmark	44,426		
„ United States of America	215,022	1,356,943	1,293,423
„ Brazil	34,003	137,642	7,881
„ Uruguay		73,096	73,096
„ Argentine Republic . .	108,769		
„ Other Foreign Countries	205,530	1,401,698	1,597,113
Total	1,999,799	11,213,564	9,838,355
Refractory goods, not elsewhere specified	507,637	2,316,586	2,883,453
All other descriptions . . .	72,908	258,627	193,033
Total of Pottery and other shaped and fired clay products . .	4,037,953	27,275,793	25,673,274

From the above it can be seen, how much British pottery exports have increased by the end of 1952 as compared with 1938:

Tiles, 10-fold; Sanitary Ware, 6-fold; China, 12½-fold; Electrical Insulators, 8-fold; Earthenware, 5-fold; Refractory Goods, 6-fold.

GLOSSARY

Acids, bases and salts : By the combination of an acid and a base (a process called neutralization) a salt is formed. – In ceramics, oxides of *non*-metals (such as silicon and boron) act as acids and combine with oxides of metals (such as sodium, potassium, magnesium, calcium) which act as bases forming glasses or glazes.

Acid refractory products : Forming those made of clay-silica mixtures or pure silica.

Alkali : A term first used to designate the soluble parts of the ashes of plants; chemically alkalis may be regarded as water in which part of the hydrogen is replaced by metallic radicals, e.g. potassium or sodium. They neutralize acids and form salts with them. – Alkalis are introduced into ceramic mixtures, e.g. by the addition of feldspar or Cornish stone and are used in the preparation of frits (*see* Frit) for glazes. They decrease the vitrification and melting points of ceramic mixtures and are also used in the preparation of casting slips (*see* Slip). – The oxides of calcium, strontium and barium are called Alkaline earths.

Alumina : Aliminium oxide (Al_2O_3), a white insoluble powder, melting point 2200° C., used in the manufacture of highly refractory material and for bedding bone china in the bisque-saggars. Produced by calcining Bauxite.

Aluminous refractory goods : Those which contain more than 45% Alumina.

Bag : a firebrick structure near the fireplace of a potter's oven which prevents the flame from striking directly on the ware.

Ball clay : A very plastic clay from Devon and Dorset.

Basic refractory materials : Those containing a large proportion of lime, magnesia or other metal oxides.

Bat : A potter's term for the thin disc of clay which is subsequently thrown on to the plaster mould for jollying plates. – The name is also used for a fired thin slab made of fireclay or other heat-resisting material to be used in kilns for placing ware.

Bauxite : Hydrated alumina (Al_2O_3 H_2O) used in calcined form to increase the heat-resistance of refractory materials.

Bisque : Pottery which has been fired once, without glaze.

Blunger : A machine in which rotating arms or propellers break up large lumps of clay and mix them with water, forming a 'slip'.

Body: Potters designate by the term 'body' both the plastic paste used for shaping an article and also the material formed by the firing process.

Bone ash: Used as an opacifier for glazes and as an ingredient in bone china bodies, and is produced by calcining the bones of oxen.

Bone China: Most of the china-ware made in England is bone china. It is characterized by its white colour and great translucency.

Buller's rings: Buller's firing trial rings indicate the work done by heat by their contraction.

Calcine: To heat a substance in order to disintegrate it or to reduce it to a powder.

Calcareous glazes: Glazes in which lime or other calcium compounds are the main fluxing agents.

Carborundum: Silicon carbide (SiC) is produced by the fusion of sand and coke in an electric furnace and is used for the manufacture of refractory material, grinding wheels and electrical resistors.

Castable: Refractory material which is mixed with water, poured into place and allowed to set like concrete.

China-ware: An expression describing porcelain, particularly porcelain table ware.

China clay: A white burning clay used for the manufacture of china (porcelain) and earthenware.

Chipping: If the glaze has a smaller thermal expansion than the body, it tends to peel off. This is called 'chipping'.

Chromite: A mineral in the chromite series of multiple oxides ($FeO . Cr_2O_3$) used as a neutral refractory material.

Chromium oxide: Used as colouring agent for green glazes, bodies and colours.

Clay: Is formed by the decomposition of feldspar; it is hydrated silicate of aluminium ($A_2O_3 . 2SiO_2 . H_2O$). If mixed with water, it is plastic and when dried becomes hard; when fired, harder still and permanent. The most important constituents of clay are crystals of sheet-like structure such as kaolinite and others. Clay never occurs in nature in absolutely pure state; it contains impurities like feldspar, mica and silica.

Clay state: A pottery article is in the clay state when it is shaped but not yet fired.

Clay-substance does not exist in nature and is a term used by ceramists for ceramic calculations, designating theoretically pure clay.

Clay ware: 1. Potter's term for shaped pottery before firing.
2. Everything made of clay.

Cone: See Seger Cone.

Cornish Stone: A mineral rich in feldspar, used in the manufacture of earthenware, bone china and porcelain.

Crazing: If the glaze has a larger thermal expansion than the body, it develops a network of fine fissures or crackles; this is called crazing.

Crucible: Small pot used by chemists, founders, etc, for melting purposes, made of fireclay, graphite and other refractory materials. (For use in the laboratory also made of porcelain.)

Crystal: Strictly speaking a body having a definite geometrical form, but also pure translucent silica, and also glass of superior clearness (crystal glass).

Crystal-glazes: Devitrified glazes in which crystallization has taken place.

Crystobalite: Crystal modification of quartz which is formed by heating the clay-silica bodies at temperatures above 1100° C.; it increases the thermal expansion and decreases the danger of crazing.

De-airing of clay: The clay is treated, shred, cut and pugged in a vacuum chamber of a pugmill, from which the de-aired clay is extruded through the mouthpiece. De-airing improves the consistency, plasticity and dry-strength of the clay.

Decalomania (Decal for short)*:* Is another term for ceramic lithos or ceramic transfers (*see* Litho).

Deflocculent: Very small amount (1/3% to 1/2%) of sodium carbonate or sodium silicate act as deflocculents and transform a plastic clay into a liquid slip.

Devitrification: The formation of crystals in glasses or glazes, taking place when the hot liquid melt solidifies in the cooling process.

Dipping: The ware is immersed by the 'dipper' in a glaze 'slip' and thus covered with a layer of glaze material.

Dobbin: Semi-automatic chamber dryer, consisting of rotating compartments, in which the clay ware, as it comes from the cup- or plate-making machines, is dried on or in the plaster moulds.

Dolomite: Calcium-magnesium carbonate. Intermediate in composition between limestone (calcium carbonate) and magnesite (magnesium carbonate). It is used as a flux in glazes (when it forms a calcium-magnesium silicate) and as a refractory material (in the absence of silica).

Dunting: The cracking of fired articles during the cooling period of the kiln, caused by too rapid cooling.

Earthenware: A slightly porous type of pottery, characterized by a white or ivory paste, covered with a translucent glaze.

Elutriation: A method of purifying clay in a slow stream of water. The heavier particles settle down, whereas the lighter ones are carried away and settle in large basins.

Enamel: A vitrified compound applied to meta or ceramic surfaces, which has lower melting temperatures than glazes.

Engobe: A ceramic mixture applied in slip form to cover the body. It does not fuse at the firing temperature like a glaze, but can be covered by a glaze if required.

Extrusion: Plastic clay is forced through a mouthpiece of a pugmill or a press, forming a rod or a tube, which can be cut to the desired length.

Faience: French term for earthenware.

Feldspar: A mineral containing potassium or sodium, alumina and silica, is the most important flux and used in many types of ceramic ware. In this country, feldspar is often introduced into a ceramic mixture by Cornish stone, a material rich in feldspar.

Fettling: Finishing the surface of a ceramic article in white hard clay state with a tool, or smoothing it with tow (towing).

Filter-cakes: The plastic body remaining in the filter-frame, when the surplus matter has been removed.

Filter-press removes surplus water from the clay slip and produces a plastic paste. The slip is pressed through chambers covered with filter-cloth.

Fireclay goods are mainly composed of fireclays with the addition of opening materials such as grog (granulated fireclay or sand).

Fireclays are used for the manufacture of refractory materials and are clays which withstand high temperatures.

Flat-ware: Saucers, plates, round and oval dishes, and trays are called flat-ware; cups, pots, bowls, vegetable dishes, soup tureens, etc, are called hollow-ware. Flat-ware deforms more easily during firing and is therefore placed in the 'easiest' places in the kiln.

Flint is a variety of quartz, a crypto-crystalline substance composed of silica. Flint pebbles from the coasts of England, Northern France or Belgium are calcined and ground and used as main source of silica by earthenware and porcelain manufacturers.

Flux is a material (or a mixture of materials) which decreases the vitrification temperature of ceramic bodies, glazes or colours.

Frit: A flux used in the preparation of glazes and colours, produced by melting water-soluble chemicals, such as sodium carbonate, potassium carbonate, borax, boracic acid together with silica and clay, in order to obtain low-melting silicates, not soluble in water.

Ganister is a clayey sand found at the base of coal seams and used in the refractory industry.

Ginetting: The smoothing and polishing of marks after glost firing.

Glass: A transparent or translucent substance formed mainly of silica and metallic oxides, produced by mixing, e.g., sand, sodium or potassium carbonate lime and melting this mixture in a refractory pot or tank in a furnace. It is shaped into the desired form in hot, soft state by mouth-blowing, machine-blowing, or pressing in dies, or in the case of sheet glass by drawing. The physicist might define glass as an undercooled liquid or an amorphous solid.

Glaze: A vitreous (glassy) coating on ceramic articles.

Graphite (pure carbon): Either mineral graphite (plumbago), or retort graphite (formed in glass retorts) used for the manufacture of refractory material, and also for many other purposes outside the scope of this book.

Glost firing means firing the glaze on ware which has previously been fired at a higher temperature (bisque fire).

Green ware: Pottery articles are said to be in the green state when they are shaped but not yet dried or fired.

Grog is a potter's term for broken granulated fired refractory clay, broken granulated saggars, crucibles, etc.

Gypsum: See Plaster of Paris.

Hard glaze is a glaze having a high melting point owing to its high silica content. It is mechanically harder than glazes fired at lower temperatures, and more resistant to chemical attack.

Hard (paste) porcelain, or true porcelain, is made of china clay, feldspar and silica, fired at 1300° C. or more and covered with a hard glaze.

Hardening-on fire: Underglaze decorated earthenware has to be fired at over 600° C. before the glaze can be applied, in order to evaporate the heavy oils used for the preparation of the ceramic colour, and allow the colours to stick on the bisque surface during subsequent 'dipping'.

Hollow-ware : See 'Flat-ware'.

Impermeable : A pottery body (paste) becomes impermeable by application of sufficient heat, which melts the fluxes contained in the body, thus closing the pores, and transforming a porous permeable body into a vitrified non-porous body.

Iron oxides : Iron and iron oxides produce brown or reddish colours in ceramic mixtures if they are fired in an oxidizing atmosphere, and greenish or bluish colours if fired in a reducing atmosphere. Iron oxides are fluxing and colouring materials. Larger particles give brown or black spots, which, particularly in the case of white ware, are a great nuisance to the potter. For this reason much care is being taken to remove iron and iron oxides from the raw materials and from the bodies used for white ware manufacture.

Jiggering and jollying : A process used extensively for making plates and cups. In jollying the plastic clay is placed on or into a plaster of Paris mould, and a profile presses the soft clay firmly on to the mould as it revolves on a spindle. One part of the article (in the case of cups the outside) is thus shaped by the mould and the other part (the inside, in case of a cup) is shaped by the tool.

Kaolin or china clay : A fine white primary clay (*see* Primary clay) used in the manufacture of porcelain, bone china, earthenware, and of refractory materials.

'*Kiln Furniture*' used for 'open' setting of the ware, replacing the time-honoured saggars. Refractory slabs or trays with intervening posts strong enough to support the ware at the high temperature prevailing in the bisque or glost tunnel kiln.

Lead oxide is used extensively in glass and in glazes for table ware. It increases the optical refractive index in glasses and thus makes them and also glazes particularly brilliant, and makes glass soft and suitable for cutting. Lead compounds act as very strong fluxes and decrease considerably the melting temperatures both in the case of glasses and glazes. They are introduced into the batch as PbO (litharge) or Pb_3O_4 (red lead). Both are very poisonous. When lead oxides combine with silica (as in the cases of glass and glaze during the firing) lead silicates are formed which are not poisonous.

Lead silicate : Since lead silicates are not poisonous, lead is nowadays introduced into the glaze batch by using a frit consisting of 65% lead oxide, 33% silica and 2% alumina, commonly called '*lead bisilicate*'.

Lime as calcium oxide is not found in nature. Calcium carbonate, which is the chief source of lime, is found in the form of the mineral calcite. Impure calcite occurs as the rock limestone in large quantities all over the world. Use of the term 'lime' in ceramics very often infers some form of calcium carbonate, chalk, or ground 'limestone'. In the form of calcium carbonate 'lime' is used as a flux in glasses, glazes and to a lesser extent in earthenware manufacture. Lime in the absence of silica is, however, a refractory material.

Lithography is the art of drawing upon and printing from stone; it is used for decorating pottery on and under glaze.

Litho is the sheet of paper on to which the design or pattern is printed, and with the aid of which it is transferred on to the ceramic article.

Magnesium carbonate (Magnesite, Magnesia) is used as flux for glazes. Magnesium oxide (burnt or calcined magnesia) is used as refractory material where a highly basic refractory is required.

Majolica: A porous type of pottery, of reddish or greyish colour, covered with white opaque tin containing glaze. Made by Arabs and Saracens. The name is derived from the island of Majorca where it was made many centuries ago.

Mangle or mangle dryer: a vertical continuous dryer used for drying clay ware and glazed bisque ware.

Marl: A clay which contains sand and fluxes like feldspar and lime.

Mica: A term applied to a number of complex alumina silicates; it occurs in granitic rocks, and, being rather resistant to weathering, is found in many raw kaolins, formed by the decomposition of such rocks. Mica is used as an electric insulating material.

Mouldable: Refractory material which is sufficiently plastic to be formed by hand to the desired shape.

Mullite $(3 \; Al_2O_3. \; 2 \; SiO_2)$: A crystal formed in clay products fired at $1200°$ C. and higher.

Nepheline and Nepheline Syanite are potassium-sodium-alumino-silicates which, in America, are nowadays frequently used instead of feldspars and allow a lower firing temperature.

Neutral refractory materials are those more aluminous than pure clay, or formed of such materials as graphite and carborundum.

Nickel oxide is used in glazes to produce blues, greens, browns and yellows.

Nitre (potassium nitrate): Used to introduce potash into frits.

On-glaze decoration is the decoration of glazed and fired pottery, the colour being applied on top of the fired glaze. After application of the decoration, the article is fired in an enamel or decorating kiln.

Opening material: Non-plastic materials, such as flint, sand, grog, used in clay mixtures to facilitate drying and reduce shrinkage.

Orthoclase, a potash feldspar (*see* Feldspar).

Orton Cones are used in the U.S.A. for heat recording; they are similar to Seger Cones, but the same numbers do not indicate the same temperatures, e.g. Orton cone 14 corresponds to Seger cone 13.

Oxidizing conditions prevail in a kiln when surplus air makes a complete combustion of the gases, carbon particles and heavy oils possible.

Pegmatite is a feldspatic rock containing mainly feldspar and quartz.

Pitcher is fired pottery ground to a powder and used as an opening material in bodies and as a flux in glazes.

Plaster of Paris: Calcined gypsum prepared originally from the deposits of Montmartre (Paris). By heating gypsum, three-quarters of the water of crystallization is removed. When mixed with water and allowed to rehydrate, the plaster-water mixture sets to a solid mass.

Porcelain: A white translucent and vitrified pottery. Feldspar is used as flux.

Potash: (*see* Alkali).

Primary clay: A clay found in the location where it was formed by decomposition of feldspatic rocks.

Pug mill is a machine which makes clay in its plastic state more homogeneous. It consists of a cylinder in which helical knives rotate and cut the clay, pressing it forward through a tapered outlet.

Pyrometer: Heat-recording electrical or optical instrument nowadays used for automatic temperature control.

Quartz (*see* Flint) is crystallized silica (SiO_2). Some varieties are:
  1. Rock crystal, a transparent mineral, from which translucent articles were cut; hence the term 'crystal glass'.
  2. Amethyst (violet).
  3. Chrysoprase (copper green).
  4. Topaz.
  5. Chalcedony.
  6. Jasper.

Quartzite: Granular crystal rock consisting almost entirely of quartz.

Reducing conditions prevail in the kiln if there is not enough air available to make a complete combustion of the carbon particles and carbon compounds in the flame possible.

Refractory material: A material which can be used at high temperatures.

Rutile (titanium dioxide) is used to stain pottery and glazes in colours from ivory to dark yellow. Also a very important dielectrical material for the manufacture of electric condensors.

Saddle, stilt, spur and thimble are refractory fireclay supports used to place the glost ware into the saggar and keep it in the desired position during the glost fire.

Saggars are fireclay boxes in which the pottery is placed for subsequent firing, to protect it from direct contact with the flame.

Salt glaze is formed by the decomposition of common salt, thrown on to the fire grates during the finishing period of the firing process.

S.C. (Seger Cone): Cones made of different ceramic mixtures for heat recording. They become soft and bend over at certain known temperatures, thus recording the work done by heat.

Scaling: If a glaze has a considerably lower thermal expansion than the body, it contracts less when solidifying after firing than the body, and tends to flake off (chipping).

Secondary clays are clays carried away by rain or streams from the location where they were originally formed, and deposited elsewhere.

Shale: A laminated clay often containing bituminous matter.

Shrinkage: During drying and firing clays contract, plastic clays more than lean ones. Opening materials reduce the shrinkage.

Silica (Silicon dioxide) occurs abundantly in nature in the form of quartz, sand, sandstone, pebble flint, and is used in the ceramic industry as opening and refractory material (*see* Acids, Flints, Quartz).

Siliceous clay is a clay containing much sand.

Silicon: (SiO) A grey crystal or brown powder. In the inorganic world, silicon plays a role in the composition of rocks and minerals comparable with that of carbon in the organic world of plants and animals.

Silicon ester: The first chemical compound manufactured in which silicon replaces carbon in a molecule in the realm of organic chemistry. One carbon atom in an alcohol molecule is replaced by silicon. One of the latest developments in the manufacture of highly refractory materials is the mixing of refractory powders with silicon ester. This operation produces a workable body which will not shrink during drying and firing.

Silicones: Are a new type of resins or greases containing SiO (Silicon) showing increased resistance to heat and chemical action and better electrical insulating characteristics compared with conventional resins or greases not containing silicon.

Silicosis: A chronic disease of the lungs chiefly affecting miners and other workers who have to work in silicon dust laden atmosphere such as workers in several branches of the ceramic industry.

Sillimanite: An alumino silicate ($Al_2O_3 . SiO_2$) is used for the manufacture of refractory materials of highest quality.

Slip is a clay diluted to the consistency of cream.

Soft glaze is a glaze softening at low firing temperature; an alternative term would be 'low temperature glaze'.

Sponging: Smoothing the surface of clay ware with a sponge before firing.

Spur: see Saddle.

Steatite (or talc) is a hydreous magnesium silicate, very soft, slightly plastic, having a smooth grease-like surface. Used in the manufacture of electrical insulating materials.

Stilt: see Saddle.

Stone: see Cornish stone.

Stoneware is a type of pottery characterized by a hard, dense and impervious body, as a rule covered with salt glaze. Stoneware is made of plastic clays containing iron oxides and other fluxes and is consequently cream or brown.

Talc: see Steatite.

Terracotta comprises all porous pottery ware which is not covered with a glaze. Its colour varies from yellow to red and brown. It is softer and more porous than earthenware and fired at a lower temperature.

Thimble: see Saddle.

Thixotropy: The quality of a paste or slip to change its plasticity or viscosity.

Throwing: Shaping a lump of plastic clay on a spinning wheel between the thumbs, fingers and palms of both hands. One of the oldest shaping methods, nowadays used only for making individual articles.

Towing: Smoothing the surface of cups and plates after drying and before firing, with tow.

Tridymite resembles quartz silicon dioxide (SiO_2), but is a high temperature variety, and has a crystal form and thermal expansion different from that of quartz and cristobalite (another high temperature quartz).

Turning is done on lathes similar to those used for turning metal or wood. The article to be turned must first be dried and in a reasonably hard state.

Underglaze decoration is applied on pottery before the article is glazed; the underglaze colours are consequently covered by a glaze.

Uranium oxide and other uranium compounds were used before the invention of the atom bomb for the preparation of lovely bright yellow, orange and red colours and glazes.

Vitreous china is a white and dense, but not translucent type of pottery, used for the manufacture of sanitary ware.

Wad clay: Rolls of plastic fireclay placed between individual saggars to prevent fumes from affecting the ware.

Waterglass: Silicate of soda is made by melting sand and soda in a furnace. The most alkaline waterglass has a ratio of 1 part alkali to 1.6 silica, and the most siliceous waterglass has a ratio of 1 alkali to 4 silica.

Waterglass mixed with powdered fireclay grog is used as a cement to repair broken saggars and cement together stoneware parts and to build up large containers.

Waterglass is also used as a deflocculent for the preparation of casting slips.

Whiting: A calcium carbonate produced by grinding in water and subsequent drying of chalk.

Zinc oxide is used in the preparation of glazes, but is not to be recommended in connection with underglaze decoration.

Zircon (Zirconium silicate – $ZoSiO_4$) and Zirconia (ZrO_2) are used for the manufacture of highly refractory materials and high frequency insulators.

INDEX

THE PENGUIN MODERN PAINTERS

Each volume in this series (which is under the editorship of Sir Kenneth Clark) contains 16 illustrations in colour, 16 black-and-white reproductions, and a 16-page appreciation of the artist's work by a well-known critic.

THE THINGS WE SEE

'They run to sixty-four pages, and are profusely and beautifully illustrated. They are marvels of the printer's and publisher's art, and should prove extremely popular.... They are aids to informed understanding, they direct the eye and mind to a cultural discrimination, and all this with subtle wit, based on expert knowledge.' Thus the *British Journal of Photography* described this series which so far includes:

The Pelican History of Art

EDITED BY NIKOLAUS PEVSNER

Slade Professor of Fine Art in the University of Cambridge

When completed, THE PELICAN HISTORY OF ART will consist of forty-eight volumes, each containing nearly 300 illustrations, most of which are full-page plates, and each being bound in a rich red cloth. It will be the first complete survey of world art and architecture ever to appear in the English language.

The first four volumes are now available:

PAINTING IN BRITAIN 1530 – 1790
Ellis K. Waterhouse
>Director of the Barber Institute of Fine Art, University of Birmingham; Slade Professor in the University of Oxford

THE ART AND ARCHITECTURE OF INDIA
Benjamin Rowland
>Professor of Fine Arts, Harvard University

FRENCH ART AND ARCHITECTURE 1500 – 1700
Anthony Blunt
>Director of the Courtauld Institute; Surveyor of the Queen's Pictures

ARCHITECTURE IN BRITAIN 1530 – 1830
John Summerson
>Curator, Sir John Soane's Museum, London

42s EACH

'If succeeding volumes are as scholarly and compact as that of Professor Rowland, who includes Afghanistan, Tibet, and Turkistan in his far-reaching survey of India, and that of Mr Waterhouse, who writes of British painting with his usual precision, urbanity, and mastery of facts, then *The Pelican History of Art* should not merely "have its place" on the shelves of the libraries, but is likely to find itself frequently in the hands of students of all sorts who care for the arts, have an inquiring mind, and are in search of enlightenment.' – *The Manchester Guardian*